COMMUNICATING
THE CATHOLIC VISION
OF
LIFE

CONTRIBUTORS TO THIS VOLUME

Helen Alvare
Director, Information and Planning, NCCB
Pro-Life Committee
Washington, D.C.

Fred S. Berlin, M.D., Ph.D.
Director, National Institute for the Study, Prevention and
Treatment of Sexual Trauma
Baltimore, Maryland

Peter J. Cataldo, Ph.D.
Director of Research
The Pope John Center
Braintree, Massachusetts

The Reverend Monsignor Frank J. Dewane
Permanent Observer
Mission of the Holy See to the United Nations
New York, New York

Richard M. Doerflinger
Associate Director, Secretariat for Pro-Life Activities
United States Catholic Conference
Washington, D.C.

The Reverend Avery Dulles, S.J., S.T.D.
Laurence J. McGinley Professor of Religion and Theology
Fordham University
The Bronx

Arthur J. Dyck, Ph.D.
Saltonstall Professor of Population Ethics
School of Public Health
Member, Faculty of the School of Divinity
Harvard Divinity School
Cambridge, Massachusetts

Kay Ek
Director Natural Family Planning Office
Diocese of St. Cloud, Minnesota

Rose Fuller
Northwest Family Services
Portland, Oregon

Robert P. George, J.D., D. Phil.
Associate Professor of Politics
Princeton University
Princeton, New Jersey

Dolores Bernadette Grier
Vice Chancellor for Community Relations
Archdiocese of New York

The Reverend John F. Harvey, O.S.F.S, S.T.D.
Director of Courage
New York, New York

Jacqueline Kasun, Ph.D.
Professor of Economics
Humboldt State University
Arcata, California

Patrick Lee, Ph.D.
Professor of Philosophy
Franciscan University of Steubenville
Steubenville, Ohio

The Reverend Monsignor Diarmuid Martin, S.T.D.
Undersecretary, Pontifical Council for Justice and Peace
The Vatican City

William E. May, Ph.D.
Michael J. McGivney Professor of Moral Theology
Pontifical John Paul II Institute for Studies on
Marriage and the Family
Washington, D.C.

The Reverend Kevin T. McMahon, S.T.D.
Professor of Moral Tehology
St. Charles Seminary
Overbrook, Pennsylvania

The Reverend Monsignor James J. Mulligan
Director for Programs for Priestly Life and Ministry
Mary Immaculate Seminary
Northampton, Pennsylvania

Julie Sly
Associate Director for Social Development and
Communications
California Catholic Conference
Sacramento, California

Victoria Thorn
Founder, Project Rachael

William J. Thorn, Ph.D.
Director, Institute for Catholic Media
Marquette University
Milwaukee, Wisconsin

Arland Thornton, Ph.D.
Professor of Sociology
Institute for Research
University of Michigan
Ann Arbor, Michigan

L. L. de Veber, M.D., F.R.C.P. (C)
Director of Hematology/Oncology
Children's Hospital
London, Ontario, Canada

COMMUNICATING THE CATHOLIC VISION OF LIFE

Proceedings of
The Twelfth Bishops' Workshop
Dallas, Texas

Russell E. Smith
Editor

THE POPE JOHN CENTER

NIHIL OBSTAT: Reverend James A. O'Donohoe, J. C. D.

Imprimatur: Bernard Cardinal Law   DATE: October 1, 1993

THE NIHIL OBSTAT AND IMPRIMATUR ARE A DECLARATION THAT A BOOK OR PAMPHLET IS CONSIDERED TO BE FREE FROM DOCTRINAL OR MORAL ERROR. IT IS NOT IMPLIED THAT THOSE WHO HAVE GRANTED THE NIHIL OBSTAT AND IMPRIMATUR AGREE WITH THE CONTENTS, OPINIONS OR STATEMENTS EXPRESSED.

Library of Congress Cataloging-in-Publication Data

Communicating the Catholic Vision of Life

"Proceedings of the Bishops' Workshop, February 1-4, 1993, Dallas, Texas"

Workshop for Bishops of the United States and Canada (12th : 1993 : Dallas, Tex.)
   Communicating the Catholic vision of life : proceedings of the Twelfth Bishops' Workshop, Dallas, Texas / Russell E. Smith, editor.
     p.   cm.
   Includes bibliographical references.
   ISBN 0-935372-36-9
   1. Human reproduction—Religious aspects—Catholic Church—Congresses. 2. Sex—Religious aspects—Christianity—Congresses. 3. Birth control—Religious aspects—Catholic Church—Congresses. 4. Population policy—Religious aspects—Catholic Church—Congresses. 5. Death—Religious aspects—Catholic Church—Congresses. 6. Catholic Church. Pope (1963–1978 : Paul VI) Humanae vitae—Anniversaries, etc. 7. Sexual ethics—Congresses. 8. Christian ethics—Catholic authors—Congresses. 9. Catholic Church—Doctrines—Congresses. 10. Communication—Religious aspects—Catholic Church—Congresses. I. Smith, Russell E. (Russell Edward) II. Title.
   BX1795.H84W67   1993
   241'.042—dc20   93-34979
                                                         CIP

Contents

The Pope John Center presented its twelfth Workshop for Bishops from February 1–4, 1993. This gathering was again made possible through a generous grant from the Knights of Columbus. Several hundred bishops from Canada, the United States of America, Mexico, the Caribbean and the Philippines gathered for a week of study, reflection and prayer.

The Pope John Center began these workshops in 1980. Workshops have occurred every year since, with the exceptions of 1982 and 1986. Each workshop concentrated on a specific topic or cluster of topics related to the field of medical ethics. These proceedings are published in book form and are all still available from the Pope John Center. The titles are as follows:

New Technologies of Birth and Death (1980)

Human Sexuality and Personhood (1981)

Technological Powers and the Person (1983)

Moral Theology Today: Certitudes and Doubts (1984)

The Family Today and Tomorrow: The Church Addresses Her Future (1985)

Scarce Medical Resources and Justice (1987)

Reproductive Technologies, Marriage and the Church (1988) (a detailed examination of the then recently published *Instruction on Respect for Human Life in its Origin and on the Dignity of Procreation* [*Donum Vitæ*])

Critical Issues in Contemporary Health Care (1989)

The Twenty-Fifth Anniversary of Vatican II: A Look Back and A Look Ahead (1990)

Catholic Conscience: Foundation and Formation (1991)

The Interaction of Catholic Bioethics and Secular Society (1992)

* * * * *

The theme of the 1993 Bishops' Workshop was "Communicating the Catholic Vision of Life." A wide variety of life issues and the place of the Church's prophetic voice in society were examined by this Workshop. In the last year, bioethical issues have been front-page news almost daily. Legislative proposals for doctor assisted suicide, health-care rationing, the human genome project, the possible approval by the FDA for RU-486, issues of gender identity and the possible lifting on the ban on electively aborted fetal tissue research are just a few subjects that constantly made the headlines.

The Catholic vision of life celebrates the importance of every human being and recognizes each one as a person of transcendent dignity. Each brother and sister of ours is dear to God and a bearer of rights that no one may violate from the first moment of life until its end.

Human sexuality too shines with splendor. As the expression of a love that is able to cure the loneliness of the human spirit, and as a reality through which new persons spring into being, sexuality is concerned with guarding basic human goods: enduring love and little children and homes and the hope of the future.

But those who wish to communicate well the Catholic vision of life must seek to understand and appreciate the reasons why that vision is so often feared and so vigorously assailed in our time. In this age of excessive and often ineffective communication they must realize how much blocks perception of what is precious and essential in the vision of life faith gives. They must take possession of those effective ways of communicating that enable us to communicate our vision as the good news it really is.

In the keynote address on Monday evening, Helen Alvare, director of the Pro-Life office of the United States Catholic Conference, presented a unified vision of the central themes that the Workshop examined. Each subsequent morning session began with a sociological, cultural and factual analysis of the way our contemporary world views the life questions on which one must reflect. Then, a theologian presented the Catholic vision that should be proclaimed in this real and struggling world. Finally, an expert in communications spoke of some of the important aspects of communicating effectively to the world a vision it needs, but finds difficult to accept.

On Tuesday morning, Professor Arland Thornton gave an account of contemporary attitudes toward sexuality and the family. Professor Patrick Lee spoke of the nature of the Catholic vision of sexuality. Professor and Mrs. William Thorn then spoke of ways of communicating this vision to a world like ours.

xii

End of life issues were discussed on Wednesday morning. Professor Arthur Dyck surveyed contemporary attitudes toward death and dying. Monsignor James Mulligan spoke of the principles that Catholic faith invokes when treating contemporary problems that touch dying. Mr. Richard Doerflinger then spoke of ways of addressing a world that is so tempted to slip into support of euthanasia and other false forms of mercy.

Professor Jacqueline Kasun provided a factual analysis of the population question at the beginning of Thursday morning's program. Monsignor Diarmuid Martin discussed the major concerns that the Church wishes to address when discussing population issues. Such concerns are sometimes difficult to articulate effectively in the contemporary world. Monsignor Frank Dewane spoke of efforts to present the Catholic vision most effectively in the international forum.

Afternoon sessions introduced a variety of subjects closely related to declaring and communicating the Catholic vision of life. On Tuesday afternoon, Doctor Fred Berlin spoke of new explanations of the possible physical origins of homosexuality, and Father John Harvey provided moral reflections on these new developments. Doctor Peter Cataldo provided a report on a Pope John Center study of the use of fetal tissue, while Professor William May evaluated new methods of treating ectopic pregnancies. An astonishingly popular program in Natural Family Planning was discussed by Kay Ek, and Rose Fuller spoke of a new course in chastity that is flourishing in Oregon.

Doctor L. L. de Veber spoke on Wednesday afternoon of pain management and the encouraging spread of hospice forms of treatment. Julie Sly gave an account of the efforts to guard life against the vigorous efforts to legalize euthanasia in California. More attractive ways of presenting the Pro-Life case were discussed by Doctor Dolores Bernadette Grier.

The final session of the program was a commemoration of the twenty-fifth anniversary of Pope Paul VI's encyclical *Humanæ vitæ*. This positive and hopeful discussion of the problems surrounding Catholic concern for responsible parenthood had three parts: Father Kevin McMahon spoke on the theological development of Catholic teaching in this field. Father Avery Dulles treated the pastoral difficulties created by massive dissent against Catholic teaching in this matter, and Professor Robert George discussed ways of presenting both faithfully and attractively what faith believes about the meaning of sexuality and the requirements of responsible parenthood.

We present this collection of essays to those who are engaged in the pastoral and health care ministries of the Church. We hope that this volume finds its way to seminary libraries and houses of religious formation to assist those who must know and communicate the message of the Church. For the same reason, we offer this volume to all the Catholic faithful, and to those beyond her borders who wish to know her teaching and understand its application. *"Tolle, lege ... fruere!"*

* * * * *

Many people contributed generously to the successful execution of the 1993 Workshop for Bishops. The planning, content and hospitality necessary for an international event of this magnitude depend on many hard-working, self-sacrificing individuals who obviously love the Church very much. We are very grateful to everyone who made this Workshop such a success.

We are very grateful to the Supreme Knight, Mr. Virgil C. Dechant, and to the Knights of Columbus for their generous sponsorship of this workshop. We are also very grateful to the faculty of this year's workshop, for their patience with the many deadlines and for their scholarly competence and presentations.

Special thanks go to the Most Reverend Charles V. Grahmann, Bishop of Dallas, for his gracious hospitality. Thanks also to the staff and seminarians of Holy Trinity Seminary at the University of Dallas for serving the Masses, singing, and acting as sacristans. In this regard, special thanks go to Father Thomas Cloherty for overseeing all the liturgical arrangements. We are also very grateful to the local councils of the Knights of Columbus and the Catholic Women's Guilds of the Diocese of Dallas for their kind assistance. Thanks also to the Spanish translators—Father Rutilio J. del Riego of Santa Lucia Parish in El Paso and Sister Margarita Cecilia Velez, O.P. of Brownsville, Texas, and the Reverend Seminarian Rolando Fonseca of Santa Lucia Parish in El Paso. Sister Margarita very graciously typed out the Spanish translations of the plenary sessions which were sent in manuscript form to the Spanish speaking bishops.

We are also grateful to the staff of the Harvey Hotel in Dallas for their graciousness and service. A very special word of thanks goes to the Nuns of the Poor Clare Federation of Mary Immaculate who prayed for the success and for the participants of the conference. Special thanks also to Father Ronald Lawler, OFM Cap, the Center's Director of Education, who so competently and graciously served as program director, and who, with Doctor Peter Cataldo and Fathers Albert Moraczewski and Donald McCarthy, crafted such a well-received conference. Thanks go also to our expanded staff in Braintree: Sister Margaret Mary Turner, RSM, the Center's Development Director (and some time travel agent!), and to Mrs. Doris Amirault and Miss Barbara Sullivan. Finally, we are deeply grateful to Mrs. Jeanne Burke and Mr. Donald Powers for their indefatigable effort and diligent assistance from the beginning of this Workshop's conception to the moment this book was delivered to your hands.

The Reverend Russell E. Smith, S. T. D.

President

Feast of the Visitation, 1993
Boston, Massachusetts

To My Brother Bishops
taking part in the Twelfth Workshop organized by the
Pope John XXIII Medical-Moral Research and
Education Center

Once again I greet you on the occasion of your yearly meeting to study the complex moral issues which you face in your ministry as pastors and teachers of God's People in the United States, Canada, the Philippines, Mexico, the Caribbean and Central America. This meeting provides you with a precious opportunity for prayer and reflection on the ethical demands of the new life we have received in Christ. I am grateful to the Pope John XXIII Medical-Moral Research and Education Center and to the Knights of Columbus for making this event possible.

Your gathering this year will concentrate on the urgent task of "Communicating the Catholic Vision of Life", and will discuss questions regarding human sexuality, death and dying, and world population. These issues are fundamental to human self-understanding in accordance with the fullness of truth revealed in Jesus Christ. Christ is the Word made flesh, "the new Adam who, in revealing the mystery of the Father and his love, fully reveals man to himself and brings to light his high calling" (*Gaudium et Spes,* 22). For this reason, the Church is convinced that only in Christ can man find the answers to his deepest questions about the mystery of human life and happiness. Today, as ever, the Church can and must offer the world a deeper anthropological vision which alone holds the promise of satisfying a man's deepest yearnings for an authentic existence lived in love and in the generous gift of self. Because "man must respect the natural and moral structure with which he has been endowed", there is a pressing need to defend and promote the moral conditions for a truly "human ecology" (cf. *Centesimus Annus,* 38).

The need to communicate the truth of the Catholic vision of life is all the more important in the light of the profound moral crisis though which society is passing. People today are desperately seeking hope and inspiration in order to live truly meaningful lives. At the same time they are torn by conflicting messages about the true sense of life, and attracted by false promises of fulfillment. The Church cannot be silent in the face of the growing confusion in people's minds and their increasing inability to perceive the clear distinction between good and evil in matters of human life.

As teachers and witnesses of faith, as well as discerners of the charisms with which God provides the Church in fulfilling her mission, Bishops have a critical obligation to promote that "culture of life" which constitutes the essential prerequisite for the humanization of society. This of course involves overseeing the teaching imparted in seminaries, Catholic schools and universities and ensuring that practices followed in Catholic hospitals and clinics are in harmony with Church teaching, and contributing effectively to the public discussion of moral issues. At the same time, Bishops have to make it apparent that "the Church is called upon to manifest anew to everyone, with clear and stronger conviction, her will to promote human life by every means and to defend it against all attacks" (*Familiaris Consortio,* 30). This is your personal responsibility, a task which may not be delegated completely and must not be neglected.

There is an urgent need to mobilize the whole Church in defense of life and in the promotion of a consistent witness to the sanctity of the Creator's gift. Amid the signs of a "culture of death" and a blunting of people's spiritual and moral sensitivities, we can also give thanks that many, especially among the laity, are deeply committed to defending life. Many of the faithful have distinguished themselves in bearing witness to the inalienable right to life. Through their action they make the Church's "yes" to life ever more concrete and efficacious (cf. *Christifideles Laici,* 38).

The issues which you will study during your meeting are especially timely in this year which marks the twenty-fifth anniversary of the Encyclical *Humanae Vitae.* With deep insight, Pope Paul VI taught that "the problem of birth, like every other problem regarding human life, must be considered, beyond partial perspectives-whether of the biological or psychological, demographic or sociological orders-in the light of an integral vision of man and of his vocation, not only his natural and earthly, but also his supernatural and eternal vocation" (No. 7). It is my fervent hope that your reflection on the perennial truth of this insight will lead to ever more effective efforts to enable the truth of the Gospel to enlighten the consciences of individuals and to assist in the promotion of an ever more humane society, responsive to the deepest human needs and concerned to favor all that promotes true human dignity.

Dear Brothers, may the Holy Spirit guide you in the ways of wisdom and understanding during these days of study. May he help you in your ministry to explain the truths of faith and to apply them with prudence and compassion. Commending all of you to the loving intercession of Mary, Seat of Wisdom and Mother of the Church, I cordially impart my Apostolic Blessing as a pledge of grace and peace in Jesus her Divine Son.

From the Vatican, January 12, 1993

Joannes Paulus PP. II

Virgil C. Dechant
Supreme Knight

Your Eminences, Your Exellencies, Reverend Monsignors, Reverend Fathers, Deacons, Religious, Distinguished Presenters, Guests and Friends:

Once again it is my privilege to convey a few words of welcome, and of greeting, at this opening session of the twelfth Workshop for Bishops. The greeting I bring comes from our more than one and a half million Knights and their families throughout the world who, essentially, are the ones sponsoring this symposium.

They do so, first of all, as a sign of affirmation for you individually and collectively in your roles as teacher and shepherd. They do so as well in the knowledge that, in the face of the many moral dilemmas that come to the fore with regard to life-and-death issues in the modern world, you can neither teach nor shepherd in a vacuum.

I recently returned from a meeting of the Pontifical Council for the Family where we discussed the importance of the fact that life begins at conception. If we really believe this, we must act as if we believe it—especially as regards defeating the "Freedom of Choice Act" (FOCA) and opposing other anti-life actions of government. I can tell you that it is the conviction of the members of the Pontifical Council that, in life matters and in other areas, "as the U.S. goes, so goes the world." Yet we see by the voting trends of Catholics in the recent U.S. elections, many of our own flock either do not believe, or are confused about, the fact that life does indeed begin at conception.

The United States Catholic Conference's Pro-Life Information and Education Campaign has been underwritten over thirty months by a

$5.5 million grant from the Knights of Columbus. Out of this effort came the development of the pro-life spokesperson, Helen Alvare, keynote speaker of this Workshop, whose appearances in the media have done much to advance the cause of life.

But there is still challenge ahead. On January 22, 1993, the new Administration in Washington took action to overturn policies that in the past had diminished the number of abortions, thus saving innocent unborn lives. It will be more and more difficult to carry out a pro-life program in such a climate.

Nevertheless, there are things that can be done, especially as regards FOCA. First among these is to inundate our legislators with postcards, phone calls, telegrams and letters demanding their vote against this bill. But of greater importance is that bishops must speak out because the Catholic electorate looks to you.

COMMUNICATING THE CATHOLIC VISION OF LIFE

Helen Alvare

If ever there was a huge topic to cover in one speech, this is it—"Communicating the Catholic Vision of Life." On the other hand, I am both an enthusiastic proponent of this vision and a fast talker—so we ought to be fine.

Roughly speaking, my presentation has two parts, which correspond to two elements of good communication—knowing your audience and speaking to them in a way that resonates with who they are and what they want to believe about themselves. I will spend a few minutes on the former, and a lot of minutes on the latter subject.

KNOWING YOUR LISTENERS

Commonly circulating truisms about the status of American opinion on abortion are so flawed as to be almost ludicrous. Secular newspapers repeatedly assert that "most Americans are Pro-Choice." The actual status of American opinion is much more complex and nuanced than this hasty generalization reflects. Knowing where your listeners stand—or are likely to stand—and why they stand where they stand can be of enormous benefit to anyone communicating about abortion.

Some of the best research ever done on the face of American opinion was commissioned by you through the NCCB in 1990 from the Wirthlin Group. This polling firm specializes in finding out not only about opinions, but about why people hold their opinions, specifically, what are the core values people hold which determine their opinions on the subject of abortion. Needless to say, once these values are known, it becomes possible to take our message of life and—without changing its core truths—communicate it with words and symbols which speak to the particular values of the group before us.

For example, we know from the Wirthlin Studies that persons who support or lean to supporting legal abortion have as their core values—independence and freedom. These values supersede even the values of salvation and caring for others. When asked to articulate how "independence and freedom" relate to abortion, these persons very often posited a situation where a woman is pregnant as a result of rape or incest, or where the pregnancy jeopardizes her life or health. They believed a large percentage of abortions resulted from these circumstances. In order to achieve freedom, they continued, women must have access to abortion. These findings tell us a lot about how we address a pro-life message to the committed or leaning abortion advocate: first, disassemble their flawed factual premise—that most abortions result from rape, incest, life or health problems. Second, consider abortion from the perspective of the value of "freedom." Inquire into its limits, its objects and its participants. Prompt them to think about the chaotic consequences of freedom without limits. Refer to the powerlessness—the utter absence of legal or physical freedom—on the part of the unborn child. There are many possibilities, but the object is the same: use the values held dear by the subject audience and apply those to the abortion context from a pro-life perspective.

The same procedure applies to a pro-life or leaning pro-life audience. Frequently, though not always, that audience will be religiously motivated. The Wirthlin Study found that the single most powerful motivating value in the pro-life community is "salvation or eternal life." Reference, therefore, to behavior consistent with salvation will motivate many pro-life listeners. This might include a variety of things, but I have found particularly helpful a discussion of Jesus' option for the poor and vulnerable in our society, and to our aim of emulating Jesus.

2

Looking at other categories which might assist you in developing a communications strategy, I offer the following findings culled from a great variety of polls and studies:

First, women tend to be more pro-life than men. Women with children and older women are particularly pro-life.

Second, the more money and education an individual has, the more supportive they are of legal abortion. With regard to abortion funding for the poor, for example, those below the poverty line oppose it by roughly two to one, and those making more than $60,000 per year support it by roughly two to one.

Third, African-Americans and Hispanic-Americans are more pro-life than non-Hispanic white Americans or Americans generally. They rest their stance often on their feelings about the fragility of life in an overly violent society and on strong feelings for the extended family. With fewer worldly goods, on average, than white Americans, they place more value on life as good or gift.

Fourth, studies show that the less one knows about the true state of abortion law and practice in the United States, the more supportive one claims to be of these laws and practices. Most Americans are woefully ignorant of the truly extreme state of abortion practice but will nonetheless claim to endorse Roe v. Wade (and will call anyone a vicious liar who claims Roe legalized abortion for 9 months for any reason).

Curing basic ignorance, appealing to the values held by the listeners—rich or poor, male or female, or whatever ethnic group—will go a good distance toward pro-life persuasion.

With regard to Catholics—study after study shows that those regularly participating in Mass are quite strongly pro-life. Those who take a Catholic label but do not attend Mass regularly have generally the same opinions as the public at large. In other words, with non-practicing Catholics, evangelization is still the primary task, and rhetoric which persuades the general public applies equally to them. Practicing Catholics most often need to be continually inspired with words about why the Church stands in solidarity with the unborn, and with the mother in crisis.

RESONANCE WITH WHO AND WHAT AN AUDIENCE WANTS TO BE

A professor-friend at Catholic University once said to me that that social movement succeeds which convinces people that its vision is the

American vision, that its ideals are the ideals Americans would most like to believe they hold. One often hears in political campaigns various politicians claiming that their vision of America resonates most closely with "who we really are." Bill Clinton told us that he represents a society whose people "work hard and play by the rules." He told us that he envisioned America as a community sharing a "new ethic of mutual responsibility." Articulating a positive vision and calling on all to work with us to create the reality, are powerful communications tools.

Note how successfully, for example, Martin Luther King and Malcolm X painted their dreams and visions for African Americans. "I have a dream . . ." is one of the most powerful—and interestingly quite Christian—vision statements spoken in American history. Catholic teaching is chock-full of inspiring visions of human society. These visions and the desire to work for them intellectually converted me to an adult Catholicism in my 20's. Unfortunately, virtually every reporter who telephones me and every student who questions me starts the same way: "The Catholic Church is against all abortions under any circumstances, right?" This question presumes there are no positive formulations of our pro-life stance. And it fails utterly to comprehend the beautiful bases of our stance. I would like to share with you now some positive formulations of the Catholic pro-life vision.

First, the Church's approach must be understood to be based on common sense, on bases rationally available to all persons of good will. It is ordinarily presumed that our teaching is based upon esoteric Catholic theology.

Second, that rational basis should be articulated in human rights terms—the terms, in fact, used in the CDF's Declaration on Procured Abortion. All can understand that there are scientific bases for our claims that what grows in the mother's womb is human and alive. All can understand us when we teach that there should not be discrimination against some human lives on the basis of size, visibility, stage of development, disability, dependency, and so forth. This appeals to our better natures. Surely, we do not want to be known for the opposite. Unfortunately, abortion is rarely discussed in these terms; abortion advocates studiously avoid even mentioning of the child. The mother, only, is allowed the status of "victim." Calling on individuals to accord dignity to all stages of human life, however, is a task Americans would like to believe they could accomplish. It calls on our better angels.

Third, "inclusivity" is another hallmark of the Church's vision. Dr. Jack Willke brought back from Latin America what I believe may be

4

the most beautiful pro-life sentiment I have ever seen. On a poster of a modern madonna and child was printed the simple phrase "love them both." This summarizes the Catholic vision beautifully. Dr. Jocelyn Elders, Mr. Clinton's appointment for surgeon general, has asked the pro-life movement to "get over its love affair with the fetus." What a mischaracterization! The pro-life movement, rather, is asking Americans to "expand their love affair with freedom and with life" to include the child. In other words, we ask: "Why not love them both?" "Why not justice for both?" Again, this is where the better angels of American nature want to be.

Fourth, a message I have found particularly appealing in High School and College settings, where students are often eager to catch me in inconsistencies, is the Consistent Ethic of Life. I was bowled over in a Catholic gradeschool two weeks ago when a 7th-grader asked me if I opposed capital punishment as a "consistent extension of respect for life." The consistent ethic is tremendously intellectually convincing to the person actually thinking about abortion. Its radical implications for action are frightening, but challenging. High school and college students, in particular—the usual participants in rallies on the Mall against racism, sexism, aid to the Contras, war, and everything else—are ripe for the challenge of considering pro-life to be on this human rights continuum.

Listeners are also quite surprised to hear about the Church's putting its consistent ethic principles to work in programs and lobbying efforts which address a wide spectrum of needs. "Targeting problems" not "sufferers" or "those who might cause suffering" is a convincing pattern of behavior. Americans like to think of themselves as caring, as inclusive, and as problem solvers. The consistent ethic is a piercing call to "our better angels" to apply these talents on behalf of the unborn as well as the born.

STATIC

Despite the numerous positive contexts in which a pro-life message can be conveyed, a good many members of the secular media and the public focus upon certain less-than-positive "hotpoints" in characterizing the Church's pro-life vision. I offer some suggestions for turning these "negatives" into "positives."

First: "separation of Church and state." Most believe this to mean that religion, even moral values, and the public square may not touch.

I usually point out not only the legal fallacy inherent in this interpretation, but two "positive" points. The first is our right as Catholics to free exercise. To exclude us from the public square on the grounds of our religious beliefs is a violation of that clause. Second, I note the desirability of having religious voices in the public square. With no vested interests in monetary profit, and a demonstrated social services commitment to human persons in need, the Church makes a credible and trustworthy advocate of human rights. As Gary Wills said in his recent book on religion in American life, the Church is the traditional moral voice against abuse of power by the strong over the weak. That role is an American tradition.

Second: "contraception." Strange as it would seem, in a country where increased availability of contraception has corresponded only with increased pregnancy rates among unmarried teens and a vastly increased abortion rate, there are still many who say that "if only" the Church approved contraception, all of our abortion problems would be solved. I always note first that there is no empirical proof whatsoever that increasingly available contraception has or can cure the abortion problem. In fact, all of the evidence is to the contrary. I also point to the empirical statistics showing that abstinence programs often do successfully lower teen intercourse, pregnancy and abortion rates, and to the mounting empirical evidence that monogamous sexual relationships within marriages open to children contribute greatly to mental and physical health.

Third: an all male hierarchy could not possibly have anything correct to say about abortion. It is helpful to point out here that the ad hominem argument is the last refuge of the person with no substantive argument. Too, this argument fails utterly to consider the substantive human rights basis of the pro-life argument—the humanity and dignity of the unborn—and manages even to throw some reverse-sexism into the mix. It also ignores the fact that women generally, including Catholic women, are even more pro-life than men. On the positive side, I point out that it is the abortion advocate who would characterize the entire Catholic Church as consisting only in its hierarchy. Catholics themselves, men and women, clergy, religious and laymen, do not understand the hierarchy to be speaking alone when they speak on abortion, but as representative of the body of believers. Finally, the Church has traditionally spoken out for those without power in society. It is not our place, or another's, to deprive any defenseless group— such as the unborn, or women in a crisis pregnancy—of an advocate. Would they stop us from speaking out against apartheid because we are not South African residents? The consequences of their reasoning are absurd.

6

CONCLUSIONS

A doctoral student researching the pro-life movement in the United States recently interviewed me regarding the status of the movement. She asked me who I considered the most persuasive abortion advocacy group in the country. After answering, I asked her what abortion advocates had said to the parallel question. She answered unhesitatingly: "The Catholic Bishops. Because their authority is moral, not merely political or financial." After 20 years of Roe v. Wade, the remarkable thing is not what a pro-abortion nation we are in, but how pro-life it is in the face of overwhelming pressure from the media, the academy, Hollywood, professional societies, and so on. Political observers are now telling us that the legal debate is over after 20 years and the moral can begin. There is also virtually universal admission that every abortion is a tragedy and that our real human task is to reduce the need for abortion. Prescinding from the reality that the moral debate has never ended (and the legal never will until the community's pro-life values are enshrined in law), these conditions are fertile ground for the Church's message. A message not about resigning ourselves to the shamelessness of 1.6 million abortions each year, but about creating a consistent, inclusive American society where each life merits respect. A call to our better angels indeed.

PART ONE

HUMAN SEXUALITY

Chapter 2

CONTEMPORARY ATTITUDES AND STUDIES OF HUMAN SEXUALITY AND FAMILY LIFE

Arland Thornton, Ph.D.

I will begin this discussion of attitudes and behavior concerning marriage, sexuality, and family life in Western societies by placing the contemporary situation in historical and comparative perspective. A comparative perspective is useful because it allows us to perceive our similarities and differences with other societies. Historical perspective is necessary because it provides knowledge to understand the past and the complex web of change and continuity that has brought us to the present.

Let us go back in time a couple of centuries—to what some call the "good old days" and others refer to as the "bad old days". In this world of the past our ancestors in Northwestern Europe, Canada, and the United States, as in many other places, had a social system that was organized largely around family units (Laslett 1965; Thornton and Fricke 1987). Family ties and relationships were key elements of society, and large fractions of human activities were conducted within family units. Individual human beings were born into families, socialized by kinsmen, protected by family members, and organized into economic units along kinship lines.

Marriage was a central institution in the past in the United States, Canada, and Northwestern Europe (Hajnal 1965, 1982; Macfarlane 1986; Thornton and Freedman 1983). In these Western societies marriage bestowed upon young people full membership in adult society. It was also accompanied by independence as master and mistress of a household and economic unit. Marriage also legitimized sexual relations and childbearing.

Family patterns in the past in Canada, the United States, and Northwest Europe were different in several respects from those observed in many other parts of the world (Hajnal 1982; Thornton and Fricke 1987). Unlike the systems of many other cultures, including those of China and India, marriage in the West generally required the newly-wed couple to establish a household and economic unit separate from either of the couple's parents. As a result, marriage could not be contracted until the couple had procured an independent household and economic unit. This system of marriage was also characterized by much later marriage than occurred in most other populations (Hajnal 1965, 1982; Macfarlane 1986). Many women did not marry until their middle twenties, and most men postponed marriage until their late twenties. In addition, substantial numbers of men and women did not marry—with the fraction remaining single throughout life reaching as high as one-fifth (Hajnal 1965). Despite the large numbers of never-married people in Western societies in the past, marriage was still strongly preferred because of the advantages associated with it.

Another unique institution of Northwest Europe, Canada, and the United States was "lifecourse servanthood" in which many young men and women left their parental homes at young ages—frequently before their teenage years—to work and live in the households of other families. Lifecourse servanthood was not limited to the wealthy taking in the children of the poor, but involved a wide range of families across the economic spectrum as both senders and receivers of young people. Consequently, large fractions of young people lived away from the parental home for extended periods of time before marriage (Hajnal 1982; Kussmaul 1981).

Late age at marriage and lifecourse servanthood was associated with a substantial amount of autonomy for young people in Western societies. Young people in the West, of course, received extensive supervision from parents and other adults, but when compared to their counterparts in other societies, they had considerable freedom to make their own decisions and form their own relationships (Macfarlane 1979, 1986).

The autonomy of young people was particularly true of marital decisions. Marriages were typically not arranged by parents, as in many societies, but were generally contracted by the young people themselves. While financial considerations were, of course, important in mate selection, love and romance were also crucial. In this world of the past young people married for both love and money (Macfarlane 1986).

Marital dissolution rates were high in Western societies of the past, as was true in the rest of the world. Unlike today, however, the main cause of marital dissolution was mortality rather than marital discord (Thornton and Freedman 1983). Nonetheless, the result was large numbers of single parent families.

Unfortunately, we have little solid data about sexual experience in the past. Nevertheless, there are indications that society in general and local communities and families in particular tried to limit sexual expression to marriage (Shorter 1975). However, with a marriage system that included youthful autonomy, courtship, and romance, it was more difficult for Western parents to control the sexual experience of their unmarried children than in societies where marriages were arranged at young ages by the older generation. Consequently, there were a significant number of pregnancies to unmarried young people. Additional young people were probably sexually experienced before marriage but had their first conception later.

In the Western past, there was an even stronger linkage between childbearing and marriage than between marriage and sexual expression. Marriage was seen as the institution that made childbearing legitimate. Consequently, many, but not all, out-of-wedlock pregnancies were legitimated by marriage. Marriage also made childbearing necessary as married couples were expected to bear and rear children.

In the old days there was also a close linkage between sexual expression and childbearing within marriage. Although various forms of birth control had been known for centuries, their use was very limited because information about them was not widespread, because their use was not considered legitimate, or because there was no widespread desire to limit childbearing within marriage (van de Walle and Knodel 1980; Himes 1970). Consequently, sexual expression was associated with the possibility of pregnancy among all married couples except those who were biologically unable to conceive.

13

In recent centuries there have been both important changes and continuities in many of these dimensions of marriage, sexuality, and family life. Of central importance is the proliferation of social institutions that have no basis in kinship relations (Thornton and Fricke 1987). With the appearance and expansion of numerous non-family institutions such as factories, hospitals, public health organizations, schools, police, the mass media, and commercialized leisure, individual lives were increasingly organized by and conducted within non-familial institutions. Families, of course, continued to be important, but numerous non-familial institutions began to organize and affect the lives of individuals. These changes subjected individuals and their families to non-family influences not widespread earlier.

A crucial change of the last two centuries has been the uncoupling of sexual expression from childbearing within marriage. In the nineteenth century married couples in substantial numbers began to separate their sexual and childbearing lives through the use of contraception and abortion (van de Walle and Knodel 1980; Coale and Zelnik 1963). The effective use of birth control increased further during the twentieth century as sterilization, condoms, IUDs, the pill, and abortion became widespread. Today, there is almost universal use of highly effective means of birth control within marriage for planning both the number and spacing of children (Mosher and Pratt 1990; Forrest and Singh 1990).

Perhaps the most dramatic indicator of the widespread separation of sex from childbearing is the emergence of sterilization as the most common form of contraception in the United States (Mosher 1990). In 1988, 47 percent of all American women between the ages of 35 and 44 reported that they or their husband or partner had been sterilized for the explicit purpose of preventing pregnancy (Mosher and Pratt 1990). Another 15 percent of the women this age reported involuntary sterility (either nonsurgical sterility or surgical sterilization that was not done for contraceptive purposes).

A second important indicator of the separation of sex from childbearing is the increase in abortion. Despite the widespread usage of contraception, more than one-half of all pregnancies continue to be unintentional (Forrest and Singh 1990). With the availability of abortion, however, the carrying of unplanned pregnancies to live births is largely a voluntary decision. In 1987, one-half of all unintended pregnancies were terminated by abortion (Forrest and Singh 1990).

Over the last two centuries there have been few long-term trends in the propensity to marry in Western societies. Perhaps the biggest story of this period was the dramatic boom that occurred in most Western societies following World War II (Cherlin 1992; Watkins

14

1981). During the immediate post-war years, marriage rates increased dramatically, age at marriage fell, and the number of people never-marrying declined. For example, in the United States, average age at marriage fell to just over 20 for women, and only about three percent of the young women living through this era never married (Thornton and Freedman 1983). However, by the 1970s and 1980s, the marriage boom had ended, and the propensity to marry declined. At the end of the 1980s, the percentage of never-married among young men had returned to the levels of 1900, and among young women, never-married levels were even higher than at the turn of the century (Cherlin 1992).

However, the rapid decline in marriage propensities during the 1970s and 1980s did not represent an abandonment of intimate coresidential heterosexual relations. During this same period unmarried cohabitation increased so rapidly that it was experienced by significant fractions of young people in many Western societies. For example, more than forty percent of Americans in their late twenties and early thirties now report that they have cohabited without being married (Bumpass and Sweet 1989; London 1991). In the early 1980s more than two-fifths of all first marriages had been preceded by nonmarital cohabitation, and the fraction of remarriages preceded by cohabitation reached three out of five (Bumpass and Sweet 1989). Furthermore, the recent increase in cohabitation has been so large that it has nearly off-set the simultaneous decline in marriage. As a result, the fraction of young people who have ever lived in a coresidential union—including either cohabitation or marriage—is now only somewhat lower than at the height of the marriage boom in the 1950s and 1960s (Bumpass and Sweet 1989; Bumpass, Sweet, and Cherlin 1991; Cherlin 1992).

This appearance of unmarried cohabitation is part of a longer-term increase in sexual expression and childbearing among unmarried people. During the nineteenth century there were significant increases in out-of-wedlock childbearing in numerous Western countries (Shorter 1975). These increases have been interpreted as being the result of increased premarital sex during the same time period. While out-of-wedlock childbearing declined in the early part of the twentieth century, this was probably due to the increased use of contraception by unmarried couples rather than to declines in premarital sex (Shorter 1975; Shorter, Knodel, and van de Walle 1971).

Recent surveys reveal that premarital sexual experience among teenagers was already widespread by the early 1970s and increased rapidly during subsequent years. In 1971 in the metropolitan United States 28 percent of all never-married women aged 15-19 reported that they had experienced sexual intercourse, and this percentage increased to 46 percent by 1979 (Zelnik and Kantner 1980). In 1988, the fraction of never married women in the United States reporting sexual intercourse was one-half for those aged 15-19 and three fourths for those 20-24 (Forrest and Singh 1990). Even higher levels of sexual experience are reported by single men, with three-fifths of all unmarried men aged 15-19 in 1988 reporting sexual experience. At age 19, the number of never-married men reporting sexual experience reached four out of five (Sonenstein, Pleck, and Ku 1991). While these numbers represent lifetime experience, large fractions of unmarried American men and women also report recent sexual experience (Forrest and Singh 1990; Sonenstein, Pleck, and Ku 1991). Even higher rates of recent sexual experience are reported by the previously married (Forrest and Singh 1990).

Despite the widespread availability of contraception and abortion, there have been rapid increases in the prevalence of pregnancy and childbearing among unmarried teenagers in the United States in recent decades. The teenage out-of-wedlock childbearing rate has increased almost uninterruptedly across the last half century (Thornton and Freedman 1983; National Center for Health Statistics 1986, 1990). In the late 1980s nearly 4 percent of all unmarried teenage women 15-19 had a child each year (National Center for Health Statistics 1990). Increasing rates of out-of-wedlock childbearing, along with declines in marriage and marital childbearing, have increased the percentage of all children born to unmarried mothers to 26 percent in 1988 (National Center for Health Statistics 1990). Accompanying this increase in out-of-wedlock childbearing has been a decline in the percentage of these children placed for adoption (Bachrach, Stolley, and London 1992).

One of the most widely recognized family changes is the expansion of divorce, which has been underway at least since the 1860s. For a century the increase in divorce was slow and steady, but picked up speed in the 1960s and 1970s and then levelled out in the 1980s (Cherlin 1992). By the 1980s, as many as 60 percent of all marriages were projected to end in divorce (Bumpass 1990). Recent high divorce rates have also been accompanied by high remarriage rates, so that the number of blended or reconstituted families has expanded (Thornton and Freedman 1983). Both the increase in divorce and out-of-wedlock childbearing have expanded the number of single-parent families in recent years. As a result, both the bearing and rearing of children have joined sexual experience in being substantially separated from the institution of marriage.

16

Data limitations prevent systematic documentation of trends in family, marriage, and sexual attitudes and norms prior to the 1960s. However, data from the subsequent three decades indicate that the numerous recent changes in familial and intimate behavior have been accompanied by equally strong shifts in attitudes, values, and norms (Thornton 1989).

Of central importance has been the decline in the normative imperative to marry (Thornton 1989). Between 1957 and 1976 the percentage of adult Americans expressing negative attitudes toward a person who did not want to marry decreased from 53 to 34 percent. In addition, the percentage believing that marriage positively changed a person's life decreased from 43 to 30 percent across the same years while the percentage saying that marriage brought negative changes increased from 44 to 59 percent. However, between the 1960s and 1980s, there was only a very small increase in the percentage of young people expecting to remain single throughout their lives (Thornton 1989).

We also have evidence of strong shifts toward the acceptance of divorce in recent decades. In a 1962 study of mothers, 51 percent disagreed with the statement that "when there are children in the family, parents should stay together even if they don't get along". Fifteen years later, in 1977, the number disagreeing with this statement had increased to 80 percent (Thornton 1989). There were, however, no additional changes in attitudes between 1977 and 1985.

There have also been significant trends during recent decades toward the acceptance of childlessness (Thornton 1989). Between 1962 and 1980, the percentage of mothers saying that all married couples who can ought to have children declined from 85 to 43 percent. These same mothers were also very tolerant about the possibility of their own children remaining childless; only one-eighth indicated they would be bothered a great deal if their children did not become parents. Parenthood is also increasingly seen as a restrictive role. Between 1957 and 1976 the percentage of adults viewing parenthood positively declined from 58 to 44 percent, while the number viewing parenthood as restrictive increased from 30 to 45 percent. However, at the same time that childlessness has become more acceptable and the number of people with positive views of parenthood has declined, there is no evidence of a rush towards wanting to remain childless (Thornton 1989).

Another area of significant change has been attitudes toward premarital sex. In 1965, almost 70 percent of young Americans (ages 18-30) thought it was always or almost always wrong for a man to have intimate relations with a woman he is engaged to and intends to marry. This widespread restrictiveness concerning premarital sex declined rapidly during subsequent years. By 1986, just twenty-one years later, only 22 percent of young women and 14 percent of young men in the United States reported that they believed it was always or almost always wrong for a man and woman to have sex relations before marriage. Interestingly enough, this trend was not limited to young people as only 45 percent of older women and 34 percent of older men (aged 30 or older) in 1986 believed that sex before marriage was always or almost always wrong (Thornton 1989).

This widespread acceptance of sexual relations for the unmarried also extends to cohabitation outside of marriage (Thornton 1989). In the middle 1980s high school seniors in the United States were asked their view of a man and woman living together without being married. Approximately one-quarter of them indicated that they believed unmarried cohabitation was a worthwhile experiment and another one-half thought that the couple were just doing their own thing and not bothering anyone. In another study conducted in 1985 nearly three-quarters of men and women in their early twenties disagreed with the idea that "a young couple should not live together unless they are married".

While there is widespread acceptance of sexual relations and cohabitation without marriage, it should not be assumed that Americans now place no limitations on sexual expression. One important area of restriction is maturity as indicated by age. When a 1986 study asked adult Americans about the acceptability of sexual relations for a couple in their early teens—14 to 16 years of age—the vast majority (over four-fifths) said that it is always or almost always wrong (Thornton 1989). However, even though most Americans are opposed to sexual relations for young teenagers, the vast majority (over three-quarters) also believe that information about birth control should be available to teenagers (Thornton 1989).

Another area of restriction is marital status, with extramarital sex being strongly opposed by the vast majority of Americans (Thornton 1989). For example, in 1985, about nine-tenths of all women and five-sixths of all men reported that they believed it was always or almost always wrong for a married person to have sexual relations with someone other than the marriage partner. Furthermore, among young (ages 18-30) American men and women, there were increases between 1973 and 1985 in the percentage saying that extramarital sex was always or almost always wrong. This suggests that the decade of the late 1970s and early 1980s was one of growing restrictiveness concerning extramarital sex.

18

Recent data suggest that these strong norms against extramarital sex are reflected in the behavior of married Americans (Greeley, Michael, and Smith 1990; Smith 1991). It appears that married men and women are quite faithful to their spouses. One and one-half percent of married people in 1989 reported having sex with someone other than their spouse in the preceding year (Smith 1991). There is also some evidence suggesting that large fractions of people have maintained marital fidelity across their entire marriages (Smith 1991).

A central conclusion to be drawn from the myriad changes in family and marriage attitudes and behavior is that there has been a substantial relaxation of the norms concerning marriage, sexual behavior, and family life. There has been an important weakening of the normative constraints to get married, to remain married, to abstain from sexual relations before marriage, to have children, and to have all of the children that would naturally come in the marital relation. Other important normative changes include acceptance of abortion and permission for less segregation in the roles of men and women. While many Americans continue to have strong attitudes about some of these issues, there has been a significant general weakening of the historical proscriptions and prescriptions.

Many of these changes in norms and values concerning marriage and family life have been institutionalized in American law. Questions of morality and the community's regulation of family and intimate behavior were previously important elements of legal philosophy, but now such matters receive little emphasis (Schneider 1985). Replacing this emphasis upon public morality and regulation has been a movement towards concern about privacy and the restriction of public involvement in personal lives. Examples of this legal trend is the universal adoption of no-fault divorce laws by American states and the protection of the right to abortion under the shield of privacy (Freed and Foster 1980; Schneider 1985).

An important component of this relaxation of social norms and legal prescriptions has been the widening of individual choice. Individuals now have much wider latitude in the ways they lead their intimate and family lives. They can undertake a much wider range of behaviors without incurring the displeasure and censure of family, friends, and the law.

This increase in individual choice and privacy is perhaps clearest in the area of sexuality and reproduction. One example of this is the privatization of sexual relationships so that they no longer require the legitimacy brought by marriage. Whereas in the past sexual relations and cohabitation were legitimated by the social, legal, and religious institution of marriage, today most Americans see marriage as irrel-

19

evant to the initiation of intimate sexual relations. The bearing and rearing of children are also less closely linked with marriage today.

It is interesting to remember, however, that this trend has given increased sexual freedom only to mature individuals who are not married. For married individuals trends in recent years have been toward more restrictiveness of sexual relationships to the marital dyad. This indicates that fidelity within relationships has become more rather than less important during recent years. Together, these trends suggest that commitment between individuals may have become more important as the sanctioning influence of the marriage institution declined.

A second example of increased individual choice is the sexual freedom brought by the widespread availability and acceptance of highly effective means of birth control. Whereas married couples in the past accepted the linkage between sexual relations and the possibility of conception and birth, today they have the ability and legitimacy to engage in sexual relations without having to face the possibility of an undesired birth.

A key feature of these important trends in family and intimate behavior and values is their ubiquity (van de Walle and Knodel, 1980; Roussel and Festy 1979; Chester 1977; Hajnal 1953; Lesthaeghe 1983; Jones and Westoff 1979). The broad general outlines of continuity and change have occurred not only in the United States and Canada, but in virtually all of the countries of Northwestern Europe, although the timing and rapidity of the trends have varied. In addition, they have been felt within virtually every subgroup of people in the United States, including those defined by region, age, social class, and religion.

While these family trends have been ubiquitous and impressively parallel for many subgroups of the population, there have also been some noteworthy differences in trends across religious groups. In the past, there were a number of significant differences between American Catholics and Protestants in family behavior and attitudes (Westoff 1979; Lenski 1963; McCarthy 1979; Greeley 1977; Mosher, Williams, and Johnson 1992; Goldscheider and Mosher 1991; Thornton 1985). These included generally higher than average fertility among Catholics and lower than average use of technical means of birth control. Catholics also held stronger norms about having children, had higher family size preferences, and were more negative towards divorce. These religious differences, however, have largely disappeared in recent years as changes among Catholics have been so dramatic that the values and behavior of Catholics have generally converged to match those of Protestants (Thornton 1985; Goldscheider and Mosher 1991;

20

Greeley 1990; Roof and McKinney 1987). There are, however, some family domains where Catholic behavior and values now depart from national averages, but in unexpected directions. For example, whereas Catholics used to have higher fertility than Protestants, they now have lower fertility (Mosher, Williams, and Johnson 1992). In addition, there is now a tendency for Catholics to be more accepting than average of premarital sex, cohabitation, and sexual unfaithfulness (Greeley 1989, 1990; Sweet and Bumpass 1990). The religious groups with high fertility and restrictive attitudes toward premarital sex and cohabitation are now Mormons and fundamentalist Protestants (Thornton 1985; Mosher, Williams, and Johnson 1992; Heaton 1992; Sweet and Bumpass 1990; Roof and McKinney 1987).

It is useful to note that family and intimate relations are not the only aspects of American society where individual freedom and privacy have increased and the need to conform to external standards has declined. In recent years there has been a substantial decline in the extent to which Americans value obedience, loyalty to church, and conformity in their children, while the value of tolerance, autonomy, and thinking for yourself has increased (Alwin 1984, 1986, 1988a, 1989). There have also been important increases in political tolerance as noted by expanded acceptance of free speech for atheists, socialists, and communists (Glenn 1987; Mueller 1988; Nunn, Crockett, and Williams 1978). There have also been increases in independent thinking in politics as political party identification has declined (Glenn 1987).

Significant changes in religious authority, practice, and values have also occurred in recent decades. Among the relevant religious changes have been declines in the legitimacy of religious leaders and institutions, declines in confidence in religious answers to life's problems, and declines in the perceived usefulness of the Bible as a decisionmaking guide (Glenn 1987; Caplow, Bahr, and Chadwick 1983; Hout and Greeley, 1987; Greeley, McCready, and McCourt 1976; Greeley 1989). Also declining have been identification with religion, attendance at religious services, and the perceived importance of religion (Glenn 1987; Greeley 1989). Parents have also become more willing to give their children the latitude to make their own religious decisions and provide their children with less religious training and encouragement to pray (Alwin 1988b).

There is also evidence that religious experience itself has been changing in recent years. American religion has become increasingly pluralistic, so that Americans increasingly accept the authenticity of others' faith and beliefs (Bellah, Madsen, Sullivan, Swidley, and Tipton 1985; Caplow, Bahr, and Chadwick 1983; Roof and McKinney

1987). Religion has also become more privatized, so that individual faith and morals are now more isolated from the larger community. This has made religion more voluntaristic, less compulsory, and less punitive towards those who behave independently. In fact, a norm of tolerance has apparently emerged to replace the former requirement of conformity to religious authority. As a result, religion itself now provides more freedom, individual choice, and tolerance for divergent behavior.

There is now significant evidence suggesting that recent declines in the degree to which Americans value obedience and participate in religious services have been greater among Catholics than Protestants. In fact, it appears that the decline in religious authority and attendance at religious services occurred primarily among Catholics (Hout and Greeley 1987; Greeley 1989). In addition, Catholics experienced much more decline than Protestants in the desire for obedience among children (Alwin 1986). This decline in the value of obedience among Catholics has been so great that young Catholics now express this value less than young Protestants (Alwin 1989).

In closing, I will offer some speculations about the concurrent trends in the decline of religious authority and the weakening of the historical normative rules concerning marriage, sexuality, and family life. While it is likely that these trends are, to some extent, merely the joint products of larger social forces, there is also good reason to believe that the two trends are mutually reinforcing (Thornton 1985; Lesthaeghe and Surkyn 1988; Lesthaeghe and Wilson 1986; Thornton, Axinn, and Hill 1992).

Scholars have long recognized the central causal role of religious institutions in creating and maintaining strong social and legal rules concerning marriage, sexuality, and family life. Numerous studies have shown that many dimensions of family and intimate life, including marriage, divorce, childbearing, and sexual behavior, are strongly influenced by religious commitment and participation (see Thornton, Axinn, and Hill 1992). For these reasons, one would expect that the historical reduction of religious authority was a significant factor in the decline of historical norms and laws concerning family life, sexuality, and marriage.

Family and intimate behavior also influence religious institutions and the religious participation and commitment of individuals. As individual family behavior and values have changed and diverged from the historical positions of the churches, religious leaders have found it necessary to modify their institutional positions to accommodate the new values and behavior of their adherents (Thornton 1985). The ra-

22

pidity and extent of such adjustments have, of course, varied across denominations.

There is also a tendency for individuals to distance themselves from their religious institutions as their intimate and family behavior and values diverge from the positions of their churches. It is likely that as behavior and values concerning marriage, sexuality, and reproduction increasingly diverged from the historical rules and contemporary pronouncements of the churches during the last two centuries, that there was also added impetus toward the decline of religious authority. There were probably also associated declines in religious participation and commitment.

This reciprocal relationship between religion and family behavior and attitudes poses a significant dilemma for religious institutions today. On the one hand, religious institutions have historically had the moral authority to influence the family attitudes and behavior of their adherents. On the other hand, when the positions of religious institutions depart too dramatically from the lives of their adherents, church leadership is frequently seen as irrelevant and without legitimacy and authority. Using and maintaining religious authority in a world of changing family values and behavior is an issue whose importance may only be transcended by its difficulty of solution.

REFERENCES

Alwin, Duane F. 1984. "Trends in Parental Socialization Values: Detroit, 1958 to 1983." *American Journal of Sociology,* 90:359–382.

Alwin, Duane F. 1986. "Religion and Parental Childrearing Orientations: Evidence of a Catholic-Protestant Convergence." *American Journal of Sociology,* 92:412–440.

Alwin, Duane F. 1988a. "From Obedience to Autonomy: Changes in Traits Desired in Children, 1924–1978." *Public Opinion Quarterly,* 52:33–52.

Alwin, Duane F. 1988b. "Religion in Detroit, 1958 to 1988." Unpublished paper, Institute for Social Research, University of Michigan.

Alwin, Duane F. 1989. "Changes in Qualities Valued in Children in the United States, 1964–1984." *Social Science Research,* 18:195–236.

Bachrach, Christine A., Kathy Shepherd Stolley, and Kathryn A. London. 1992. "Relinquishment of Premarital Births: Evidence from National Survey Data." *Family Planning Perspectives,* 24(1):27–32.

Bellah, Robert N., Richard Madsen, William M. Sullivan, Ann Swidley, and Steven M. Tipton. 1985. *Habits of the Heart.* New York: Harper and Row.

Bumpass, Larry L. 1990. "What's Happening to the Family? Interactions Between Demographic and Institutional Change." *Demography,* 27(4):483–498.

Bumpass, Larry L., James A. Sweet. 1989. "National Estimates of Cohabitation." *Demography,* 26(4):615–625.

Bumpass, Larry L., James A. Sweet, and Andrew J. Cherlin. 1991. "The Role of Cohabitation in Declining Rates of Marriage." *Journal of Marriage and the Family,* 53:913–927.

Caplow, Theodore, Howard M. Bahr, and Bruce A. Chadwick. 1983. *All Faithful People.* Minneapolis: University of Minnesota Press.

Cherlin, Andrew J. 1992. *Marriage, Divorce, and Remarriage,* Revised and enlarged edition. Cambridge, Massachusetts: Harvard University Press.

Chester, R. 1977. *Divorce in Europe.* Leiden, The Netherlands: Martinus Nijhoff.

Coale, A. J. and M. Zelnik. 1963. *New Estimates of Fertility and Population in the United States.* Princeton: Princeton University Press.

Forrest, Jacqueline Darroch and Susheela Singh. 1990. "The Sexual and Reproductive Behavior of American Women, 1982–1988." *Family Planning Perspectives,* 22(5):206–214.

Freed, Doris Jonas and Henry H. Foster. 1980. "Divorce in the Fifty States: An Overview as of August 1, 1980." *The Family Law Reporter,* 6(42):4043–4066.

Glenn, Norval D. 1987. "Social Trends in the United States: Evidence from Sample Surveys." *Public Opinion Quarterly,* 51:S109–S126.

Goldscheider, Calvin and William D. Mosher. 1991. "Patterns of Contraceptive Use in the United States: The Importance of Religious Factors." *Studies in Family Planning,* 22(2):102–115.

Greeley, Andrew M. 1977. *The American Catholic.* New York: Basic Books.

Greeley, Andrew M. 1989. *Religious Change in America.* Cambridge, Massachusetts: Harvard University Press.

Greeley, Andrew M. 1990. *The Catholic Myth: The Behavior and Beliefs of American Catholics.* New York: Charles Scribner's Sons.

Greeley, Andrew M., William C. McCready, and Kathleen McCourt. 1976. *Catholic Schools in a Declining Church.* Kansas City: Sheed and Ward.

Greeley, Andrew M., Robert T. Michael, and Tom W. Smith. 1990. "Americans and Their Sexual Partners." *Society,* 27(July/August):36–42.

Hajnal, John. 1953. "The Marriage Boom." *Population Index,* 19:80–103.

Hajnal, John. 1965. "European Marriage Patterns in Perspective." In D. V. Glass and D. E. C. Eversley (eds.) *Population in History.* Chicago: Aldine Publishing Company.

Hajnal, John. 1982. "Two Kinds of Preindustrial Household Formation System." *Population and Development Review,* 8(3):449–494.

Heaton, Tim B. 1992. "Demographics of the Contemporary Mormon Family." *Dialogue: A Journal of Mormon Thought,* 25(3):19–35.

Himes, N. E. 1970. *Medical History of Contraception.* New York: Schocken Books.

Hout, M. and Andrew M. Greeley, 1987. "Church Attendance in the United States." *American Sociological Review,* 52:325–345.

Jones, E. F. and C. F. Westoff. 1979. "The End of 'Catholic' Fertility." *Demography,* 16:209–217.

Kussmaul, A. 1981. *Servants in Husbandry in Early-Modern England.* Cambridge: Cambridge University Press.

Laslett, P. 1965. *The World We Have Lost.* New York: Charles Scribner.

Lenski, G. 1963. *The Religious Factor.* New York: Anchor Books.

Lesthaeghe, Ron J. 1983. "A Century of Demographic and Cultural Change in Western Europe: An Exploration of Underlying Dimensions." *Population and Development Review,* 9:411–435.

Lesthaeghe, Ron J. and Johan Surkyn. 1988. "Cultural Dynamics and Economic Theories of Fertility Change." *Population and Development Review,* 14:1–45.

Lesthaeghe, Ron J. and C. Wilson. 1986. "Modes of Production, Secularization, and the Pace of Fertility Decline in Western Europe, 1870–1930." In A. J. Coale and S. C. Watkins (eds.) *The Decline of Fertility in Europe,* pp. 261–292. Princeton: Princeton University Press.

24

London, Kathryn A. 1991. "Cohabitation, Marriage, Marital Dissolution, and Remarriage: United States, 1988." *Advance Data from Vital and Health Statistics*, No. 194. Hyattsville, Maryland: National Center for Health Statistics.

Macfarlane, Alan. 1979. *The Origins of English Individualism: The Family, Property, and Social Transition*. Cambridge: Cambridge University Press.

Macfarlane, Alan. 1986. *Marriage and Love in England: Modes of Reproduction, 1300–1840*. Oxford: Basil Blackwell.

McCarthy, J. 1979. "Religious Commitment, Affiliation, and Marriage Dissolution." In R. Wuthnow (ed.) *The Religious Dimension: New Directions in Quantitative Research*. New York: Academic Press.

Mosher, William D. 1990. "Contraceptive Practice in the United States, 1982–1988." *Family Planning Perspectives*, 22(5):198–205.

Mosher, William D. and William F. Pratt. 1990. "Contraceptive Use in the United States, 1973–1988." *Advance Data from Vital and Health Statistics*, No. 182. Hyattsville, Maryland: National Center for Health Statistics.

Mosher, William D., Linda B. Williams, and David P. Johnson. 1992. "Religion and Fertility in the United States: New Patterns." *Demography*, 29(2):199–214.

Mueller, John. 1988. "Trends in Political Tolerance." *Public Opinion Quarterly*, 52:1–25.

National Center for Health Statistics. 1986. "Advance Report of Final Natality Statistics, 1984." *Monthly Vital Statistics Report*, 35(4)suppl. Hyattsville, Maryland: Public Health Service.

National Center for Health Statistics. 1990. "Advance Report of Final Natality Statistics, 1988." *Monthly Vital Statistics Report*, 39(4)suppl. Hyattsville, Maryland: Public Health Service.

Nunn, Clyde Z., Harry J. Crockett, Jr., and J. Allen Williams, Jr. 1978. *Tolerance for Nonconformity*. San Francisco: Jossey-Bass.

Roof, Wade C., and William McKinney. 1987. *American Mainline Religion*. New Brunswick, NJ: Rutgers University Press.

Roussel, L. and P. Festy. 1979. "Recent Trends in Attitudes and Behavior Affecting the Family in Council of Europe Member States." *Population Studies*, No. 4. Strasbourg, France: Council of Europe.

Schneider, Carl E. 1985. "Moral Discourse and the Transformation of American Family Law, 1803–1879." *Michigan Law Review*, 83(8):1803–1879.

Shorter, E. 1975. *The Making of the Modern Family*. New York: Basic Books.

Shorter, E., J. Knodel, and E. van de Walle. 1971. "The Decline of Non-Marital Fertility in Europe, 1880–1940." *Population Studies*, 25:375–393.

Smith, Tom W. 1991. "Adult Sexual Behavior in 1989: Number of Partners, Frequency of Intercourse and Risk of AIDS." *Family Planning Perspectives*, 23(3):102–107.

Sonenstein, Freya L., Joseph H. Pleck, and Leighton C. Ku. 1991. "Levels of Sexual Activity Among Adolescent Males in the United States." *Family Planning Perspectives*, 23(4):162–167.

Sweet, James A. and Larry L. Bumpass. 1990. "Religious Differentials in Marriage Behavior and Attitudes." NSFH Working Paper No. 15.

Thornton, Arland. 1985. "Reciprocal Influences of Family and Religion in a Changing World." *Journal of Marriage and the Family*, 47:381–394.

Thornton, Arland. 1989. "Changing Attitudes Toward Family Issues in the United States." *Journal of Marriage and the Family*, 51:873-893.

Thornton, Arland and Deborah Freedman. 1983. "The Changing American Family." *Population Bulletin*, 38(4):1–39.

Thornton, Arland and Thomas E. Fricke. 1987. "Social Change and the Family: Comparative Perspectives from the West, China, and South Asia." *Sociological Forum*, 2(4): 746–779.

Thornton, Arland, William G. Axinn, and Dan. H. Hill. 1992. "Reciprocal Effects of Religiosity, Cohabitation and Marriage." *American Journal of Sociology*, 98(3):628–651.

van de Walle, E. and J. Knodel. 1980. "Europe's Fertility Transition: New Evidence and Lessons for Today's Developing World." *Population Bulletin*, 34(6):1–44.

Watkins, S. C. 1981. "Regional Patterns of Nuptiality in Europe, 1870–1960." *Population Studies*, 35:199–215.

Westoff, C. F. 1979. "The Blending of Catholic Reproductive Behavior." In R. Wuthnow (ed.) *The Religious Dimension: New Directions in Quantitative Research*. New York: Academic Press.

Zelnik, Melvin and John F. Kantner. 1980. "Sexual Activity, Contraceptive Use and Pregnancy Among Metropolitan Area Teenagers: 1971–1979." *Family Planning Perspectives*, 12(5):30–36.

26

Chapter 3

THE CATHOLIC VISION OF HUMAN SEXUALITY: ITS REALISM

Patrick Lee, Ph.D.

Few would deny that the Church on this continent has not succeeded well in communicating to people and persuading people of her teaching on sexual morality. Specific parts of the Church's teaching have, of course, been constantly challenged. But my topic this morning involves characteristics of the teaching as a whole. I shall discuss three contemporary objections. (1) The Church is accused of being negative and restrictive in her teaching on sex. (2) The Church is accused of being too severe. (3) The Church is accused of being unrealistic in requiring everyone to live up to her strict teaching. The combined effect of these objections is, not so much to argue that the Church's conclusions are wrong, but that the Church's teaching on sex is not something which we should insist on, that perhaps we should remain silent about it. I will consider these objections one by one, and I will argue that they are based on a misunderstanding of Catholic teaching.

I.

Catholic teaching on sexual morality has acquired the image of being totally negative. Many people have the feeling that Catholic teaching on sex is a restriction, a limitation, a straight-jacket. Catholic teaching seems to them to exclude a whole host of fulfilling experiences. But this attitude has things exactly upside down. It is the Church's teaching which is positive and the opposite, secular culture's view, which is negative and limiting.

It is true that the scholastic theology manuals of thirty or more years ago defended Church teaching on sex by means of a legalistic ethical theory. The arguments appealed to abstract human nature, backed up by divine will, rather than to real human goods or to aspects of human persons. Thus, moral norms, especially those regarding sex, often appeared to be arbitrary and revocable *rules* imposed from outside rather than *truths* indicating the direction of true human flourishing.[1]

Many theologians in the last thirty years have argued that the way to respond to this accusation of negativity is to modify the teaching, that is, make it less strict.

However, along with John Paul II and many able contemporary moral theologians, I believe that, first, an effort is needed to understand more deeply the personalistic basis of the Church's constant teaching on sex, but, secondly, the teaching itself is true and absolutely essential to the flourishing of the life of faith. Here, as elsewhere, we should clearly distinguish between the teaching itself—which in its main lines has been a constant part of the Gospel from the very beginning—and the reasons put forward to support and explain that teaching.

The Church's teaching is positive and a defense of important and central values in the lives of all people. In the first place, Catholic teaching presents to us as normative, as what we husbands or wives should and with God's grace can bring about, an unbelievably lovely and beautiful reality: we married people are called to leave father and mother and cling to our wife or husband and become one flesh, to build a two-in-one flesh unity founded on self-giving love, which unfolds or is crowned by children as concrete images of that love; [2] we are called to cooperate intimately with God in creating new personal human life, and to build up—again with God's grace—a home, a domestic church, a warm and loving environment in which children and parents can flourish.[3] That is a wonderful and inspiring teaching. Moreover, following Catholic teaching on sex leads to happy, fruitful, holy lives. The

28

Church truly has good news about sexual and family living! By no means should this teaching be hidden under a bushel basket.

Because this teaching is beautiful and because it does speak to our heart, young people, even in a culture saturated with immoral sexual attitudes, receive this teaching well and even enthusiastically when it is presented clearly and forthrightly. I see this first-hand at the university in which I now teach, the Franciscan University of Steubenville. We see this many times in the history of the Church. After all, the sexual mores of the Roman empire were quite similar to the unfavorable moral environment we have in our culture today. But Christianity spread rapidly, and partly because the Church's teaching on sex, marriage and family was articulated clearly, as we see for example in St. Paul.

Moreover, the teachings which lead people to think that the Church's doctrine is negative are not actually fundamentally negative. We can see this briefly with respect to some of the moral norms which elicit the accusation of negativity.

On divorce and remarriage: the Church says no to divorce and remarriage, but that is to exclude a negative action, namely, the attempted dissolution of a marriage. The Church's teaching stands up for fidelity in marriage and the permanence and sacredness of this bond, and that is positive.

The same is true on contraception. As its very name indicates, contraception is a choice *against* conception, that is, against new life. Thus, it is an anti-life act—not the choice to destroy a new life, but still a choice contrary to new life, in that the content of the choice is that a new life not come to be. Moreover, since the child is the concrete unfolding or fulfillment of the spousal personal communion, a choice contrary to the procreative good is also against the unitive good. The Church's teaching is positive: new life is very good, and spousal love is very good, and this teaching entails the exclusion of negative actions against new life and against spousal love.

A similar point is true regarding fornication. The Church's teaching defends the goodness of the body and the sacredness of the Christian body.

In every case it is the same. The accusation of negativity views matters upside down. When the Church preaches against divorce, contraception, and so on she is preaching against negative actions. The defense of basic goods of the person, and of the reality of God's covenant must involve excluding actions against those goods, but to exclude negations is not a fundamentally negative action. It calls us to a respect and a reverence for those goods.

Moral truths are distinct from arbitrary rules. Moral truths or norms direct us to real basic human goods or real fulfillment for ourselves and for others.[4] Christian moral norms direct us to our actual fulfillment in Christ, the eternal kingdom, which includes both divine life and human fulfillment (*Gaudium et Spes*, #39). Such norms, then, are not alien impositions, that is, they are not alien or extrinsic to what is in our own best interest. But they are extrinsic to irrational desires. Following them does involve setting aside or detaching ourselves from desires for things which are not in reality good or fulfilling for us. Now, to the extent that people identify themselves with desires which are not yet integrated with their respect for basic human goods and with their commitment of faith, to that extent moral truths have the appearance of being negative and restrictive. But this is mere appearance. The Church's teaching merely insists on reality rather than fantasy.

II.

A second and widespread contemporary objection to Catholic teaching on sex is that the Church places entirely too much emphasis on sex, that she is too severe in her teaching on sex. The Church views sex as so serious that the traditional teaching has been that all deliberate sexual sins (immoral choices of sexual pleasure or arousal in oneself or another) are grave matter, that is, these are the sorts of acts which if done with sufficient reflection and full consent cause one to lose the divine life within one. Some who accept the teaching of the Church with respect to what is right and what is wrong have explicitly or quietly taken the position that while the Church's teaching on sex is true it is not nearly as important as previous generations mistakenly held.

However, the doctrine that intentional violations of the marital good, whether by the married or by the unmarried, are grave matter, is, I think, not a position which can be set aside. This doctrine was for several generations taught as something to be held definitively and by virtually all authorized teachers in the Catholic Church. This teaching, then, seems to fulfill the criteria laid down by *Lumen gentium* (#25) for a teaching infallibly proposed by the ordinary magisterium.[5] Common sense supports this point: if virtually all the authorized teachers in the Church have for generations said of a list of acts that doing these things with sufficient reflection and full consent excludes one from the kingdom of God, then if that teaching were wrong the Church would have misled many people on an issue central to salvation. To say that this teaching in wrong is to imply that the Church is responsible for untold misery in this life and the next. Such an organization could scarcely be called "the pillar and the bulwark of the truth" (1 Tim. 4:2). So, it does not seem that this teaching on the gravity of the matter of sexual sins can change. But this point also shows that the moral truths concerning sex are extremely important, and are central to leading a good and faithful Christian life.

The experiences of the last thirty years provide something like a laboratory experiment which confirms this point. Thirty years ago one might have asked, "What would happen if it became generally accepted that traditional sexual morality is either wrong or unimportant?" Today we have the answer to that question: the sexual revolution, instead of leading to healthier and less repressed sexual lives, which was expected, has led to immense suffering and has ruined lives. The results are well documented: broken marriages, women in poverty, abandoned children, abused and neglected children, loss of faith stemming from irregular marriage-situations, a plague of sexually transmitted diseases. These realities can be traced to infidelity and to vehement sexual desires not integrated with respect for real human goods and commitment of faith.

Thus, the first reason why the Church's teaching on sex is central and must be clearly and forthrightly articulated, is that the goods at stake in sexuality are fundamental human goods, and by one's relationship to these goods one organizes—for good or bad—a large part of one's life. As to the gravity of sexual sins: intentionally to impede or damage a basic human good—which occurs in such acts as masturbation, fornication, contraception, and so on—is gravely wrong.

The second reason why uprightness in the sexual domain is central to Christian life is that not only basic human values, but also values of the faith or Christian values are at stake. The marital and familial relationships are images of the relationships within the Godhead and also of ourselves to God. For this reason central truths of revelation are communicated in marital and familial language: God is Father, Son and Holy Spirit; Christ is related to the Church as a bridegroom is related to his bride; Christ teaches us to call God "Father" in the Lord's prayer. Sexual sins weaken the bonds of family and to that extent make it impossible to understand God's self-revelation.[6]

Thirdly, heavenly communion is not just spiritual but includes a bodily union with the Lord and with those who have accepted our Lord in heaven. Marriage, the giving of self in a two-in-one flesh unity, foreshadows this bodily communion. Thus, respect for the body is an aspect of respect for the Body of Christ. On the other hand, sexual sins violate not only the capacity to give oneself in marriage, but also violate the greater good which marriage foreshadows: the body of Christ. St. Paul makes this point succinctly in his argument against fornication:

> The body, however, is not for fornication (*porneia*) but for the Lord, and the Lord is for the body; God raised the Lord and will also raise us by his power. Do you not know that your bodies are members of Christ?. . . . Avoid fornication. Every other sin a person commits is outside the body, but the fornicator sins against his own body. Do you not know that your body is a temple of the holy Spirit within you, whom you have from God, and that you are not your own? (1 Cor. 6: 13–20)

Respect for our bodies, then is an essential part of reverence for heavenly communion.[7]

Fourthly, sexual immorality is closely tied to temptations against faith. In sexual sins the person chooses a sexual act not because it contributes to the real human good of marriage, but rather for the pleasure it brings or for the illusion of contributing to personal communion.[8] In such acts the person uses his or her body as a tool for producing conscious satisfaction or as a tool for producing the feeling of personal communion. In marriage sexual desire is integrated with love for real human goods: in marriage the sexual act is chosen as an embodiment or a concretion of the many levelled, one-flesh unity which is marriage (a unity whose crowning point or fulfillment is the procreative good, as *Gaudium et spes*, #50 teaches). Outside marriage, or within marriage if the total marital good is not respected, sexual desire is not integrated with respect for real goods, and the result is that the body is viewed as a mere instrument or tool for gratification. The body is viewed as subpersonal. A habit of such acts gradually changes the way one views one's own body and the bodies of others. Gradually, the body seems to be insignificant, something which of itself lacks meaning but can acquire whatever meanings one chooses to impose on it. But with such a view of the body and matter it is hard to take seriously central Catholic teachings on the Eucharist, the resurrection of the body, the importance of Mary's role in salvation, the need for Sacraments by which to be joined to Christ's salvific acts, and, indeed, the Incarnation itself. In short, habitual unchastity leads to depersonalizing the body, and depersonalizing the body leads to a Gnostic view of salvation.[9]

It seems to have been precisely this Gnostic tendency that led St. Paul and his immediate disciples to address so emphatically sexual problems. Referring to sexual sins, the author of the letter to the Ephesians writes: "Let no one deceive you with empty words, for because of these things the wrath of God comes on those who are disobedient." (Eph. 5:6) The "no one" the author refers to is apparently those who wish to downplay the seriousness of sexual sins. We know from Paul's first letter to the Corinthians and also from writings very soon after this that the basis for the objection to the Church's teaching was the same as it frequently is today: namely, that the merely physical or biological of itself lacks personal significance.[10] This is not to say that all of those who argue in this way are guilty of unchastity, but it is to say that unchastity leads to this serious blind-spot and that such a blind-spot leads to difficulties of faith.

Many people object to the Church's teaching on sex that too much emphasis is placed on isolated acts, that what is really important is the orientation of one's life, not this or that single action. And it is objected that isolated acts should not be classified as grave matter.[11]

It is true that in scholastic theology texts the orientation or organization of one's life was not sufficiently considered or clarified. Moreover, it also is true that not all choices are equally important. Yet, it remains that it is by conscious choices that we accept communion with the Lord, and it is possible by one conscious choice to reject explicitly or implicitly communion with the Lord.

The moral act is the choice, and a choice is not the same as the external behavior which carries out the choice. The external behavior may be very brief and once done is over with. But when one chooses one not only selects among objects to pursue, one also determines one's self to be in one way rather than another. And this determination of the self, or this shaping of oneself is not transitory. Rather it lasts, it remains as an aspect of oneself, unless and until one reverses that choice. Thus, each choice is important because by it one determines oneself to be as one chooses, one shapes a certain type of self. A mortal sin is a choice which constitutes oneself outside communion with God and his friends. It is an act which is incompatible with the commitment by which one accepted communion with God and with all of those who have accepted God's invitation of common life. As there are certain choices which are simply incompatible with a commitment of friendship to another human person—for example hatred of him, or choices seriously to harm his children—so there are certain choices which cannot co-exist in us with our act of accepting God's invitation to friendship and cooperation with him.[12]

To locate our communion with God on a level below that which we can immediately affect by our conscious choices would be to make our everyday choices, and the life which we consciously fashion by our choices, extrinsic to the salvation and communion with God and his friends which is the kingdom of God being built up in mystery. If justification and salvation operated at a so-called deep level below our conscious choices, as some fundamental-option theories maintain, then justification and salvation would be things which simply happened to us without our conscious, active cooperation.[13] Such notions of justification and salvation are contrary to the definitive teaching of the Church: God's strategy is to save us with our conscious, active cooperation, our active cooperation itself being part of God's gift.

Our individual free choices are extremely important. We all recognize this with respect to good or heroic actions: the heroic act of a St. Stephen or of a St. Maximilian Kolbe, or the deathbed conversion of a sinner. But we cannot logically hold that good moral acts can be decisive but at the same time deny that bad moral acts also can be decisive.

The gift God offers us is not extrinsic to ourselves. That is, while heavenly communion includes more than our good deeds and human fulfillment—for it principally consists in sharing in the divine life itself, seeing God as he is in himself—nevertheless, not even the sharing in divine life is an extrinsic reward which can be imposed on us regardless of the kind of self we have constituted by our choices with or without God's grace. If we reject the offer of communion with God and his friends explicitly or implicitly, then we have constituted a self which is outside communion with God and his friends, and then God cannot impose communion on us. God cannot do what is intrinsically contradictory; he cannot, for example, build a boulder so large he cannot lift it. Similarly, God cannot bring it about that I both am outside communion with God (by my choices) and am not outside communion with God (by God's action). Intentional violations of the goods at stake in sexuality are inconsistent with communion with God and his friends. But this stern point is just the logical corollary of the previous point, namely, that marriage and sex are central to our lives as Christians.

Moreover, talk of isolated sexual sins ignores the dynamic situation of sexual desire. Temptations to sexual sins are quite different from temptations leading to many other sins, for example stealing or lying (sins which do admit parvity, i.e., types of acts which are grave matter, but some instances of which are such small offenses that they are not grave matter). Temptations to lie or steal arise from external circumstances. Furthermore, satisfying the desire to lie or steal does not by itself lead to a habit of lying or stealing. Temptations to sexual sins, however, stem from an interior, deep and constant desire, and one which is difficult to control. Also, sexual pleasure is quite intense. Sexual acts done simply for pleasure, that is, sexual acts not integrated

34

with commitment to real goods, intensify the desire for sexual pleasure and establish a habit. Non-integrated sexual desire is like the desire for drink by an alcoholic or the desire for narcotic drugs by someone who has tried them and liked them: a single instance tends to set up more intense desire for repeated experiences. Thus, so-called isolated sexual sins quickly tend to cause habits of sinning.[14]

Furthermore, talk of isolated sexual sins suggests that many sexual sins, for example masturbation, are purely private. But this is not the case: the one who masturbates will most likely fantasize about someone, and thus reduces others to objects, thus affecting the way he relates to others. Sexual sins are far from private but color the way people relate to others in other areas of their lives.[15]

To conclude this second part, on the importance and centrality of Catholic teaching on sex: it is understandable to wish that the Church could perhaps lighten the burden a bit with respect to her teaching on sex, or not insist on it so much. Nevertheless, this is not a realistic wish. First, to remain silent on these issues would simply abandon people to the immense amount of suffering which sexual immorality causes. Moreover, the wish seems to be based on a legalistic view of the Christian life or at least a legalistic view of Christian sexual morality. The wish implicitly views the reward of being in God's grace and heavenly communion as something extrinsic, something outside the life we live, so that God can give us the reward even if we haven't passed the test—God can as it were grade us on a curve, give everyone an extra fifteen points on his or her final exam, so to speak. But the reward which God offers us is not separate from the life of good deeds to which he calls us. As the letter to the Ephesians says: "For we are his handiwork, created in Christ Jesus for the good works that God has prepared in advance, that we should live in them." (Eph. 2:10) In other words, part of the gift which God wishes to give us is a life of good deeds, by which we actively cooperate with God in preparing the materials of the heavenly banquet. (see *Gaudium et spes,* 39) To ask that this burden be lightened is really to ask God to change the gift he wills to give us.

III.

The last objection I want to consider is closely related to the second. This is the objection that Catholic teaching on sex is unrealistic: It is too difficult, most people cannot live up to it. So, the appeal is made, let us reclassify it: Catholic teaching is still true, only it describes the ideal, not what is required. Regarding this objection, there are four points I wish to make.

First, Christian teachers should not fear asking Christians to make strenuous efforts and expend great dedication. Christianity is or includes a grand and noble communal work or enterprise: we are called to actively cooperate with God in building up the kingdom of God, to do our part in preparing the materials for the eternal banquet. But great works generally require strenuous effort and often require heroism. High school football or basketball coaches, for example, do not flinch from asking their players to participate in grueling daily practices and to discipline themselves in food, drink and sleep. Christianity is a call to inconceivable greatness. There should be no surprise if this call entails discipline and strenuous effort. It is really surprising that people think it should be otherwise.

Secondly, many Christians today do live up to Catholic teaching on sex. The difficulties should not be exaggerated. There are some few people for whom living up to Catholic teaching on sex requires heroic efforts: special circumstances make it especially difficult for them. God will give them extra graces to do the heroic. But for most people, while chastity is difficult, it is not so difficult that one should call it heroic.

Thirdly, both Scripture and the Church teach clearly that God will give us the grace we need to follow his commandments. The Church definitively teaches this in the Council of Trent:

> But no one, however much justified, should consider himself exempt from the observance of the commandments; no one should use that rash statement, once forbidden by the Fathers under anathema, that the observance of the commandments of God is impossible for one that is justified. For God does not command the impossible, but by commanding admonishes you to do what you can and to pray for what you cannot, and aids you that you may be able. (DS, 725 1536)

As the letter to Ephesians says, in the text I quoted a moment ago, God has destined us to a life of good deeds. And this life of good deeds is part of the good news which God has promised us. But leading an upright life in the sexual domain is an integral part of a life of good deeds. So, we know by faith that God will give us the grace we need to live uprightly in the sexual domain. Put otherwise: God is faithful to his promises, but part of the good news is that God really does will us to be good and holy men and women!

Fourthly, and finally, there are many for whom Catholic teaching is realistic only if it is articulated clearly, defended, and given community or institutional support. Following Catholic teaching on sex is *not* possible for someone who does not see any appeal in it: and that is likely to be so if one is not shown that it is important (even if he or she does not understand why—although that is really more desirable). In other words, the widespread view that sexual sins are not serious tends to ensure that people will fall into sins of unchastity and then habits of unchastity. For, given the power of sexual desire and the power of external temptations to sexual sins in today's culture, if one sees little point in avoiding them then one probably will not do so.

Resisting temptations to sexual sins is also quite difficult for people acting in isolation, without communal support. I have seen positive community support at the Franciscan University of Steubenville. What characterizes this effective support, it seems to me, are two things: (1) the leaders view living chastely with positiveness and enthusiasm; (2) they enlist the active cooperation of young people in the administration of the programs. We need widespread efforts of this sort in the Church as a whole.

Catholic teaching on sex is not negative, nor is it too severe, nor is it unrealistic. God is calling us to a life of love, respect and fidelity for the noble goods of personal communion, new life, and a share in Christ's covenant with his Church, and that truly is Good News!

NOTES

1. Cf. Germain Grisez, *Contraception and the Natural Law* (Milwaukee: Bruce, 1964), Ch. 3; Germain Grisez, *The Way of the Lord Jesus*, Vol. I, *Christian Moral Principles* (Chicago: Franciscan Herald, 1983), Ch. 1, Ch. 4 F–H.

2. *Gaudium et Spes*, #48.

3. On the family as domestic church: John Paul II, *Familiaris consortio*, #49–50.

4. Cf. Germain Grisez, *The Way of the Lord Jesus, Vol. I: Christian Moral Principles* (Chicago: Franciscan Herald, 1983), Chs. 4, 7, 8 A and 8 F. A very lucid presentation of much of what is discussed in detail in Grisez's work: Russell Shaw, *Why We Need Confession* (Huntington, Ind.: Our Sunday Visitor, 1986).

5. Cf. John Ford, Germain Grisez, Joseph Boyle, John Finnis and William E. May, *The Teaching of Humanae Vitae: A Defense* (San Francisco: Ignatius, 1988), pp. 7–32, 117–219.

6. Cf. Germain Grisez, *The Way of the Lord Jesus, Vol. II, Living a Christian Life*, forthcoming, Ch. 9 E.

7. Ibid.

8. Germain Grisez, *Way of the Lord Jesus*, Vol. 2.

9. Ibid.

10. Cf. St. Irenaeus's description of the Gnostic view of matter in the second century: "For, as it is impossible for the earthly element to partake in salvation, not being susceptible of it, so it is impossible for the spiritual element (which they pretend to be themselves) to suffer corruption, whatever actions they have indulged in. As gold sunk

in filth will not lose its beauty but preserve its own nature, and the filth will be unable to impair the gold, so nothing can injure them, even if their deeds immerse them in matter, and nothing can change their spiritual essence. Therefore the most perfect among them do unabashed all the forbidden things of which Scripture assures us 'that they which do such things shall not inherit the kingdom of God.' " (St. Irenaeus, *Adversus haereses*, I, 6, 2–3, cited in Hans Jonas, *The Gnostic Religion* [Boston: Beacon Press, 1963], pp. 270–271).

11. For example, Philip S. Keane, S.S., *Sexual Morality, A Catholic Perspective*, (New York: Paulist Press, 1978), pp. 35–40; also see the disparaging remarks on this position, although she does not explicitly reject it, in: Lisa Sowle Cahill, "Catholic Sexual Ethics and the Dignity of the Person: A Double Message," *Theological Studies* 50 (1989), pp. 120–150.

12. On the nature of grave matter and mortal sin, see: Germain Grisez, *The Way of the Lord Jesus, Vol. I, Christian Moral Principles*, loc. cit., Chs. 15–17.

13. There are various theories which use the term "fundamental option." I am disagreeing here with those fundamental-option theories which hold that self-determination or self-disposition is distinct from conscious choice with respect to concrete actions. That is, I think it is important to see, as I argue in the text, that self-determination is an aspect of our concrete (categorial) choices rather than a reality lying "below" these choices. On the latter theory, the relationship between this "core-level" self-determination and concrete free choice (of determinate actions) becomes quite ambiguous.

For example, in his *Sexual Morality, A Catholic Perspective*, Philip Keane writes: "The term 'fundamental option' means the stable orientation or life direction that exists at the core level of the human person. One's fundamental option can be either toward God or away from God. When we sin we separate ourselves from God at the core level and thus break our fundamental option for God. The term fundamental option implies the nuances of religious anthropology mentioned above, i.e., that the human person is a complex in such wise that we cannot simplistically argue the character of a person's fundamental option based on individual external acts taken out of context," (Philip S. Keane, S.S., *Sexual Morality, A Catholic Perspective*, p. 38). The last statement is true with respect to *external* acts, but it is evident from the rest of Keane's book that he also applies it to *single* free choices, and that is the disputed point. Keane writes: "In the area of sexuality it seems quite unlikely that in certain types of sexual behavior a person totally estranges himself or herself from God in a single act. This and other implications of fundamental option for sexuality will be developed in subsequent chapters." (Ibid, p. 40)

Richard McCormick complains that recent attacks by John Finnis and Germain Grisez on certain fundamental-option theories are based on misunderstandings of the theory (see Richard McCormick, S.J., *The Critical Calling, Reflections on Moral Dilemmas Since Vatican II* [Washington, D.C.: Georgetown, 1989], pp. 181–188.) However, the crux of the issue concerns the relationship between self-determination and free choice of actions bearing on basic human goods, referred to by many as "categorial choices." Authors of fundamental-option theories criticized by Finnis, Grisez and myself in this article maintain, in various ways—for the theory is not uniform—that self-determination is not identical with free choice. Though free choices may *cause* or *occasion* a self-determination or self-orientation, the latter (according to these theories) is in some way on a deeper level than free choices, so one's orientation is not likely to be reversed by a single choice. Finnis, Grisez, others and I hold that it is precisely in our choices that we determine ourselves and thus one cannot say a priori that it is unlikely that people reverse their fundamental orientations by single free choices. Once we recognize, however, the significance of free choices themselves, and their self-determinative aspect, the appeal of fundamental-option theories which locate self-determination below free choice lose whatever logical appeal they originally had. For a development of this point, see: Joseph Boyle, "Freedom, the Human Person, and Human Action," in *Principles of Catholic Moral LIfe,* ed. William E. May (Chicago: Franciscan Herald, 1980), 237–266.

14. Germain Grisez, *The Way of the Lord Jesus, Vol. II, Living a Christian Life,* forthcoming, Ch. 9 E.

15. Ibid.

Chapter 4

COMMUNICATING THE CATHOLIC VISION OF HUMAN SEXUALITY

William J. Thorn, Ph.D.
Victoria Thorn

I. William J. Thorn Ph.D.

Good morning. Bon jour, buenos dias, buon giorno.

I'm happy to be here. I hope I can give you something from my small area of expertise which will help you shepherd your flock.

In communicating the Church's teaching on sexuality you place yourself in the position Paul wrote the Corinthians about regarding preaching Christ crucified: for many in our time the teaching is a stumbling block and folly compared to the wisdom of the world.

This means you, teaching a view of sexuality rooted in God's creative plan and something other than personal pleasure and self fulfillment, will be caught in the swirl of controversy, simultaneously derided and applauded. Like Paul, you will be the target of stones from opponents who, in this media age, aim for your public image rather than your ribs or head. Also like Paul, you will need to remind us of the teaching. As the father of 6, I and my family need the encouragement of your public witness and the truth of the Church's teaching. We are in this together.

In giving this talk, I recognize that my orientation will be heavily skewed to the United States. and Canada, for we have similar mass media systems. I understand that the amount of media saturation is different for us in the metropolitan societies than for you who come from more rural societies in the Caribbean, Latin America, and the Philippines. Despite these differences, we share an underlying communication process upon which you can build a strong effort to convey the Church's teaching. You, of course, will have to make the application to your own context.

When a small group of us were brought to Rome from different parts of the world to draft the foundation for what became *Aetatis Novae,* we were in full agreement on one central phenomena which had changed from the days of *Communio et Progressio:* we now live in an age in which reality itself is shaped by mass media. Communicating the Church's teaching on sexuality will come in the context of mass mediated culture.

Each of you has your own experience of both the power and vicissitude of contemporary mass media, the context within which you teach. Some of my colleagues claim the classic philosophical query about the tree falling in the forest should be revised to this: If a tree falls in the forest and the news media don't report it, did it actually happen?

Just over 20 years ago Avery Dulles wrote that we have passed into an age as fundamentally changed by electronic media as the 16th century was changed by the introduction of the printing press, an age in which the great challenge will be to get people to focus on the transcendent when media immerses them so thoroughly in the tangibles of this world. Walter Ong shares that view, articulating the profound differences between the literate culture which began in the 1600's from the second stage oral culture which began with radio and blossomed with the age of television. I share their view that teaching (a form of communicating) in this age requires adaptation to the oral culture and the influence of mass media.

The Christian vision presents sexuality as the fundamental understanding of our own identity and its location within the creative plan of our Father. Yet, the entertainment and news media view contradicts this in two ways. First, portraits of the Church's view of sexuality have been reduced to that of the village scold: don't, can't, shouldn't. Second, the vision of sexuality promulgated through entertainment media is limited to sexual action and titillation, turning us into a nation of voyeurs who find it increasingly difficult to visualize the difference between love and lust.

Your role was made substantially more difficult 25 years ago because you collectively and individually were selected as the most strategically advantageous group to make the "enemy" in the drive for legalized abortion, as Bernard Nathanson noted in *Aborting America*. Any discussion about communicating the Church's teaching in sexuality has to recognize that you enter the public discourse painted with the unflattering image skillfully projected by opponents to minimize the Church's credibility.

In addition, we are a house divided. Since *Humane vitae,* religious educators and other "professional" Catholics have consciously set themselves up as legitimate bearers of Catholic teaching on sexuality. Planned Parenthood of America made much of the fact that its new president, Pamela Maraldo, is a Roman Catholic: "Like most Catholics in America," she declared in announcing her selection, "I support the right to contraception and the right to choose." The Church, she said, is "out of touch" with its own followers. That Church is you and the Pope. Thus, the hierarchical Church is set against the People of God.

In a nutshell, this is the communication problem:

—Gain the audience's attention in the present media saturated environment.
—Break the stereotypes and images projected upon you so that you are seen realistically.
—Replace erroneous impressions with the Church's teaching.

As Helen Alvare so well showed last evening, you have a beautiful and coherent teaching for which the world hungers.

The question I am equipped to address by my background is how you can teach given the context created by mass media. Fear not: I am no proponent of big media solutions to this communication problem for reasons which come from communication research and the clear lesson of every Church which has tried to compete with the networks.

How powerful are the media? We used to believe they were so powerful that we used a medical model: the hypodermic effect, and we theorized about inoculation against propaganda. However, research has clearly shown that the media, while powerful as socializing agents over time, are subordinate to primary groups. Wilbur Schramm, one of the early giants of mass communication research visualized the primary groups as an interpretive body which helped make sense of mass media messages just as it helped make sense of every other experience in life.

Note that there are a variety of primary groups. Some, like extended families, have a rich array of connections to other primary groups. Think of these as people with a variety of links through professional and trade associations, social groupings, parish work, neighborhood ties, and the like. Some of these groups are almost totally resistant to media of the larger culture because they are immigrants who bring their media and culture with them. In a study funded by the Catholic Communication Campaign, I found that over 75% of migrant Mexican workers in the San Jose area have VCRs and televisions. Why? They watch Mexican movies and taped programs. Other groups here have limited primary groups, and some have virtually none. Think of the latter as isolated senior citizens, and the former as loners moving from one part of the country to another.

There is another kind of primary group, which come together temporarily for a specific purpose. Marriage preparation is one of these, so is an adult education class, a parish council on retreat, a sacramental preparation group, or a parish prayer discussion group. While they are together, they greatly influence each other as they work to make sense of their experiences. This is the power of group media: the media experience is shared in common, and the group discussion which follows leads to common understanding, though not necessarily full agreement.

After studying the effect of television on children in Denver in the 60's, Schramm concluded that it was less what TV brought to children than what they brought to TV that accounted for the effects. He had found the influence of primary groups and individual psychology. Subsequent research by Schramm, Paul Lazarsfeld and others has consistently demonstrated that primary groups and even secondary groups modify and interpret mass media messages as part of their normal process of helping the group maintain its values and apply them to new situations.

Think about this from the standpoint of the Church. How does it fit into the primary or secondary groups? What does the Church do to help its people make sense of the media environment? What does it do to help parents teach their children to make sense of it? How does it help the average Catholic understand the contemporary world's view of faith or Jesus in contrast to the Church's? How does it take advantage of natural teaching moments in media life or real life? Answering these questions leads to strategies for effective teaching.

Reflect with me for a moment upon teaching about sexuality. I mean here not body plumbing and how babies are made, but the

44

broader self understanding of being a man or a woman. How does each of us learn about our own sexuality and learn to see it through the lens Christ brought to us? It begins at infancy with the primary socializer—the family—and continues there, augmented as we go through life by school, friends, peer groups, professional associations, and close friends. This learning continues to the day we die, because our sexuality in the deepest sense changes as we change. Mid-life crisis, for example, is all about adapting to change, particularly in sexuality.

Where in all of this is official Church? It is but one of a host of would-be teachers. How does it help me or my children make sense of the sexuality presented by Oprah Winfrey or Days of Our Lives? Do you as Church directly teach about sexuality? Surely, you do in formal programs and schooling and speeches and the way you live out your own sexuality. But most often the Church's teaching comes indirectly: through others, first and foremost the family and social groups, second through teachers and peers, and third, through the image of the teaching which appears in media.

As teachers, we are always inclined to assess our task from our own perspective: how can I communicate *this* to *them* (described by one of my colleagues in a fit of despair as casting artificial pearls before real swine). The first media theorists saw it the same way, because they didn't give the audience sufficient credit. We now know that the more accurate model is this one:

WHO hears WHAT from WHOM in which MEDIUM for what PURPOSE

It is important to remember that we teach by actions, by speech, by images, but people learn most efficiently when they are making sense of their experiences and their observations.

As teachers, we need to understand that the audience is active, not passive, and it is motivated by specific needs. This audience-centered approach to communication will lead you to different teaching strategies than a source-centered approach, because it begins with the motivation of those you would reach.

Let me quickly review a few key points:

Gaining the audience's attention in the media environment is no small task because of the enormous volume of media options. Gaining attention is a task parents and children also face daily with each other, for media replaces time they might otherwise spend talking with each other.

How Catholics respond, as audience, differs according to their self-identified relationship to the Church. In research funded by the Catholic Communication Campaign, I have found significant differences in communication among three types of Catholics described by John Haughey: institutional, autogenic, and pneumatic. These differ very little on demographic items, including age, education, and income, but a great deal in how they view official sources and what they want.

The *institutional Catholic* perceives the Church as the authority on matters of faith, and looks to you and the Pope for guidance on moral and religious issues. Obedience and faithfulness to Church teaching are among the most important elements of this groups' way of life. Their primary and most credible source of teaching comes from the institution: sermons, publications, and addresses. For them, the hierarchy is important because it represents the universal Church.

The *autogenic Catholic* perceives the Church as a divinely inspired institution run by flawed and manipulative humans, one source among several on moral and religious issues. Personal analysis of important issues is the dominant concern of autogenics, for they give greater significance to an individual's decision process than to obedience (to which they add "blind"). They consider secular media coverage of Catholicism more credible because it is less likely to be manipulated by Church leaders for their own purposes. For them, the local worshipping community is the most important, and both diocese and Vatican are administrative levels of less import.

The *pneumatic Catholic* perceives the Church primarily as a source of spiritual growth and tests all to discern the movement of the Spirit. For pneumatics, the most important sources of communication are books and adult education, with Church publications secondary.

If you teach effectively from the authority of tradition and Church as bishop, you will surely reach the institutional Catholics and the pneumatics as well. However, you will reach the autogenics only by persuasive arguments, for Church authority is inadequate of itself. Moreover, autogenics limit their concern for Church teaching to issues with which they currently are wrestling. If they have already made up their mind or judge the issue irrelevant to them, they pay scant attention to Church teaching.

Our audience is diverse in its sources of information, diverse in its perspective of the role of the Church in its moral decision making, and not always interested when you want to speak. Is that hopeless? Not at all. It is the human condition.

How do you enter this stream to teach?

First, you need to undertake this in full battle dress—with prayer. Like Paul, we have to recognize that this is part of a larger struggle, and that we rely on Christ and the Spirit.

Second, you have the Church in praxis, in direct contact with the lived experience of your flock. A quick review of the later topics in this conference highlight some of them: NFP, ectopic pregnancies, in vitro fertilization, contraception. Out of this lived experience you have people open to the Church's teaching because they are wrestling with a fundamental issue.

Focus on small groups. You have access to many groups for whom you can tailor specific group media programs. Our educational system has thousands of teachers involved in sacramental preparation, parochial schools, adult education, RCIA, and the like. In each of these you have an audience of people available for specific purposes and open to the Church's teaching at a level they can understand. Prepared group media programs overcome the ignorance and confusion of specific instructors and move into the lived experience of the participants.

Third, we have a substantial communication system within the Church. Imperfect, but our own. Journalists in this system, like teachers, need to know both what the Church teaches about sexuality (not just that we oppose abortion) and what the bishop's strategy is for communicating that teaching. My experience with members of the CPA tells me that they are people of good will, somewhat tired of writing editorials against abortion, but often uncertain about the communication strategy of the diocese. Indeed, research I have done on bishops and editors disclosed that they spend far too little time discussing the editorial strategy of the paper together. You need to work with them to develop an effective strategy. They are the media professionals; you are the official teachers.

Fourth, you need to take up the issue in the public arena whenever possible and directly and immediately counter the errors which appear. This can be a very frustrating task, but it is an essential one.

Fifth, and perhaps most importantly from my perspective, you need to begin a major full blown campaign to teach parents how to pass their faith on to their children in this mass media age. Sexuality will surely be part of this, as will other elements of our tradition and teaching: the life of Christ, the Holy Family, our superheroes (saints) and our prayer forms.

The family is the first and most powerful primary group for all of us, augmented from middle childhood on by close friends, co-workers, and professional colleagues. Renew basic Christian communities, aim at precisely that phenomenon: the power of small groups to develop and reinforce values and beliefs.

47

My parents' generation relied on nuns, priests and parochial schools. That was a different world. I believe we should embrace the strategy long used by Jews and Mormons: make the family the basic educational unit by empowering and assisting parents as teachers. Teach parents how to develop their children's faith, and provide materials to assist them. I have long been impressed by how the Mormons support the parents in religious education through annual instructional manuals for Monday nights.

Parental education in the faith must begin as the child learns to speak and continue systematically through the pre-school years. First Communion preparation is far too late to begin; by age 7 the average child has spent over 10,000 hours in television's world. It is precisely during the preschool years that children form a world view based on their experience of the world around them. My formative experience in this area came when my oldest daughter was 2. As we drove in a business district in Milwaukee, she pointed out the window at the golden arches and said "Ronald McDonald". If we all—you bishops and we parents—are doing our job, every Catholic child should be able to recognize Jesus and the cross at the same age, because the child is capable of it. This is the reality of raising children in the media age.

Each teacher of my children has repeated the standard line: parents are the first and most influential teachers of religion to their children. Four of my children have gone through First Communion preparation, and each time the line is repeated, insistently. We all seem to agree to the reality, but what is your diocese doing to help parents? If we agree to the statement, then logic tells us that the Church should do more to prepare parents to teach their children than it does to prepare its formal teachers.

From my perspective as father and communication scholar, the Church provides too little assistance to parents in their role as first teachers of their children. Where are the parish-based or diocesan programs that teach parents how to teach their children? Where are the guidebooks? the supporting audio-visual materials? the curriculum keyed to age level and liturgical seasons?

When I served on the education commission of the Archdiocesan Synod in Milwaukee, I learned in our hearings that parents of young children regularly sought assistance from the diocese in teaching their children what the Church teaches because as products of post-Vatican II religious education, they said they didn't know what the Church teaches. Without substantial assistance from you, they will pass that ignorance on to the next generation.

What about reaching the larger community? The better communication strategy is to prepare a public relations effort which will take

48

advantage of the teaching moments which are sure to appear: municipal debates over sex education in the schools, state battles over funding welfare payments for single mothers, even pedophilia. You should also be prepared as a matter of common practice to correct errors as they appear in public forum. My archbishop, Rembert Weakland, observed that he spent more time dealing with press and press errors after the pastoral on the economy was adopted than he did during its preparation.

The lesson of public relations is this: Anyone who holds a press conference or speaks out publicly has at least temporary credibility. As long as you, the official teachers of the Church, do not consistently and immediately correct errors which appear in the public forum, the errors can become the accepted wisdom, by both Catholics and the larger community. And, if you do not speak out, the teaching will be unheard. This is a tiring and relentless struggle, but it is the nature of teaching in the media age.

We can complain, for example, that pedophilia has become an obsession with the media, but we ought to recognize that it offers a powerful teaching moment as well. Once gone, it will not come again. Surely it is embarrassing, but so was Peter's denial of Christ. Peter turned his denial into a teaching moment, over and over again. I believe Thomas did the same with his doubt, and that the other Apostles acknowledged their personal error and used it to teach others about redemption through Christ. We should do the same because these teaching moments lead people to a better understanding of Christ.

Communicating the Church's teaching, then, is both an internal and external communication task. I have focused more heavily on the internal task in the time allotted me because it seems to me that the higher priority is teaching the next generation and reducing confusion among the faithful. Through this effort you will also reach the larger public, many of whom may still reject the teaching. Leading Catholics and others to understand the Church's teaching on sexuality requires a prolonged and multi-level effort, and it should begin with the greatest attention to the context within which we first learn about our sexuality—the family. Improve the education here by helping parents teach their children, and you will move a great distance toward that end.

References

American Psychological Association. *Small Window, Big World: Children and Television*, 1992.

Chaffee, Steven. "Interpersonal and Mass Communication," *Inter Media*, 3rd Edition, 1986.

Dulles, Avery SJ. "The Church Is Communication," *Multimedia International*, 1(1972).

Haughey, John SJ. *The Conspiracy of God*, 1973.

Lazarsfeld, Paul et al. *Personal Influence*, 1955.

Ong, Walter SJ. "Communications Media and the State of Theology," *Cross Currents* 19(1969).

Schramm, Wilbur. *The Science of Human Communication*, 1963. *Television in the Lives of Our Children*, 1961.

I. Victoria Thorn

It is indeed an honor and a pleasure to have been invited to share my reflections with you on communicating the Church's teaching on sexuality in light of my experience.

I'd like to take just a minute to frame my experience for you. I am a wife and the mother of 6 children. I have been a diocesan Respect Life director and involved in the state and national context of the pro-life movement. I am a spiritual director and retreat director. I have been a crisis pregnancy counselor, the friend of aborted women, the aunt of several aborted babies and the foundress of Project Rachel and the National Office of Post-Abortion Reconciliation and Healing. But of all these, the single thing that best qualifies me to share with you is that I have held the hearts of women and men whose misguided sexuality has left indelible scars on their lives. It is their wisdom that I share with you today.

Sexual promiscuity, divorce and abortion are destroying the fabric of family in the culture. Our young are living in a sexually saturated society, where serial monogamy is the mode, where unrelated males enter family structures as mates of parents and unrelated children bounce in and out of households. The culture continues to subscribe to "if it feels good, do it." Our children continue to be victimized sexually and emotionally. Furthermore, the family with an unresolved abortion experience is especially at risk for child abuse, addictive behaviors, potential domestic abuse, and divorce as well as psychological problems.

The Church, while it speaks clearly, has a difficult time being heard. I want to touch on a couple of the problems briefly. Undoubtedly, our society with its message of unfettered sexual gratification flies in the face of the Church's teaching. We live in a society that pays lip service to preserving marriages but where in reality, the media and entertainment industries glorify uncommitted sexual adventures. We must never underestimate the impact the media has on our society. Their pro-abortion bias is known and recognized by those of us working in the area, but not the public at large. As a society we have come to worship the T.V. as the "truth speaking oracle." In addition, the entertainment/media industry is filled with high profile aborted women, such as Gloria Steinem, Kate Michelman, Whoopi Goldberg, Sinead O'Connor, Linda Ellerbe, Jill Clayburgh, Rita Moreno, Polly Bergen, Margot Kidder and Ally Sheedy to name a few. In excess of 90% of the people who participated in the pro-abortion march in Washington, D.C., knew someone who had had an abortion. Everyone has been brainwashed in some way by this exposure.

Catholics for Free Choice receive huge amounts of money from foundations (including Playboy) to counter the Church's teaching on abortion and birth control, here and in Latin America.

Our society has a multitude of families in conflict over their own values. The family, which should be transmitting values that correspond to those of the Church often can't articulate a set of values of any kind—and so a vacuum exists that the media steps into. The family excuses this by saying they want to let their children make up their own minds.

And the church which should be presenting a unified vision of life and beliefs can not do so. We are plagued by appearing to have no consensus on any of these issues. In all the ranks below the Pope, there are dissident voices, all of who claim to have the truth. Let me point out that we never see the other side disagree in public; only unity of purpose there. It is no wonder that the people looking for moral guidance can't sort out the forest for the trees. All those voices make convincing arguments and our own perception is colored by our own brokenness and biases. Furthermore, while we would like to believe that there is sound teaching within our Churches for those who manage to go with any regularity, the fact of the matter is that our own priests have been scared off. They've been told they are only men and they don't understand. Additionally, the external and internal politicization of many topics keeps them at bay. For example, many priests have told me they don't homilize on abortion because it's too political.

Furthermore, we have difficulties within the house that people see and are quick to use to dismiss any teaching voice. So we struggle with pedophilia, trying to balance compassion and help for the victims while seeing that justice is done with regards to the perpetrator while reminding ourselves that most perpetrators were themselves abused at one time and in justice, they too are in need of our concern and care in seeing that they receive the best treatment. And people misunderstand. We are plagued by scandals of a sexual nature and it is front page news. We struggle with a multitude of sexual issues (homosexuality, birth control and celibacy) as Church, but always now in the public forum.

And finally we are under constant direct and indirect attack from the "loyal" opposition. These people are Catholic by Baptism but hold to very few, if any of the tenets of Catholicism. Unfortunately, they promote themselves as the enlightened voices who are out to convert the Church. They too have the ear of the media and people are further confused.

We need to be conscious of the fact that the majority of people who are only somewhat Churched are vulnerable to all these counter messages because of their own incredible brokenness. We want to hear the things that support our lifestyle. We want things that we can concur with that don't challenge us to reevaluate our own lifestyle. We err when we assume a truly informed conscience on the part of those we are trying to reach. Many of these people were lost in the Vatican II shuffle. Many people my age and younger, have said to me, "I wish I knew what to teach my kids. You know I came through school right after Vatican II and I don't think they knew what to teach us. I feel so inadequate in my faith."

I have come to believe that sexual brokenness is the single most pervasive wound in our society. The women who come to Project Rachel are 7 to 10 years past their abortions, often having had them as adolescents who were involved in inappropriate sexual activity that looked like love to them. They found themselves abandoned by parents or boyfriends, pressured by one or both of these forces directly or indirectly. These were not mature women who made this decision rationally. They acted out of fear. Many did not give an ounce of consideration to the wrongness or rightness of abortion, nor were they aware of the facts of fetal development until after the fact. Many of them have sexual abuse in their history. (At least 60% of aborted women have been sexually abused.) At the time of the abortion, most of these women were basically areligious. Furthermore, I am appalled at how many parents insist on abortion for their pregnant daughters— good Church-going parents, who should know better. Consistently these women share that the sexual experience was not great, that they had sex to get love. They were used and abused. These are not "bad" women. These are wounded, abandoned, hurting women. For many that abortion is just one more symptom of incredible dysfunction. And the men who come are profoundly wounded. They wanted their children. They are filled with rage and grief, interestingly vowing never to touch that woman sexually again.

Sexual abuse and incest leave a hole in the soul of the victim that forever impacts the relationship with God. That trusted figure who abused them represents God and they can't come to trust the God experience until they have undergone profound healing. They question why God let this happen to them. If they can't trust God, they can not trust the Church which represents authority to them. Complicating these issues, the aborted woman describes herself as having turned her back on God. She fears punishment from God and stays as far away as she can. (Research indicates that only 20% of aborted American Catholic women attend services regularly.) These people are not attuned or predisposed to hear or believe anything the Church says. People using birth control can not seem to make the connection to the logic of "wanted life" and the disposal of unwanted life. They are blind to the consequences of "controlling" our fertility.

Let me add that I see little hope of reversing the abortion mentality on a national scale without legislation, for the law is a teacher. Even then abortion will remain easily accessible through RU-486 and menstrual extraction that the radical feminists are looking to promote. Furthermore, it will take at least a generation of illegal abortion for our young people to internalize that value once again.

Despite the bleak picture I have painted so far, the good news is that I believe there is hope. Indeed all is not lost to us as Church in the transmission of values. However, what I am about to suggest may require a changed heart, a new and expanded vision and courage. It is a call to rise up prophetically in the midst of the insanity that surrounds us.

I believe that we too often speak as an authority without a heart. We expect people to listen to us just because we are on the side of good. But Scripture reminds us that without love, the words are empty.

In Scripture, while Jesus spoke to the masses, he converted the individuals. He heard their story and their pain. He dealt with that pain with compassion, love and healing and then he called them to conversion. I believe that that is the model for the Church of today in this computerized, dehumanized age when everyone is just a number. People are longing to be recognized in their humanness and longing to be healed in their brokenness.

I want to commend and thank the Bishops of the United States for their prophetic teaching given in the Pastoral Plan for Pro-Life Activities. There is great wisdom in those documents. And I have seen recently that priests are beginning to recognize the truth of those and other documents based on their own pastoral experience.

Now, let me make my suggestions for some possible ways to change how we are heard.

First, I suggest that healing ministries for those touched by abortion and survivors of sexual abuse be a priority. We must pick up the pieces. To minister to the broken does not condone the action but rather re-enforces the message of the evil of abortion and abuse. Not only is the child lost, but all these other people are injured as well. Do we run the risk of the opponents using this ministry as a way to promote abortion? Of course we do, but I believe it is a risk we must take. I don't care how smooth their sales pitch is, if a woman makes the choice to abort her child, her life is irrevocably changed. Her pain is no less because a clinic provider told her the Church will forgive her. However, in a perverse way, the irony is that if she begins her healing closer to the time of her abortion, much pain can be avoided. Project Rachel is attacked by pro-abortion Catholics. They find it offensive because it acknowledges the pain as well as the sin that needs to be reconciled. The good news is that people who undergo this healing experience are evangelized in a powerful way. These are the people who come to church, who listen to the teaching and who understand in a deep way the truth of the Church's teaching on sexuality. They practice and teach NFP, they promote chastity with teens, they speak of their experience that others might understand, they work at their marriages, they bond with their children, they counsel pregnant teens and women, and they pray for an end to abortion. As one woman said to me, "when you recognize that the Church spoke the truth about abortion, then you must stop and look for the truth in the other areas of Church teaching."

Furthermore, we need to expand our teaching framework in this area to include discussions of abortion's impact on the family. I am convinced that the "great gray middle", those people who are personally opposed to abortion but wouldn't impose their beliefs on someone else stand in that posture because they know someone who has had an abortion, someone who is dear to them. If they own that abortion is murder, then the one they love is a murderer. They can not do this. However, by explaining abortion's aftermath, it is my experience, that they readily identify the brokenness they see in their loved one. It allows them to own their belief about abortion and still love their loved one. More than 28 million abortions in the United States alone have impacted many millions of people. We need to recognize the circle of impact from an abortion and not dismiss these "fence sitters" as bad people as is often done in the pro-life movement. We need to understand where they are coming from and help them.

54

Secondly, we must own our brokenness as humans within the Church. Have we failed to handle pedophilia properly? Perhaps, so let's own that fact and get better. If we are sanctimonious, people will dismiss us. Have we erred in the way we have treated people? Perhaps, but people are very forgiving of those who recognize their own weakness. We need to acknowledge that many people have had hurtful experiences within the Church. Many souls have been turned away by the pat answer "Oh, that was so long ago. Why don't you just forgive and forget?" However, our understanding and our willingness to say we're sorry it happened, will go a long way to healing the wounds. There's a charming story of John XXIII and an old drunken priest whom he visited. When the priest returned to his old ways, the others scolded the Pope for having reached out. Pope John replied "if you can take away the bitterness, then, maybe, later the life will change. But if you don't take away the bitterness, nothing else you do is of any worth." Let us begin to take the bitterness away. People want to come home.

Thirdly, let us take advantage of the fact that the behavioral and medical sciences are on our side. Let us use this knowledge in our teaching to our benefit. When talking to engaged couples about NFP I used to talk about the risks of birth control as well as the health and psychological benefits of this method. People expressed surprise at those things as though what the Church teaches exists in a vacuum. And I was surprised to discover how ignorant people were of the fertility cycle. An example of how to use the knowledge in the secular world in promoting our message is a wonderful little book from Canada called "Hang on to Your Hormones", written by an aborted woman. It deals with the facts, and documents everyone of them. Let's show statistics about how chastity positively impacts marriage. Teens want the truth. When you level with them, they will hear you!

Fourth, let's better prepare our clergy in the seminary for the real world they are going to face when they come out. We need to be aware that our seminarians too have grown up in this same sick culture. Let us teach them about post-abortion reconciliation—those skills will only enhance their other pastoral encounters. Let's teach them enough about NFP so they can truly help couples understand the beauty of it and how it works. Let's teach them about marriage and celibacy; let's invite some couples in to share with them about the struggles of marriage and about our understanding of the marital celibacy that we are called to live. Let's hear from couples who have used birth control and come to an understanding of why that was not a good choice in their lives. Let's talk about intimacy issues openly and help priests understand and own their sexuality. And let's develop better ways to support our priests later when they struggle with these issues. Let us recognize that we are all sexual beings, with our own struggles, but that everyone of us has an experience of lived sexuality that gives us perspective on this issue. Let us resolve to make amends for the times our brokenness has harmed someone else.

Fifth, let us assume a proclamation stance. The wonderful thing about undertaking the national advertising campaign on abortion was that it proclaimed the truth. It caught people off guard. It got people talking. We weren't just reacting for a change. We were leading and that was good. We have the Good News. Let us proclaim it without embarrassment. Let us enter the fray, but let us lead the way for a change.

Sixth, let us proclaim to the world through our actions that we are the lovers of the world and remind people that Jesus came to save the sinners, the broken. He came to the heal the broken hearted and he did it one at a time. If he and a hand full of fishermen could change the world so radically, in the days before TV, telephone and fax, think what we can do today. Ours is a broken world, filled with lonely isolated people. Let us follow the model that Jesus gave us and let us love the people back to wholeness, that they might hear the good news and in turn proclaim it to all whom they meet.

So often I hear from people "I can't believe the Church has a ministry like this for me. Why does the Church care? I can't believe that the Church wants me back after what I have done." And as often I hear how we as individuals and as a community have failed to reflect the loving face of Jesus. When an abuse victim shares their plan with us, let us respond with "I'm so sorry that happened to you. I admire your courage for sharing that with me." One picture is worth 1000 words, the expression goes. I have an image indelibly etched in my mind of the essence of Project Rachel and the ministry that will restore wholeness to our people. I was in a diocese doing a training. The first presenter was a woman who had had an abortion. As she left the podium, the bishop of the diocese who had heard her story, came forward, opened his arms to her and embraced her as a father would embrace a lost child. He just held her. I assure you there were not many dry eyes in that room and his lesson of love, compassion and hospitality was lost on no one.

Seventh, let us continue to develop ways to reach our young people and keep them in Church. Let us offer them substance and truth. Fr. Andrew Greeley in an article in *America* (July 11, 1992) found that "of those who attend church regularly, only 10% have had an abortion, regardless of religion." Religious devotion also impacts virginity rates:

"44% of Catholic women who attend services regularly are still virgins as opposed to 27% of those who don't attend regularly." He goes on to conclude that we need to reenforce those who choose to adhere to the teaching of the Church in spite of enormous pressure. He suggests that we may want to point out that virginity in both sexes is not obsolete. I recall my own experience of being asked by a priest friend to participate in a Confirmation preparation program where I would speak about my experience of virginity before marriage in a program with an aborted woman, a woman who kept her child, one who placed a child for adoption and one who married the father of her child. I recall feeling embarrassed to be talking about this and thinking to myself, "I wonder what I will say?" If I, who worked within the Church and within the pro-life movement was embarrassed to admit and talk about this life choice, what about all the others who live in the societal milieu where free sexual activity is the norm and peer pressure to fit in is strong. A priest friend shared about several couples he's encountered in marriage preparation who have made the choice to maintain their virginity. He says other couples whom they share with are fascinated and challenged to implement secondary virginity in their relationships. Somehow, we need to give people permission to live healthy lives. Perhaps we can take advantage of all the focus on "healthy" living to our advantage. Virginity means freedom from AIDS, sexually transmitted disease, concern about pregnancy. Research indicates a lower divorce rate among virgin and secondary virgin marriages. A Swedish study and a Wisconsin study both indicated that couples who lived together before marriage had an 80% higher divorce rate than those who didn't. Who wouldn't want to do everything possible to insure a sound marriage with odds like that?

Eighth, let us find ways to have people tell their stories of wholeness and brokenness. Television and print media tell stories of individuals. Perhaps we can find a way to tell the stories of people who have happy marriages, who have made healthy choices as well as the stories of those who have not made good choices but who in the healing of the brokenness can look back and share with others. Let us provide role models among the ordinary folk so people can identify with them. We have few models these days of virtuous living.

Ninth, we need to think long and hard about how to reach our young people on the abortion issue. A recent survey done of Church going college students indicates that while they themselves are anti-abortion, they do not want the ban for others. Have we lost a sense of objective right and wrong?

A friend observed that our sexuality must be one of the greatest gifts God gives us as human beings because Satan so consistently seeks to pervert it and destroy its life giving properties. In light of that insight, then, let us stand together, Bishops, clerics and laity, and vow to proclaim to one and all, that our sexuality is our gift; that it needs to be understood, treasured and protected; and that we, recognizing our own sexual brokenness, will promise to judge no one in theirs. However, we will hold up the ideal of sexual wholeness for all to see and proclaim that it is good and holy. Let us resolve to snatch back this holy gift from the Evil One and return it to the life-giving sanctity that God intended.

Chapter 5

NEW THEORIES OF PHYSICAL CAUSES OF HOMOSEXUALITY AND MORAL BEHAVIOR

Fred S. Berlin, M.D., Ph.D.
The Reverend John F. Harvey, O.S.F.S, S.T.D.

A. FRED S. BERLIN, M.D., PH.D.

I. What is Homosexuality?

The eminent neurologist Huhlings Jackson stated that, "the study of causes must first be preceded by the study of things caused". If one wishes to search for the cause or causes of homosexuality it is therefore critical first to define the nature of the phenomenon itself. If an incarcerated male prisoner were to engage in sexual activity with another male, all the while imagining that he was with a female partner, should the inmate in question be thought of as homosexual?

In the example just given, the observable behavior is certainly homosexual to the extent that it involves an erotic liaison between two men. However, in terms of covert mental phenomenology, the primary, if not exclusive orientation of the inmate in question, may be heterosexual. If one wishes to maximize the probability of discovering causal factors that distinguish persons who differ from one another in sexual makeup, one must first be certain that they do indeed so differ.

In the case of the inmate referred to above, labeling him homosexual and then searching for causal factors that distinguish him from heterosexuals would likely be a futile venture. Indeed, outside of the prison setting that person's behavior would likely quickly reveal him to be fundamentally heterosexual himself.

II. Homosexuality from the Scientific Perspective

If observable behavior can sometimes be misleading with respect to an individual's underlying mental sexual orientation, what, then, are the critical issues from the scientific perspective?

First, it should perhaps be noted that the idea of considering differences in sexual makeup from the scientific point of view is historically rather new. For many years, such matters were considered to be much more the province of moralists than of scientists or physicians. Good people were thought to be those who experienced attractions to age comparable members of the opposite gender. Those who experienced other kinds of attractions, particularly if they responded to them, were judged, and in many cases still are judged, differently.

The introduction of scientific medical inquiry into the area of human sexuality has, perhaps, paralleled (though historically much more recently) the entry of science and medicine into our understandings about alcoholism. A few hundred years ago, perhaps longer, alcoholism was considered predominantly a moral issue. The male alcoholic was seen as "a bum in the gutter". The female alcoholic was perhaps viewed in an even more negative light. Today we have the Betty Ford Clinic. We recognize that there are indeed still important moral issues to be discussed and resolved, but we have also come to appreciate the importance and legitimacy of scientific inquiry as well.

From the scientific point of view, when it comes to issues of human sexuality, one can ask a number of important questions. (1) Why am I, as a heterosexual man, attracted to females rather than males? (2)

Why is the person afflicted with a pedophilic sexual orientation attracted to children rather than adults? (3) Why is the homosexual person attracted to individuals of similar rather than opposite gender?

Put another way, in the case of a given individual, what factors determine what sorts of thoughts and behaviors will acquire the capacity to elicit within him (or her) feelings of erotic arousal. A man cannot volitionally will his penis to become erect even though he can by volition will his right arm to move about. A man can obtain an erection by thinking certain thoughts. For the heterosexual man, these are thoughts about women; for the homosexual man, thoughts about men. How did the homosexual and heterosexual man come to differ from one another in such a fashion?

III. The Role of Learning

In trying to address these issues, a distinction has frequently been made between the role played by nature versus nurture. Many early theories of homosexuality stressed the alleged importance of certain types of early learning experiences. Without valid scientific evidence, homosexuality was often attributed to, or blamed upon, a weak father or an overly dominant mother.[1]

Even if sexual orientation is to some extent learned, rather than biologically determined, it is important to appreciate that there are different types of learning. Some things that are learned can be easily unlearned. Others cannot. Furthermore, learning itself likely results in certain biological changes within the brain.

Responses that are classically conditioned can be easily unlearned. The prominent Russian scientist, Pavlov, showed how a hungry dog would readily learn to salivate to the sound of a bell if ringing of the bell regularly preceded the presentation of food.[2] Subsequently, if the bell was rung repeatedly, now without food being presented, the learned, or classically conditioned, salivation response was soon unlearned, or "extinguished".

The eminent ethologist, Konrad Lorenz, demonstrated a different type of learning called imprinting.[3] His classic studies involved work with young ducklings. If one has ever had the opportunity to observe a mother duck with her recently born chicks, the sight of the youngsters lined up in a row, diligently following mother as she moved about may be vividly recalled.

What Lorenz discovered is that young ducklings are preprogrammed genetically so that they will learn to follow whomever, or whatever, happens to move about in front of them during a critical period of time shortly after birth. This is usually mother. However, when Lorenz himself replaced mother as the first moving object the ducklings were able to follow, it was he rather than she whom they subsequently continued to follow. Of equal interest, once they had learned to follow in such a fashion, it was very difficult to have them unlearn the behavior. It was as though it had somehow been biologically stamped in, or permanently "imprinted". In Lorenz's studies, some of the young ducklings became so bonded to him through imprinting that they tried to feed him live worms, attempting to force them into his ears if he closed his mouth. It has been shown that such early life imprinting can influence the nature of an adult animal's subsequent sexual attractions.

It appears that human sexuality may have certain similarities. Most heterosexual males who are attracted exclusively to women report that it is extremely difficult, if not impossible, for them even to imagine losing their attraction to women, or to imagine replacing it with an attraction towards men. Sexual orientation, once acquired, (whether by nature or nurture) appears for many to become a reality of mental makeup quite resistant to alteration. If sexual orientation is learned, it may be learned through imprinting rather than classical conditioning.

IV. The Role of Biology with Respect to Sex Drive and Gender

Persons do not acquire their sexual drive per se, as a consequence of either learning or volitional choice. None of us read books as youngsters about human sexuality which after having been read, enable us to decide whether or not subsequently we are going to experience sexual feelings. The origins of sexual drive are rooted deeply in biology. Fundamentally, heterosexual persons differ from homosexual persons primarily in terms of the gender of individuals towards whom that drive becomes attached.

Biologically, gender itself is ordinarily determined by genetics. Most persons have 23 pairs, or a total of 46, chromosomes.[4] Each chromosome contains millions of genes. One half of each chromosome pair is obtained from mother and the other half from father at the moment of conception. Twenty-two of the twenty-three chromosome pairs are termed autosomes, and as far as is known these have no effect upon gender. If the twenty-third pair, when viewed under a microscope, looks like two X's next to one another, the individual in question is ordinarily female. If the twenty-third pair of chromosomes looks like an X next to a Y, that individual is ordinarily male.

When an individual's twenty-third chromosome pair is the typical male pattern (XY), as an embryo he will develop testes. The testes in turn will produce the hormone testosterone, which will then cause what otherwise would have become the female clitoris to enlarge and form the male penis. The testosterone will also cause what otherwise would have become the female labia majora to alter and become the male scrotal sack. If, for some reason, the testes of the male fetus fails to produce testosterone, that biologically genetic male (i.e., that individual with an XY chromosome pattern) will nevertheless be born looking like a female. All males would look like females if it were not for testosterone.

Testosterone also masculinizes the brain during early fetal development.[5] For example, once per month the brain of a young adult female ordinarily puts out a surge of a substance known as leutinizing hormone. This causes a woman to begin her monthly ovulation. The male brain does not put out that monthly surge of leutinizing hormone. It does not do so because it was exposed to testosterone during early fetal development. Thus, biology ordinarily plays a profound role in determining gender differences.

V. Possible Effects of Medical Anomalies on Gender Identity and Sexual Orientation

A somewhat rare medical condition exists which is known as Klinefelter's Syndrome.[6] In Klinefelter's syndrome, the twenty-third chromosome pair is neither XY (the normal male pattern), nor XX (the normal female pattern). Rather than having a twenty-third chromosome pair, persons with Klinefelter's Syndrome have instead a triplicate pattern made up of two X's and one Y. Thus, genetically speaking, such persons can be thought of either as male (XY) with an extra X chromosome, or as female (XX) with an extra Y chromosome.

Some patients with Klinefelter's syndrome have requested so-called sex change operations, feeling as though they are trapped in the body of the wrong gender.[7] But, genetically speaking, which gender is the "right" gender in Klinefelter's Syndrome. Other patients with Klinefelter's Syndrome have reported that they are sexually attracted to members of the same gender.[8] It is often assumed that we are "supposed to be" sexually attracted to members of the opposite gender, but in Klinefelter's Syndrome, genetically speaking, which gender is the opposite.

Although Klinefelter's patients are born with a penis, appearing to be male at birth, laboratory tests of hormone profiles, and other blood tests, would identify them as females.

The point to be made here is that a question seemingly so simple to answer on the surface, such as, "Is this person a male or is this person a female?" becomes much more complicated at the level of biology.[9] A given individual can be genetically male (XY), have the external anatomy of a female, and have a mixed, or confusing, male/female pattern hormonally. Thus, at the level of biology, such matters can become quite complex, attesting to the awe and grandeur of man's remarkable nature.

VI. The Role of Biology in Determining Sex Related Behaviors in Animals

In many species of birds, only the male sings. Their songs are an important aspect of courtship. If a female zebra finch is given the hormone estradial as an embryo, plus androgen hormones as an adult, she will sing a male courtship song without having heard it previously.[10] In addition, she will display typically male mating behavior and like normal males (but unlike normal females) will have an increased number of cells in certain brain regions.

In most species of rats, normally only males mount. Mounting is a behavior that involves placing the forepaws on the back of another animal while posturing the body in a fashion conducive to intercourse. Adult female rats, given testosterone at a specific time in utero will also show this behavior, which normally predominates in males.[11] Male rats do not normally build nests or care for their young, but they will build nests and show other kinds of "maternal behavior" if electrical stimulation is applied to certain brain areas.[12]

Certain species of animals are genetically preprogrammed to respond sexually either to sounds or to visual stimuli. The sound of the wing beat of the female is the stimulus which attracts male crickets and mosquitoes.[13] Male Siamese fish are preprogrammed genetically to respond aggressively to the sight of another male, and sexually to the sight of a female. The great scientist Tinbergen described in exquisite detail how the seemingly complicated mating behavior of the male and female stickleback fish in reality reflects a preprogrammed sequence of movements elicited in response to various specific visual configurations.[14] Do some men find the shape of a woman's legs to be more arousing when she wears high heels because that visual configuration is more likely to produce a genetically preprogrammed arousal

64

response? We do not yet know the answer to such questions, but such a possibility is by no means implausible.

VII. The Role of Biology in Determining Sexual Orientation in Humans

Given the above noted marvels and complexities of constitutional makeup, what then is the evidence if any, that it is biology that ordinarily plays the more dominant role in determining sexual orientation and sexual expression in humans. Over the years there have been a number of studies addressing this issue.[15-36] Some have lent support to the idea that biology is a major determinant of sexual orientation. Others have failed to replicate earlier findings. Still others have refuted such findings. Such studies have looked for differences in (A) the anatomical structure of the brain, (B) levels of various sex hormones in the blood stream, and (C) the pattern of release of sex related hormones from the brain in response to the injection of certain biologically active substances. Other investigations have looked at identical twins in an attempt to find evidence supporting a genetic predisposition towards homosexuality.[37]

Simply put, the final verdict is not yet in regarding the degree to which biology affects human sexual orientation. There is evidence that some non-sexual human responses are genetically pre-programmed. It has been shown that human infants respond instinctively and universally in specific ways to certain stimuli.[13] A loud sound causes a startle reaction. The visual perception of height causes hesitation. The sight of a familiar face causes smiling. It seems probable, though current data is still equivocal, that future research will discover biological factors that are important in human sexual reactions and orientation as well.

VIII. The Politics of Homosexuality

The issue of the origins of human sexuality, especially homosexuality, has in many instances now come to carry with it political overtones. Some have seemed to suggest that if homosexuality can be linked to a biological etiology, the issue will then become more one of science and less of morality. However, if one of the many moral issues involved relates to the question of volition, then whether homosexuality is unlearned and due to nature, or learned and due to nurture, may be somewhat moot. As already noted, even if it is learned, this does not necessarily mean that it can be easily unlearned.

IX. What Homosexuality is *Not* Due to

There is still, then, much knowledge that needs to be accrued regarding the etiology or causes of homosexuality. However, one can already come to certain conclusions with respect to factors that in general are *not* etiological.

As a heterosexual male, I did not as a child weigh my options, debating whether I wished to grow up as a person who is attracted to women, to men, or perhaps even to children.[38] Rather than deciding, I discovered, in growing up, that I am attracted to females. In our society, that discovery has certainly made my life much easier.

Similarly, the man who is attracted perhaps exclusively to other men, did not come to experience such attractions because he was a bad youngster who decided to be different. How could he, even if he had wanted to, have programmed himself so that thoughts of other males would cause him to develop an erection, while thoughts of females would not. Rather, in growing up he *discovered* his attraction to other males. This is often a very painful and difficult discovery in our society for a young and vulnerable adolescent to have to make.

X. The Driven Nature of Sexual Behavior

One could perhaps accept the argument that homosexuality is discovered rather than decided, and yet still argue that the individual in question should refrain from acting. It is a common belief in our society that anyone can do whatever they want simply by putting their mind to it. There is a growing body of evidence, however, which suggests, particularly when it comes to behaviors which are enacted in the service of a biologically based drive (and sex is a biologically based drive), that it may not always be so simple.

Currently, many Americans are spending in total literally millions of dollars per years trying hard to change their eating behavior through a variety of diets. The outcome in the overwhelming majority of cases, unfortunately, is often disappointing. There is a growing body of data suggesting that some people may experience great difficulty in dieting because they are, in effect, "fighting nature". It now appears that biology may in some cases, through the drives and cravings of hunger, be pushing behavior towards a predetermined level of daily caloric intake.[39]

66

Not too many years ago, researchers discovered that the brain contains within it receptor sites to which opiates can bind. They also discovered that the brain produces its own supplies of opiate-like chemicals known as endorphins.[40]

Even more recently a new technology called PET scanning (Positron Emission Tomography) has been developed.[41] This technology now allows scientists to address an issue that philosophers have pondered for centuries. What is the relationship between the brain as a biological organ and the mind as subjective experience? This technology has allowed researchers to study changes in brain chemistry that occur in association with the subjective experience of sexual arousal.

Though the results are still very preliminary, early data suggests that endogenously produced opiates may be released in the brain during sexual arousal.[42] If this indeed turns out to be the case, it may help to explain why, for some individuals, sexual behavior (whether heterosexual or homosexual) sometimes seems to become addictive in nature. Perhaps an excessive release of endorphins from the brain will turn out to be the basis for this phenon. non. Whether, ultimately, the basis for the driven nature of human sexuality turns out to be endorphins or something else, because sexual behavior is, indeed, "driven", in some cases, as with the overeater trying his best to diet, professional assistance in helping to achieve proper behavioral control may be required.

XI. Concluding Remarks

In conclusion, there is still much that we do not know about human sexuality. The complexity of man's biological makeup is both mysterious and challenging, attesting to the wonderment and majesty of human existence. In addition to being spiritual beings, we are also remarkably put together in our biological makeup. Clearly the sex drive itself is rooted deeply in that biology.

When an individual develops a homosexual orientation, the subjective knowledge of its existence emerges as a discovery rather than being the product of a volitional choice. Biologically based drives, by virtue of their very nature, crave recurrent satiation. Once satisfied, in time, they crave satiation again.

Just as a heterosexual individual can yearn for a loving affectionate and at times sexually intimate relationship, so does the homosexual individual. Just as it would ordinarily be virtually unthinkable, if not impossible, for the heterosexual man to yearn for such a relationship with another man, it may be equally difficult for the homosexual man to yearn for such a relationship with a woman. His yearnings, though quite the same in content, are simply not oriented towards the same sorts of partners.

A challenge for all of us as conscientious human beings relates to how we can integrate the ongoing emerging scientific discovery of man as a complicated biological entity, with our sense that man is also a spiritual and knowing being; a being who ought to be guided in life by principals that are both ethical and virtuous. In meeting this difficult challenge, maintaining a sense of compassion and enlightenment regarding all men and women, even towards those who may differ from us in ways that we find difficult to understand, can itself represent a worthy moral effort. Hopefully, such an approach does justice both to science, and to religious conviction, as well as to the dignity of the human spirit.

REFERENCES

1. Bell AP, Weinberg, MS, Hammersmith SK. *Sexual Preference: Its Development in Men and Women; Statistical Appendix.* Indiana University Press, Bloomington, 1981.
2. Pavlov IP. *Conditioned Reflexes* (Anrep GV, Translator), OUP, London, 1927.
3. Lorenz KZ. *King Solomon's Ring: New Light on Animal Ways,* Thomas T. Chromwell, New York, 1952.
4. Stern C. *Principles of Human Genetics.* W. H. Freeman and Company, San Francisco, 1960.
5. Goy RW, McEwen BS. *Sexual Differentiation of the Brain,* The MIT Press, Cambridge, Mass., 1977.
6. Klinefelter HF, Reifenstein EC, Jr., Albright F. A Syndrome characterized by gynecomastia, aspermatogenesis without A-Leydigism and increased excretion of FSH. *J. of Clinical Endocrinology, 2,* 2, 615, 1942.
7. Baker HJ, Stoller J. Can a biological force contribute to gender identity? *American Journal of Psychiatry,* 124, 1653–1658, 1968.
8. Raboch J., Mellan J., Starka L., Klinefelter's Syndrome: Sexual development and activity. *Archives of Sexual Behavior, 8,* 4, 333–339, 1979.
9. Berlin FS. Sex Offenders: A biomedical perspective and a status report on biomedical treatment. In *The Sexual Aggressor: Current Perspectives on Treatment II* (Greer, JB and Stuart, IR, Eds.), Van Nostrand Reinhold Co. New York, 1983.
10. Miller JA, A song for the female finch. *Science News, 117,* 58–59, 1980.
11. Money J. Clinical aspects of prenatal steroidal action on sexually dimorphic behavior. In *Steroid Hormones and Brain Function* (Sawyer CH, Gorski RA, eds.), University of California Press, Berkley, 325–338, 1971.
12. Fisher AE. Behavior as a function of Certain neurobiochemical events. *Current Trends in Psychobiological Theory,* U. of Pittsburgh Press, Pittsburgh, 70–86, 1960.
13. Foss BM. *New Horizons in Psychology.* Penguin Books, Baltimore, 185–208, 1966.
14. Tinbergen N. The curious behavior of the stickleback. In *Psychobiology: The biological basis of behavior* (McGaugh JL, Weisberger NM, Whalen RE, eds.), Freeman, San Francisco, 5–9, 1966.

15. Barlow DH, Abel GG, Blanchard EB, Mavissakalian M. Plasma testosterone levels and male homosexuality: a failure to replicate. *Archives of Sexual Behavior, 3,* 571–575, 1974.
16. Birk L. Williams GH, Chasin M, Rose LI. Serum testosterone levels in homosexual men. *New England J. of Medicine, 289,* 1236–1238, 1973.
17. Birke LIA. Is homosexuality hormonally determined? *J. Homosexuality, 6,* 35–49, 1981.
18. Doell RG, Longino HE. Sex hormones and human behavior: A critique of the linear model. *J. Homosexuality, 15,* 55–78, 1988.
19. Doerr P. Pirke KM, Kockiott G, Dittmar F. Further studies on sex hormones in male homosexuals. *Archives of General Psychiatry, 33,* 611–614, 1976.
20. Dorner G. Sexual differentiation of the brain. *Vitam Horm, 38,* 325–381, 1980.
21. Ellis L, Ames MA. Neurohormonal functioning and sexual orientation: a theory of homosexuality - heterosexuality. *Psychological Bulletin, 101,* 233–258, 1987.
22. Feder HH. Hormones and Sexual behavior. *Annual Review of Psychology, 35,* 165–200, 1984.
23. Gladue BA, Green R, Hellman RE. Neuroendocrine response to estrogen and sexual orientation. *Science, 225,* 1496–1499, 1984.
24. Gooren L. The neuroendocrine response of lutenizing hormone to estrogen administration in heterosexual, homosexual and transexual subjects. *J. Clinical Endocrinological Metabolism, 63* 583–588, 1986.
25. Gooren L. The neuroendocrine response of luteinizing hormone to estrogen administration in the human is not specific but dependent on the hormonal environment. *J. Clinical Endocrinological Metabolism, 63,* 589–593, 1986.
26. Hendricks SE, Graber B, Rodriguez-Sierra JF. Neuroendocrine responses to exogenous estrogen: no differences between heterosexual and homosexual men. *Psychoneuroendocrinology, 14,* 177–185, 1989.
27. Jaffee WL, McCormack WM., Vaitukaitis JL. Plasma hormones and the sexual preferences of men. *Psychoneuroendocrinology, 5,* 33–38, 1980.
28. Livingstone IR, Sagel J, Distiller LA, Morley J., Katz M. The effect of luteinizing hormone releasing hormone (LRH) on pituitary gonadotropins in male homosexuals. *Horm Metab Res, 10,* 248–249, 1978.
29. MacCulloch MJ., Waddington JL. Neuroendocrine mechanisms and the etiology of male and female homosexuality. *British J. Psychiatry, 139,* 341–345, 1981.
30. Meyer-Bahlburg HFL. Psychoendocrine research on sexual orientation: Current status and future options. *Prog Brain Res, 61,* 375–398, 1984.
31. Newmark SR, Rose LI, Todd R, Birk L., Naftolin F. Gonadotropin, estradiol and testosterone profiles in homosexual men. *American J. Psychiatry, 136,* 767–771, 1979.
32. Pillard RC, Rose RM, Sherwood M. Plasma testosterone levels in homosexual men. *Archives of Sexual Behavior, 3,* 453–458, 1974.
33. Rohde W., Stahl F, Dover G. Plasma basal levels of FSH, LH and testosterone in homosexual men. *Endokrinologie, 70,* 241–248, 1977.
34. Schiavi AC, White D. Androgens and male sexual function: a review of human studies. *J Sex Marital Therapy, 2,* 214–228, 1976.
35. Tourney G. Petrilli AJ, Hatfield LM. Hormonal relationships in homosexual men. *American J. Psychiatry, 132,* 288–290, 1975.
36. LeVay S. A difference in hypothalamic structure between heterosexual and homosexual men. *Science, 253,* 1034–1037, 1991.
37. Bailey JM, Pillard RC. A genetic study of male sexual orientation. *Archives of General Psychiatry, 48,* 1089–1096, 1991.
38. Berlin FS, Krout E. Pedophilia: Diagnostic concepts, treatment and ethical considerations. *American Journal of Forensic Psychiatry, 7,* 1, 13–30, 1986.

39. McHugh PR, Moran TH. Accuracy of the regulation of caloric ingestion in the Rhesus monkey. *American J. Physiology, 23,* 29–34, 1978.
40. Pert CB. Type I and Type II opiate receptor distribution in brain - what does it tell us? In *Neurosecretion and Brain Peptides,* (Martin JB, Reichlin S, Biche KL, eds.), Raven, New York, 117–131, 1981.
41. Frost JJ, Wagner HN, Dannals RF, Ravert HT, Links JM, Wilson AA, Burns HD, Wong DF, McPherson RW, Rosenbaum AE, Kuhar MJ, Snyder SH. Imaging of opiate receptors in human brain by positron tomography. *Journal of Computer Assisted Tomography, 9,* 231–236, 1985.
42. Frost JJ, Mayberg HS, Berlin FS, Behal R, Dannals RF, Links JM, Ravert HT, Wilson AA, Wagner, Jr. HN. Alteration in brain opiate receptor binding in man following arousal using C-11 Carfentinil and positron emission tomography. Proceedings of the 33rd annual meeting of the Society of Nuclear Medicine, *Journal of Nuclear Medicine, 27,* 6, 1027, 1986.

B. THE REVEREND JOHN F. HARVEY, O.S.F.S., S.T.D.

Moral Reflections on Theories Concerning Biological Factors in the Etiology of Homosexuality

Dr. Berlin has reviewed studies concerning the origins of homosexuality from a scientific perspective. I found his observations on Conrad Lorenz' experimentations with duckling learning fascinating, but I have reservations concerning the analogy between the sexual behavior of ducklings and that of human persons. Can the condition of homosexuality in human persons be learned through "imprinting"? Human sexuality may have "certain similarities" with brute or duckling sexuality, but in the perspective of philosophy human sexuality is different from brute animal not only in degree, but in kind or species. For example, in the *Summa Theologica* St. Thomas Aquinas makes this point several times, arguing that the spiritual powers of the soul are meant to integrate the lower sensitive and vegetative powers,[1] that the virtue of temperance is meant to put reason into the control of our emotions,[2] that sexual desire in the human person does rebel against reason, and that such lust is a defect in humans,—an effect of original sin.[3]

Dr. Berlin also makes the point that sexual orientation, once acquired, whether by nature or nurture, "appears for many to become a reality of mental makeup quite resistant to change." I note that he does not say that **no one** can change his orientation, but that "many" find change difficult. With reference to the role of biology in the determination of sexual orientation in humans he says that "the final verdict is not yet in regarding the degree to which biology affects human sexual orientation."

70

On the complex factors involved in the development of a homosexual orientation he is on target in stressing that humans do not choose such, but discover it at a certain point, and usually with a great deal of pain. He also adverts to the potential which sexual desire, whether homosexual or heterosexual, has to become addictive, or in his language "driven." It will not be overcome, he says, by sheer will power. Something more is needed.

In short, Dr. Berlin makes a good case for the importance of the biological in the genesis of sexual-genital desire, while making room for me to integrate many points in his perspective into a moral and pastoral viewpoint. I will begin by reviewing recent studies concerning the etiology of homosexuality, and then conclude with moral-pastoral reflections based upon my vision of the human person.

I. The State of the Question

During the early months of 1992 I studied the research of Simon Le Vay, as well as the Bailey-Pillard Study of Male Twins. Both studies posited an organic substrate for homosexual orientation. Before examining these studies, however, I find it necessary to make some philosophical distinctions concerning the usage of terms.

The first is that between a contributing factor and a true cause. I find no difficulty in accepting the theory that certain generic factors can contribute to the body structure of a given individual, and that a body structure, such as the size of the hypothalamus, could constitute a certain predisposition to homosexual behavior. But, were one to grant that such a predispositive factor existed in a given individual, one is not speaking of a cause. In the case of Simon Le Vay's hypothesis, one would have to say that the entire reason for the existence of a homosexual orientation in a given individual was the reduced size of the hypothalamus. But the homosexual condition is very complex, having many forms. Authors speak of homosexualities, and forms of bisexuality.

From many studies over the last hundred years, there seem to be other factors besides the biological involved. In short, Simon Le Vay's attempt to explain the condition of homosexuality in terms of reduced hypothalami fails to explain the psychological complexities of this orientation.

In the area of human behavior, a second distinction must be made, namely, that between a predispositive factor and a determinative factor, which is really equivalent to a cause. One may theorize that a given individual has a homosexual orientation because of early familial environment, which has contributed to his lack of masculinity or her lack of femininity. This may or may not be true, but in no way does it determine him to perform homosexual acts. It may predispose him to homosexual activity, but he remains radically free not to do so. This radical freedom remains whether one is speaking of genetic/hormonal factors or of psychological factors.

Another point worthy of our consideration are the limitations of our human freedom. Suppose, for the sake of the argument, that one could gather so much data about the relationship between brain structures and the condition of homosexuality that one could say that such a relationship was probable; or again that certain hormones, given to the mother in the fifth month of pregnancy, led to a homosexual orientation. One could say, then, that these organic factors predisposed the person to engage in homosexual behavior. But it does not follow that this individual *must* engage in such behavior. He can be sexually abstinent. To be sure, this is a limited freedom, but it is freedom.

The work of Le Vay and Pillard-Bailey, moreover, presuppose that in seeking the cause or causes of homosexuality psychogenic factors are not significantly involved, and that the various psychological theories from Freud onwards have no merit whatsoever. But the effort to ignore the copious data of many psychologists and psychiatrists indicating that there are psychological predispositions to homosexual behavior has failed. In more recent years authors like Judd Marmor and John Money, for example, have tended to favor the hypothesis that both organic and psychological factors converge in the development of a homosexual orientation in a given individual. In their viewpoints it is not clear that the organic (and that includes hormonal) predominates over the psychological, or vice versa. Money, however, does hold that, once the orientation is established, it is irreversible.

Still other authors, like Gerald van den Aardweg and Charles Socarides, insist that the homosexual orientation is primarily learned, and can be reversed. There are two other areas in this complex question which most studies ignore. The first is the failure of all concerned to come up with a good definition of bisexuality as a condition of both men and women. This failure adversely affects the conclusions of Le Vay and of Bailey-Pillard. The second is the dearth of truly scientific studies concerning female homosexuality.

It is necessary to review both the Le Vay study, and the research of Bailey-Pillard on identical twins. The research of Simon Le Vay on the brains of 19 homosexual men received media coverage in the fall of 1991 which tended to create the impression that homosexuality was inherited.[4] Le Vay himself draws no such conclusion. He points out

72

that "the anterior hypothalamus of the brain participates in the regulation of male-typical sexual behavior. The volumes of four cell groups in this region . . . were measured in post mortem tissue from three subject groups: women, men who were presumed to be heterosexual, and homosexual men."[5]

The hypothalamic structure was found to be twice as large in the heterosexual men as in the women studied. It was also, however, more than twice as large in the heterosexual men as in the homosexual men. This finding indicated INAH (interstitial nuclei of the anterior hypothalamus) is dimorphic with sexual orientation, at least in men, and suggests the sexual orientation has a biological substrate."[6]

I suspect that many reporters did not read beyond the above quotes from Le Vay's abstract. Le Vay who admits that he is homosexual raises problems with his own tentative conclusions. "Brain tissue from individuals known to be homosexual have only become available as a result of the AIDS epidemic. Nevertheless, the use of this tissue raises several problems. First, it does not provide tissue from homosexual women because this group has not been affected by the epidemic to any great extent."[7] Thus, the prediction that the hypothalamus structure is larger in homosexual men than in homosexual women remains untested.

Secondly, the small size of the hypothalamus structure in homosexual men may be the result of AIDS, or its complications, and may not be related to the men's sexual orientation. Although Le Vay argues against this possibility, he honestly admits that it is possible. Looking honestly, moreover, at exceptions in his sample (presumed heterosexual men with small hypothalami, and homosexual men with large ones) the author conjectures that sexual orientation may not be the sole determinant of the size of the hypothalamus. He concludes modestly that "the discovery that a nucleus differs in size between heterosexual and homosexual men illustrates that sexual orientation in humans is amenable to study at the biological level . . . Further interpretation of the results of this study must be considered speculative. In particular, the results do not allow one to decide if the size of INAH 3 and sexual orientation covary under the influence of some third unidentified variable.[8]

A later study involving E. Marshall and Le Vay[9] found "structural differences in the anterior commissure of the brain—the part that connects the two hemispheres of the brain. But, like the previous study, it was done on AIDS patients and the AIDS virus is known to have affinity for brain tissue. . ." (Jeffrey Keefe, *Catholic Sun*, September 9, 1992). From a study of Le Vay's research, it is clear that he does not claim that the structure of the hypothalamus in the homosexual men in the sample is a causal factor for their sexual orientation.

The Pillard-Bailey Study

Among the motives which induced Drs. Pillard and Bailey to undertake this study was the increased interest in a biological explanation of homosexual orientation. They point to the "continuing tension between those who view homosexuality as an illness, or a sign of moral weakness, and those who see it simply as an alternative phenotype without moral or pathological implications. It appears that one's etiological theory of homosexuality may contribute importantly to one's views on this larger issue.[10]

The authors obviously hoped that their research would tend to support the claim that homosexuality was inherited, and not learned.[11] They point out that in American psychiatry "it has been those holding psychodynamic theories about the origin of homosexuality who have been most closely associated with the position that the homosexual is ill . . . A recent survey found that those who believed that 'homosexuals are born that way' held significantly more positive views towards homosexuals than subjects who believed that homosexuals 'choose to be that way' and/or 'learn to be that way.' "[12]

Before describing their own research, the authors refer to the previous research of Pillard and Weinrich, where it was noted that "brothers of homosexuals were about four times more likely to be homosexual than were brothers of heterosexual controls, although this familiarity could be due to genetic or shared environmental determinants."[13] Thus, from what has been said so far, the authors leaned toward a genetic theory concerning the origin of homosexuality, but they were not sure exactly what was inherited. This led them to formulate two goals for their research: (1) To determine whether there is a genetic contribution to male sexual orientation; and (2) to investigate the behavioral nature of this contribution.[14] In short, the authors reveal their own bias. Now we need to look at the experiment itself.

The authors conducted 161 interviews: 115 with male twins, and 46 with adoptive brothers. 150 described themselves as gay/homosexual, and 11 described themselves as bisexual. The subjects interviewed had a total of 174 relatives of interest: 116 co-twins and 58 adoptive brothers. In their investigation of the orientation of the relatives, the authors had only two categories, heterosexual and non-heterosexual, i.e., gay or bisexual. The principal results of the study were: Of the 95

74

pairs of twins, 50 were found to be identical (monozygotic), and 43 were found to be non-identical (dizygotic) and two were not categorized. Keeping in mind that the authors collapsed homosexuality and bisexuality under homosexuality, the rates of homosexuality among identical twins was 52% (29 of 56); among non-identical twins the rate of homosexuality was only 22 percent (12 of 54); and among adoptive brothers only 11 percent were homosexual (6 of 57). Thus, the proportion of homosexuals and bisexuals was significantly greater for identical twins than it was for either non-identical twins or adoptive brothers.[15]

From these data the authors draw several conclusions: (1) Genetic factors are important in determining individual differences in sexual orientation. But (2) "the mere finding that the rates of homosexuality in different types of relatives are consistent with some genetic influence does not provide an estimate of the *magnitude* (authors' italics) of that influence."[16]

Efforts, however, by the authors to measure that "magnitude" are not convincing. For example, they seek to calculate heritabilities of sexual orientation from rates of homosexuality in relatives of the twins, identical and non-identical, but they hold that this can be done only if we can establish the base rate of male homosexuality in the general population. Here they run into a snag, because reliable statistics are almost impossible to obtain, and there is no agreement on such a base rate. They mention the two most commonly given figures, 4 percent, which they term the low "extreme" and 10 percent, termed the high "extreme" (10 percent is the unchallenged but unsubstantiated media figure).[17]

There are also assumptions about sampling of populations, and about our ability to really discern whether a given tendency or pattern of behavior is due to heritable factors, or environmental factors, or both. The authors do not tell us whether they used the 4 percent estimate or the 10 percent estimate in their efforts to measure the "magnitude" of heritable sex orientation traits. Indeed we have no reliable statistics on the incidence of either male or female homosexuality in the general population, and it is not likely that we will arrive at such in the near future, particularly when there is disagreement on the very definition of homosexuality. The authors' collapsing of bisexuality into homosexuality should also be called into question.[18] Such is really a form of reductionism, ignoring the fact that there are different forms and degrees of homosexuality.

At no point in the study is the complex intermeshing of environmental and hereditary factors adequately treated, as it is in the writings of John Money.[19] There is, however, one important reference to environmental influences: "Perhaps the rate of homosexuality in non twin brothers differs according to whether the proband (subject of study) is a twin. This could occur if the causes of homosexuality in twins and singletons were different, i.e., if a special twin environment contributes to the development of sexual orientation."[20] But if such an environment contributes to the development of a homosexual orientation, is it not as significant as the supposed hereditary factor?

In fairness to the authors, however, their conclusions are very tentative. While reiterating, for example, that in the question of twins heredity is a strong factor, they caution that "heritability is not informative regarding the development of sexual orientation (or for that matter of any trait) that is, given any heritability estimate, there are a variety of possible developmental mechanisms . . . These data are consistent with heritable variation in prenatal brain development, or in some aspect of physical appearance that, by way of differential parental treatment leads to *differences in sexual orientation* (italics mine)."[21]

Thus, the authors definitely recognize environmental influences in the person of the parents and family upbringing. Nonetheless, they do not succeed in demonstrating that there is "substantial heritability" in their study of male twins. With regard to prenatal brain development, there is no clear distinction made between hereditary factors and hormonal factors. While in the broad sense of the term, heredity does play a role in the instances of the identical and non-identical twins,—a role termed "substantial" by the authors—it is not clear how substantial it really is, particularly since they fail to acknowledge the comparative role which environment seems to play in the lives of these male homosexual twins.

Ricketts' Critique of Above Theories

Among the critiques of the studies of Le Vay and Bailey-Pillard, the most trenchant is that of Wendell Ricketts. In evaluating the medical and biological research, he adverts to the "more or less accurate methods of hormone assay, uncertainty over the process of brain sexual differentiation in humans, lack of agreement regarding the role of various gonadotropins on human behavior, small samples and lack of adequate controls. . . . These difficulties from within the studies themselves are secondary in importance to the conceptual naiveté and theoretical barrenness that characterize most of the biological research. . . . We must rid ourselves of the belief that biological research is somehow more pure, more objective, more scientific than any other.

And we must reject the idea that medical-biological research is immune to the influence of politics and personal prejudice. It is necessary to distinguish between the *objectivity* of data and the unquestionable subjectivity of the context in which research questions are asked in the first place."[22]

Ricketts continues by admitting that human sexual behavior can be affected by biological processes, but "there is no reason to believe that such behavior is the direct, immediate result of variations in hormones, of sexual differentiation of the brain or of genetic factors. . . ."[23] There is good reason why the effort to find a direct cause and effect relationship between biology and sexual orientation fail: "They cannot embrace the complexity and variety of human sexual behavior. Not only must they account for exclusive homosexuality, heterosexuality, and bisexuality, but also exclusive sexual behavior with one sex coupled with fantasies about the other."[24]

Some Conclusions Concerning the Above Theories

(1) One is not able to demonstrate that the condition of homosexuality or bisexuality is primarily innate.

(2) Those holding that homosexuality is primarily environmental are willing to concede that in some kinds of situations, such as identical twins, hereditary influences may contribute to the orientation.

(3) Individuals having a homosexual orientation remain free to live a life of sexual abstinence. (This conclusion I shall develop in the moral-pastoral section).

Some Moral-Pastoral Reflections Flowing from our Study

There is a widespread assumption that the condition of homosexuality is innate, natural, and morally good in sexual expression. The reasoning goes like this. If it is innate, it is natural, and if it is natural, it is morally good to express the orientation. If, however, it is not innate, but **determined** by familial environment, then it becomes morally good to express the tendency, because one had no choice in having the orientation, and no one should be expected to live without sexual-genital expression. Whether one is determined biologically or psychologically it does not matter. One has a right to sexual-genital expression.

Contrary to these positions, Catholic moral theology holds that even if the person's orientation was determined genetically, hormonally, or psychologically, it does not justify him in giving into the inclination through genital expression. For the sake of the argument, let us also suppose that one is not able to get rid of the orientation, that is, to move toward heterosexuality. We need to look at the *objective* morality of homosexual activity. Recently, Sister Reneé Mirkes develops the Church's argumentation, pointing out that the Church's evaluation of homosexual orientation and activity prescinds from considerations of the etiology of homosexuality. Whether it is acquired or innate, the objective morality of homosexual activity remains the same, that is, it is always immoral.[25]

Mirkes goes on to point out that even were Le Vay's Hypothesis proven, and it is far from that, it would not negate the teaching of Revelation regarding the divine plan for the meaning and proper use of human sexual powers. I develop the position of the Church in my book, *The Homosexual Person,* arguing from Revelation and from reason to the conclusion that homosexual activity cannot fulfill the two purposes of human sexual activity, that is, permanent union of man and woman and procreation.[26]

The Need for a Total Vision of the Human: Beyond the Biological and the Psychological.

What we need to do is to integrate the spiritual dimensions of man with the psychological and the biological in our consideration of sexual orientation and sexual activity. If man's behavior is determined by biological forces, or instincts, or early familial environment, then he is not free. To be sure, such factors can predispose a person to a certain course of action, but they do not take away a man's freedom to overcome such obstacles to the exercise of his free will.

From the teaching of Divine revelation in Holy Scripture and Divine Tradition we believe that that man can make free choices. He can overcome the effects of Original Sin, which tends to limit his freedom, particularly when he lapses into bad habits or even compulsions. Through the constant help of Divine grace man is able to overcome powerful emotions of lust and to free himself from sexual addictions. In this regard spiritual support groups, like *Sexaholic Anonymous* and *Courage,* become instruments of God's grace.

It is the constant teaching of the Church, moreover, that God always gives the person the grace necessary to overcome any sinful tendency,[27] and in the situation of the homosexual person to be sexually abstinent. Some homosexual persons do live lives of sexual abstinence, and there is no argument from empirical sources to prove the contrary. With due attention, then, to the biological and the psychological we present a total vision of man in which his spiritual dimension and the power of grace integrate all his other dimensions and powers.

More recent studies of *Exodus International,* Le Anne Payne, Elizabeth Moberly, and others indicate that some persons who were diagnosed as homosexual in early life and indeed into adulthood have been able to become heterosexual through sound therapy, prayer, and spiritual support groups. But that is not the issue in this paper. Our thesis is that persons with a homosexual orientation who have not made the transition to heterosexual marriage can live a life of celibacy by the grace of God and with the help of spiritual support groups, like **Courage.** We do need more study to disprove the commonly held beliefs that homosexual persons cannot change their orientation, or cannot be chaste.

NOTES

1. *Summa Theologica,* 1, 81, 3 and 2.

2. *Ibid.,* 2-2, 141, 3.

3. *Ibid.,* 2-2, 153, 2.

4. Simon Le Vay, "A difference in Hypothalamic Structure Between Heterosexual and Homosexual Men" *Science,* vol. 253 (30 Aug., 1991, 1034–1037). The same issue contains commentaries on Le Vay's article.

5. Simon Le Vay, *ibid,* 1034, abstract of article.

6. *Ibid,* 1034.

7. *Ibid,* 1036.

8. *Ibid,* 1036.

9. See *Science,* vol. 257, 620–621, July 31, 1992.

10. J. Michael Bailey, Richard Pillard, "A Genetic Study of Male Sexual Orientation" *Archives of General Psychiatry,* vol. 48, Dec. 1991, 1089–1096 at 1089.

11. *Newsweek* (Feb. 24, 1992), "Born or Bred" uses this very dichotomy, "science and psychiatry are struggling to make sense of new research that suggests that homosexuality may be a matter of genetics, not parenting." 46. Despite the slanted reporting, the authors do present the viewpoints of researchers who are not at all convinced that 'genetics is the answer'. They ask the question; "how could two individuals with identical genetic traits and upbringing wind up with totally different sexual orientation?" 52. The authors also point out that the nature-nurture argument is no longer as polarized as it once was: "Scientists are beginning to realize that there is a complex interplay between the two, still to be explored." 52.

12. *Ibid,* 1089–1090.

13. *Ibid,* 1090. The research referred to in the text: R. C. Pillard, J. D. Weinrich, "Evidence of Familial Nature of Male Homosexuality," *Arch Gen. Psychiatry,* 1986 vol. 43, 808–912.

14. *Ibid,* 1090. While lamenting the lack of research on female homosexuality, the authors restrict their research to male homosexuals. Further indications of the authors' viewpoint is the fact that they followed up their published research with an op-ed article in *The New York Times.* "Science is rapidly converging on the conclusion that sexual orientation is innate," the researchers wrote. (*The Chronicle of Higher Education,* Feb. 5, 1992, "Studies Linking Homosexuality to Genes Draw Criticism from Researchers" A, 7-9 at 8.)

15. *Ibid,* (Bailey-Pillard) 1092.

16. *Ibid,* 1093.

17. *Ibid,* 1093.

18. Jeffrey Keefe, "A Sharper Focus on Homosexuality" in *The Homosexual Person* (Harvey), 65–74. See also Allan Bell and Martin Weinberg, *Homosexualities,* Simon and Schuster, 1978.

19. See *Lovemaps,* Irvington Publishers, Inc., NY, 1986.

20. *Ibid,* (Bailey-Pillard) 1094.

21. *Ibid,* 1095.

22. "Biological Research on Homosexuality: Ansells' Cow or Occam's Razor" *Journal of Homosexuality,* vol. 9. no. 4, 1984, 65–93 and 82–83.

23. *Ibid,* 83.

24. *Ibid,* 88.

25. "Science, Homosexuality, and the Church", *Ethics and Medics,* vol. 17, no. 6, 1–3, (June, 1992).

26. Ignatius Press, San Francisco, 1987, chapter 6, 95–104.

27. Session VI, Council of Trent, which quotes St. Augustine: "God does not command impossible things, but, in commanding, He admonishes us both to do what we can do, and to seek His grace to do what we cannot do." *De natura et de gratia,* ch. 43, n. 50, Migne, vol. 44, col. 271.

UPDATE ON SELECTED ETHICAL QUESTIONS: THE DEBATE ON FETAL TISSUE RESEARCH

Peter J. Cataldo, Ph.D.

Introduction

The current debate over human fetal tissue transplantation, and in particular the debate over the source of tissue, is permeated with the larger debate about abortion. Abortion opponents have good reason to be interested in this debate since the use of fetal tissue from induced abortions represents one more lethal assault upon the preborn child in the vast onslaught which it faces today. Abortion statistics from The Guttmacher Institute are continual reminders of the magnitude of the offence against these innocents. The Institute reports for the most recent year available that:

In 1988, there were 1.6 million abortions in the United States. From 1973 through 1988, more than 22 million legal abortions took place in the United States. Since 1967, when many states began liberalizing their abortion laws, almost 24 million legal abortions have been performed. Each year nearly 3 out of 100 women aged 15–44 have an abortion— 40% have had at least one previous abortion and 45% have had a previous birth. The abortion rate—the number of abortions per 1,000 women aged 15–44 in 1975 was 22; in 1980, 29; in 1985, 28; and in 1988, 27.[1]

Worldwide, it has been reported that, as of 1990, "[f]orty percent of the world's population now lives in countries where induced abortion is permitted on request . . . ," and that, "[i]n 1987, an estimated 26 to 31 million legal abortions . . . were performed worldwide."[2] Fetal tissue transplantation is rightly seen as another crossroads for stemming the tide of abortion.

Not only is there an argument against the use of tissues from induced abortions based upon the evil and extent of abortion, but also from a medical point of view there may be no need to secure tissues from induced abortions. The potential of tissues from miscarriages and ectopic pregnancies may be a solution both to the moral objection of abortion and to the medical need of viable tissue. In this way, the therapeutic goods of fetal tissue transplantation need not be jeopardized by becoming another battleground for the abortion debate.

This report will first summarize the key medical and ethical elements of the human fetal tissue transplantation debate. The medical-moral solution to the problem as framed by the Pope John Center Task Force on Human Fetal Tissue Transplantation will then be presented.

Clinical Utility of Human Fetal Tissue

Parkinson's disease is a neurodegenerative disease in which the neurons of the midbrain begin to disintegrate, impairing the production of dopamine (a neurotransmitter). As a result, someone afflicted with Parkinson's disease can experience motor difficulty, rigidity, tremor, and even dementia, and can be rendered incapable of normal functions.[3] This debilitating disease is estimated to affect 500–650 thousand people.[4] Severe Combined Immunodeficiency disease (SCID) is a disorder of the immune function and can lead to death from opportunistic infections before the age of 1 year. Diabetes mellitus is a disease which inhibits the production or effectiveness of insulin. This disease affects an estimated 5 million people to varying degrees.[5] These are only a few diseases in an estimated ten or more categories of neurologic, immunodeficient, and hematologic disorders for which human fetal tissue transplantation holds out potential for therapeutic benefit to people afflicted with these diseases. Drug and bone marrow transplants have proven effective against certain diseases of these disorders with only varying success rates.

Most recently, optimistic results were reported in *The New England Journal of Medicine* of three studies involving human fetal tissue transplantation for patients with Parkinson's disease induced by the drug MPTP, and with idiopathic Parkinson's disease (i.e., Parkinson's disease with unknown causation).[6] The dramatic improvement of two patients with MPTP-induced Parkinson's was documented on the American-produced NOVA television program around the time of the New England Journal publication. The continued publication and broadcasting of these kinds of results will most certainly bolster optimism within the medical research community and the general public.

Why does human fetal tissue show promise for treatment of the different kinds of disorders that have been mentioned? The Councils on Scientific Affairs and on Ethical and Judicial Affairs of the American Medical Association summarized the therapeutic advantages in this way:

> Fetal cells have four basic properties that make them clinically useful for grafting or transplantation applications: (1) the ability to grow and proliferate, (2) the ability to undergo cell and tissue differentiation (intrinsic plasticity), (3) the ability to produce growth factors [i.e., factors which promote new cell growth, the survival of the fetal cells themselves, and the regeneration of damaged tissue], and (4) reduced antigenicity compared with adult tissue [i.e., a reduced antibody reaction by the recipient].[7]

Sources of Human Fetal Tissue

Much of the recent media attention on the issue of human fetal tissue transplantation has focused on the viability of tissue from miscarriages. There is little data on the viability of this tissue, and yet, positive results from studies which have been completed are ignored in most writings on the issue. It is usually concluded that tissue from miscarriages is not suitable for transplantation. However, while most reports attempt to discredit the use of tissue from miscarriages, they are at the same time silent on the suitability of tissue from induced abortions. It will, therefore, be helpful to compare some of the key data on the viability and volume of tissue from miscarriages and induced abortions for use in transplantation.[8]

It is estimated that about one in seven recognized pregnancies, or 10–15%, ends in miscarriage. Data from the Hospital Discharge Summary up to 1988, the most recent year available, indicate that 840,650 women were hospitalized for miscarriage.[9] This number is an increase in the incidence of miscarriages per year from 750,000 during the years 1980–1985.[10] A large survey of 3318 miscarriages done in New York from 1977 to 1981 found that about 7% would be anatomically and chromosomally normal and fresh enough to be used for research.[11] These data come from the largest and most comprehensively examined series of miscarriages to date. Seven percent of 840,650 is a total of 58,845 miscarriages per year, from which tissues might be used for transplantation. The percentage of ectopic pregnancies with fetal tissue suitable for transplantation is very small, but some of this tissue may also be usable.

Miscarriages can occur at any time during pregnancy, although most occur in the 1st and 2nd trimester, while 90% of induced abortions occur in the 1st. The remaining 10% of induced abortions are usually performed for medical reasons, which may make the tissue unsuitable for transplantation. Since miscarriages most frequently occur without active interventions, the tissues are more intact, less macerated for use in transplantation. This also may result in lower levels of contamination, which is very high in tissues from induced abortion.[12] On the basis of current information, the combination of contamination and tissue damage from induced abortions disqualifies 75% of that tissue, particularly fetal liver, from being suitable for transplantation. However, the remaining 25% is not excluded from the possible problem of genetic mutation and other problems with the tissue. The use of prostaglandin and oxytocin to induce labor and to ripen the cervix in induced abortions may cause ischemic changes (i.e., consequences of insufficient blood supply) in the fetus that could impair the process of engraftment. Moreover, in the future, it is likely that the availability of tissue from induced abortions may become very rare because of the advent of early pregnancy abortifacient drugs (e.g., RU-486). Thus, not only is it likely that the maximum percentage of abortions suitable for transplantation is actually smaller than 25%, but the total number of surgical abortions itself is also likely to shrink with the legalization of abortifacient drugs such as RU486 and its progeny. Some have argued that these circumstances could also lead to pregnancies begun for the purpose of harvesting fetal tissues.[13]

84

The Ethical Dimension of Human Fetal Tissue Transplantation

Given the status of the medical question concerning human fetal tissue transplantation, we may now ask what are the moral and immoral uses of the tissue. There are three central reasons why the use of human fetal tissue from induced abortions is immoral: 1) the use of this tissue entails an implicit formal cooperation in the evil of abortion; 2) its use perpetuates the evil of abortion; and 3) its use violates the principle of consent.

The cooperation with the immorality of induced abortion can occur as a cooperation with current abortions, or as a cooperation with future abortions. Some have also argued that the procurement of this tissue is a tacit complicity with past abortions.[14] There is a cooperation in the immorality of current abortions if the procurement of the tissue influences in any way the abortion procedure itself. No government regulated separation between transplant clinician and abortion doctor can prevent the institutional partnership which must exist between the two parties in order for the transplant clinician to make requests for tissue with his or her specifications. Researchers are already developing modifications of the abortion procedure to accommodate better the medical requirements of transplantation. The use of such modified procedures in any given case is an immediate formal and material link to the abortion, which would not have otherwise taken place with the particular modifications.

Cooperation in future abortions may occur if the use of tissue from induced abortions in any way influences the woman's decision to abort her child. Statistics on the decision-making process of a woman contemplating an abortion substantiate the fact that a reason such as donating tissue to a family member or friend, or for the benefit of humanity, is just the sort of reason which could influence the decision to abort.[15] Even the separation of the transplant team from the abortion cannot prevent this work from contributing to public knowledge about the use of tissue from induced abortions, which in turn can directly affect a woman's choice to abort her child. A revision of the Universal Anatomical Gift Act allows for consent to human fetal tissue donation before the abortion. This revision has already been adopted by seven states.[16] The transplant clinician, in these ways, implicitly, but inescapably, joins in the decision to abort.

The use of human fetal tissue from induced abortions can perpetuate the evil of abortion by creating a medical demand for tissue from induced abortions, which will either help to sustain the incidence of induced abortions, or effect an actual increase in the incidence of induced abortion. Such a trend may strengthen public legitimacy of abortion, the abortion industry, and any support which is given to abortion. The general undesirability of abortion, even on the part of its proponents, would somehow become "redeemed" by the good that may come of it to those whose illnesses can be treated by the tissue from induced abortions.

The moral question about cooperation is never a self-contained one in which the mere fact of availability of tissue from induced abortions makes its availability immune from any moral dimension. The very point at issue is that the actions of the researcher and clinician can have significant effects upon the "availability" itself, for which they become morally accountable irrespective of their intentions.

Finally, as with any organ or tissue donation, there must be proper consent; either from the person whose organ is being donated, or from one who may legitimately speak on behalf of the donor. There is no sense in which a woman who has chosen to kill her preborn child can be said to speak on behalf of that child. One who is given the authority to consent on behalf of a child is allowed to do so on the basis of evidence that he or she will preserve and protect the life and health of that child. Even if it can be said that the woman does not believe that the life she carries is another human life, or that the human life she terminates is not a person, she has at a minimum demonstrated that she is not at all concerned with preserving the individual life developing within her. She therefore does not fulfill the minimum qualification for giving consent on behalf of her child.

The Pope John Center Task Force on Human Fetal Tissue Transplantation: A Medical and Ethical Solution

Given all of the moral barriers to the use of fetal tissue from induced abortions, is there a morally permissible use of tissue from miscarriages? This in point of fact was one of the central questions asked by the Pope John Center Task Force on Human Fetal Tissue Transplantation. The Task Force answered in the affirmative by proposing a nationwide network of Catholic hospitals which would collect, process, store, and distribute fetal tissues for transplantation with the following ethical conditions:

1. Fetal tissues from induced abortions are not to be used;
2. The tissues or cells are obtained from miscarriages or ectopic pregnancies which meet specified medical requirements and the embryo or fetus is certifiably deceased;

3. Appropriate consent has been obtained from the mother or proxy.
4. The participating hospitals have the proper equipment and trained personnel to carry out the requisite procedures;
5. Effective public relations programs are mounted to instruct hospital staff, the medical and nursing community as well as the general public regarding the nature of the fetal tissue network, its moral acceptability, and its avoidance of complicity with induced abortions;
6. It can be judged by the organizers that the proposed network would not contribute to false expectations and lead to increased demand for induced abortions;
7. Efforts are made so that the poor and others without adequate financial resources would have reasonable access to fetal tissue transplants for the management of their treatable medical disorders.

The organizational structure, and the professional and logistical requirements for the network have also been formulated by the Task Force. Funding for a prototype of the network is now being sought under separate auspices.

The seed of the Pope John Center Task Force on Human Fetal Tissue Transplantation was sown one year ago at this Workshop. Upon hearing about the advances in fetal medicine and therapy, and about the possible supply of fetal tissue from miscarriages from one of our speakers, Dr. Maria Michejda, His Eminence, Cardinal Law suggested that a good project for the Pope John Center might be to study the medical and moral feasibility of a Catholic network of fetal tissue banks. From that point onward we began the work of developing the goals, objectives, and structure of a task force.

The specific goals and objectives of the Task Force originated from a desire to reaffirm and protect the dignity of the preborn human being, in light of the potential good from fetal tissue transplantation. The work of the Task Force was conducted by two committees: the Fetal Tissue Bank Committee and the Ethics Study Committee. Maria Michejda, M.D. was appointed Chair of the Fetal Tissue Bank Committee, and The Reverend Albert S. Moraczewski, O.P., Ph.D. was appointed Chair of the Ethics Study Committee. The goal of the Fetal Tissue Bank Committee was to investigate the feasibility of establishing a network of tissue banks at Catholic centers across the country which would coordinate the retrieval, processing, storage, and distribution of human fetal tissues for experimentation and transplantation, solely from miscarriages and certain ectopic pregnancies. The goal of the Ethics Study Committee was to study the ethics of the proposed network of human fetal tissue banks, and to complete a comprehensive ethical analysis of human fetal tissue transplantation. This study will be published this year by the Pope John Center. In addition to the publication of the ethics study, the Task Force has set the groundwork for a fully operating network of tissue banks. It is our hope that the network will commence this year.

An interdisciplinary group of 25 experts representing the fields of medicine, biology, hospital administration, theology, philosophy, law, and government were invited to participate in the Task Force as members of either of the two committees. An opening plenary meeting of the Task Force was held in June 1992 in Braintree, Massachusetts. This was followed by separate committee meetings in Pittsburgh and Washington, D.C. The formal meetings of the Task Force ended in December 1992 with a plenarium of all the members in Braintree. During these meetings the Fetal Tissue Bank Committee investigated the questions of quality and quantity of fetal tissue from miscarriages and ectopic pregnancies. They also addressed the question of the network's organization and operation. The Ethics Study Committee first identified the necessary moral conditions for the establishment of a network and began research on a set of central ethical issues, the results of which will be published in the book mentioned above. The work of the committees was marked by professionalism, collegiality, and dedication. The dialogue between the members of this interdisciplinary group was exemplary and their commitment truly edifying. We at the Pope John Center are deeply grateful to all those who contributed to the Task Force.

If the network becomes a reality, the challenge for Catholic health care will be to recognize the opportunity it has to make a direct contribution to the advancement of medicine for the alleviation or cure of several disorders, while at the same time fulfilling its mission to the most vulnerable of our society—the preborn children whose dignity and rights are equal to all others. The recognition of this opportunity will entail a commitment to several things: to the education of health care providers about the medical and ethical aspects of this work; to the provision of facilities; and, perhaps, to some financial support. The Task Force investigation showed that education is paramount for both staff and patients so that they will be convinced of the network's medical utility and its ethical soundness.

During the development and work of The Pope John Center Task Force on Human Fetal Tissue Transplantation, a government ban on federal funding for research using tissue from induced abortions existed in the United States. President Clinton has recently lifted this restriction. Federal funding priorities will now shift from research with miscarriage tissue to tissue from induced abortions. This policy change does not affect the medical and ethical merits of using miscarriage tissue. Given the medical problems with tissue from induced abortions and the likely reduction in surgical abortion, tissues from miscarriages may become the only reliable source for transplantation therapies. It is all the more relevant, then, in light of these points, that the proposed network begin its task as soon as possible.

Thus, Catholic health care institutions may once again be called to witness the dignity of the human person as created in the image of God, in and through their contribution to the advancement of medicine. As *Donum vitae* has taught us, criteria for guidance in science and technology cannot come "from mere technical efficiency, from research's possible usefulness to some at the expense of other, or, worse still, from prevailing ideologies."[17] Analogous to Catholic moral teaching about the new reproductive technologies, fetal tissue transplantation need not be condemned as such, but only that research which is not truly at the service of the human person, whose life is a supreme gift of God.

NOTES

1. See "Abortion in the United States," *Facts in Brief,* The Alan Guttmacher Institute, 1991.

2. Stanley K. Hernshaw, "Induced Abortion: A World Review, 1990", *Family Planning Perspectives,* 22, 2 (March/April 1990), p. 76.

3. See Scott B. Rae, Th.M. and Christopher M. DeGiorgio, M.D., "Ethical Issues in Fetal Tissue Transplants", *The Linacre Quarterly,* 58, 3 (August 1991), p. 12.

4. See "Neurografting: Preparing the Brain and Spinal Cord" in *New Developments in Neuroscience,* Congress of the United States Office of Technology Assessment, 1990.

5. See Dorothy E. Vawter, et al., *The Use of Human Fetal Tissue: Scientific, Ethical, and Policy Concerns,* University of Minnesota Center for Biomedical Ethics, 1990.

6. See Stanley Fahn, M.D., "Fetal-Tissue Transplants in Parkinson's Disease", *The New England Journal of Medicine,* 327, 22 (November 26, 1992), pp. 1589–1590.

7. "Medical Applications of Fetal Tissue Transplantation", Council on Scientific Affairs and Council on Ethical and Judicial Affairs, American Medical Association, *Journal of the American Medical Association,* 263, 4 (January 26, 1990), p. 566.

8. The data presented has been taken from a letter in preparation to the editor of *The New England Journal of Medicine,* written by Maria Michejda, M.D. and Julianne Byrne, Ph.D., who are members of The Pope John Center Task Force on Human Fetal Tissue Transplantation.

9. Reported by the National Center for Health Statistics for the years up to 1988. Based on the National Survey of Family Growth published in *Vital Statistic Series,* 41, 6, 1992.

10. See E. D. Thorne and M. Michejda, "Fetal Tissue from Spontaneous Abortions: A New Alternative for Transplantation Research" in *Fetal Diagnosis and Therapy,* 4,

(1989), pp. 37–42; and M. Michejda, "Utilization of Fetal Tissue in Transplantation" in *Fetal Diagnosis and Therapy,* 21, 3 (1988), pp. 129–134; "Transplant Issues" in *The Interaction of Catholic Bioethics and Secular Society,* edited by Russell E. Smith (Braintree, MA: The Pope John Center, 1992), pp. 115–130.

11. See J. Byrne et al, "Morphology of Early Fetal Deaths and their Chromosomal Characteristics", *Teratology,* 32 (1985), pp. 297–315; and J. Byrne, "Miscarriage Study" (letter), *Science,* 257 (July 17, 1992), p. 310.

12. See H. E. Rice, M. H. Hedrick, and A. W. Flake, et al., "Bacterial and Fungal Contamination of Human Fetal Liver Collected Transvaginally for Hematopoietic Stem Cell Transplantation", *Fetal Diagnosis and Therapy,* 8 (1), pp. 42–47; and K. M. Gottesdiener, "Transplanted Infections: Donor-to-Host Transmission with the Allograft", *Annals of Internal Medicine,* 110 (1989), pp. 1001–1006.

13. See, for example, Rae and DeGiorgio.

14. See James Bopp, Jr., "Fetal Tissue Transplantation and Complicity with Induced Abortion" in *The Fetal Tissue Issue: Medical and Ethical Aspects,* edited by Peter J. Cataldo and Albert S. Moraczewski, O.P. (Braintree, MA: The Pope John Center, forthcoming).

15. See *Ibid.*

16. Vawter, pp. 176–177.

17. *Donum vitae,* Introduction 2; see also *ibid.*, I, 4 concerning research and experimentation on the corpses of human embryos and fetuses: ". . . the moral requirements must be safeguarded, that there be no complicity in deliberate abortion and that the risk of scandal be avoided."

Chapter 7

UPDATE ON SELECTED ETHICAL QUESTIONS: NEW METHODS OF HANDLING ECTOPIC PREGNANCIES

William E. May, Ph.D.

Here I will (1) describe ectopic pregnancies and their frequency, (2) identify medical procedures currently adopted for handling them, (3) note relevant teaching of the magisterium, and (4) offer a moral evaluation of the methods proposed for coping with pregnancies of this kind.

Ectopic Pregnancies and Their Frequency

An ectopic ("out of place," from the Greek *ek topos*) pregnancy occurs when a developing new human being implants, not in the uterus, where it belongs, but in some other place, usually the fallopian tube or, more rarely, the ovary, the cornua, the abdomen, or the cervix. Such pregnancies pose serious risks to the mother's life because of the danger of hemorrhage.

During the past two decades there has been an alarming increase in the number of ectopic pregnancies, particularly tubal pregnancies.[1] Among the factors contributing to the dramatic increase in the number of ectopic pregnancies in our society are the following: the increasing number of sexually transmitted diseases, in particular pelvic inflammatory disease; tubal sterilization; the use of intrauterine devices and of progesterone contraceptive pills; and *in vitro* fertilization.[2]

Medical Procedures for Managing Ectopic Pregnancies

1. Tubal Ectopic Pregnancies

John A. Rock describes four treatment procedures for managing tubal ectopic pregnancies: (1) "expectant" therapy, (2) drug therapy through the use of methotraxate (MTX), (3) conservative surgical treatment through linear salpingotomy or salpingostomy or segmental resection, and (4) radical surgical treatment through salpingectomy.[3]

(1) "Expectant" therapy simply means that nothing is done. Rock states that "the natural history of ectopic pregnancy suggests that a majority of these tubal pregnancies may resolve without treatment"; indeed, such spontaneous resolution may occur in as many as 64% of patients.[4] In short, in the majority of cases no medical intervention is required to protect the mother's life, since there is a spontaneous abortion or miscarriage. Expectant therapy demands careful monitoring of the ectopic pregnancy which today, thanks to remarkable developments in monitoring pregnancies, can be discovered at a much earlier time than in previous years. If the tubal pregnancy does not spontaneously resolve, then medical interventions are necessary to protect the mother's life.

(2) Methotraxate (MTX) is also used today to manage tubal pregnancies. MTX is a highly toxic drug, and its use must be carefully monitored. MTX, recommended for "patients with small unruptured ectopic pregnancies or if there is evidence of persistent ectopic pregnancy after conservative surgery,"[5] interferes with the synthesis of DNA (deoxyribonucleic acid) and cell multiplication. It resolves the tubal pregnancy primarily by attacking the trophoblast,[6] i.e., the outer layer of cells produced by the developing baby, connecting it with its mother. The trophoblast is indeed a *vital organ* of the baby during ges-

tation. Although it is discarded later on, it must be regarded as an integral part of the body of the developing baby. Once the trophoblast has been dissolved by MTX, the unborn baby dies and is aborted.

(3) Two conservative surgical treatments for tubal pregnancies are now recommended: linear salpingotomy (or, at times, salpingostomy) and segmental resection. In linear salpingotomy an incision is made over the distended part of the tube, and the unborn baby is removed from the tube.[7] In segmental resection the portion of the fallopian tube affected by the ectopic pregnancy is removed and the remaining segments of the tube are then connected.[8]

(4) The most radical surgical treatment of a tubal pregnancy is a salpingectomy, or removal of the entire tube with its contents. This is necessary "when a tubal pregnancy has ruptured, causing intraabdominal hemorrhage that must be quickly controlled."[9]

2. Ovarian Ectopic Pregnancies

Such ectopic pregnancies are quite rare; however, they have recently increased in number because of the use of IUDs.[10] One author claims that many ovarian pregnancies go to term.[11] The medical literature recommends surgical resection of the ovary to handle this type of ectopic pregnancy, i.e., the removal of the section of the ovary affected and reconnecting its remaining portions.[12]

3. Abdominal Ectopic Pregnancies

These are quite rare[13] and are of two types: primary and secondary. A primary abdominal pregnancy occurs when the baby implants originally in the abdomen. A secondary abdominal pregnancy, which is more common, occurs when a tubal pregnancy ruptures with secondary implantation in the abdomen.[14] Such ectopic pregnancies can ordinarily be managed in such a way that the child will come to term and can be delivered by a laparotomy, or incision in the abdomen.[15]

4. Cervical Ectopic Pregnancy

This is a rare but highly dangerous kind of ectopic pregnancy, and one completely incompatible with development of the unborn baby to viability. The standard treatment is abdominal hysterectomy. Rock notes that it is possible to evacuate the pregnancy by a skillful D&C,

but this procedure "is usually complicated by profuse hemorrhage, which generally necessitates an abdominal hysterectomy."[16] Another possibility is MTX therapy, used at times in connection with hysterectomy in order to lessen blood loss.[17]

Relevant Teaching of the Magisterium

The Church teaches that every human life is of incalculable worth and that it is *always gravely immoral* intentionally to kill an innocent human being.[18] The Church's teaching on this matter is the basis for its teaching on the absolute immorality of directly intended abortion.[19] The magisterium has made it clear that what is condemned as absolutely immoral is *direct* abortion, as distinguished from *indirect* abortion. Two passages from Pius XII are most important in understanding this distinction. In the first, in which he was explaining the meaning of the fifth commandment, "Thou shalt not kill," as this had been traditionally understood by the Church, he wrote: "So long as man commits no crime, his life is intangible, and therefore every action which tends directly toward its destruction is illicit, whether this destruction be the *end intended* or only a *means* to an end, whether this life is embryonic, or in full flower, or already approaching its term."[20] In a second text Pius XII said:

> We have on purpose always used the expression *"direct attack on the life of the innocent,"* *"direct killing."* For if, for instance, the safety of the mother-to-be, independently of her pregnant condition, should urgently require a surgical operation or other therapeutic treatment, which would have as a side-effect, in no way willed or intended, yet inevitable, the death of the fetus, then such an act could not any longer be called a *direct* attack on innocent life. With these conditions, the operation, like other similar medical interventions, can be allowable, always assuming that a good of great worth, such as life, is at stake, and that it is not possible to delay the operation until after the baby is born or to make use of some other effective remedy.[21]

The magisterium of the Church has so firmly condemned as absolutely immoral every direct abortion that in my opinion, and in that of other theologians, we can conclude that the teaching of the magisterium on this matter has met the conditions set forth in Vatican Council II's Dogmatic Constitution *Lumen gentium* required if a

94

teaching of the ordinary magisterium is to be regarded as *infallibly proposed.*[22] This is an irrevocable, irreformable teaching of the Church.

Moreover, the magisterium has not only condemned direct abortion in the strongest terms, but it has also addressed specific issues relevant to the subject of ectopic pregnancies. It has done so in a series of decrees issued by the Holy Office (today called the Congregation for the Doctrine of the Faith) during the final years of the nineteenth century and the first years of the twentieth.[23]

Commenting on these decrees T. Lincoln Bouscaren wrote as follows in his classic work on ectopic pregnancies: "The question is whether these decrees absolutely forbid *every removal* of an ectopic fetus before viability, or whether they apply only to such removals as are *directly death-dealing* to the child."[24] After a painstaking study of the matter, in which he first showed, on the basis of massive medical evidence, that a tubal pregnancy so damages the fallopian tube that its removal is necessary to protect the mother's life, Bouscaren concluded that these decrees do not forbid *every removal* of a nonviable ectopic pregnancy, but only those that are *directly death-dealing.*[25] In short, Bouscaren held that the fallopian tube was so damaged by the ectopic pregnancy that it was a pathological organ seriously endangering the mother's life. Its removal (by salpingectomy) had as a foreseen consequence the death of the unborn child, but this evil effect was not directly intended and was simply an unavoidable concomitant of a medical procedure that was itself morally justifiable as a life-saving intervention. The abortion of the unborn child was not direct, but indirect.

The Bouscaren thesis won the approval not only of the moral theologians of his day but also of the bishops of the United States. Thus, both in their *Ethical and Religious Directives for Catholic Hospitals,* published in 1949, and in their *Ethical and Religious Directives for Catholic Health Care Facilities,* published in 1971, they accepted as morally justifiable the excising of a fallopian tube (salpingectomy) containing a nonviable fetus. In the 1971 document they wrote:

In extrauterine pregnancy the dangerously affected part of the mother (e.g., cervix, ovary, or fallopian tube) may be removed, even though fetal death is foreseen, provided that: (a) the affected part is presumed already to be so damaged and dangerously affected as to warrant its removal, and that (b) the operation is not just a separation of the embryo or fetus from its site within the part (which would be a direct abortion from a uterine appendage), and that (c) the operation cannot be postponed without notably increasing the danger to the mother.[26]

From what has been said here, it is evident that salpingectomies can legitimately be used as means of managing ectopic pregnancies when the condition of the fallopian tube itself is such that it poses a serious threat to the mother's life. It should also be noted here that Bouscaren rejected salpingo(s)tomy as immoral, on the grounds that it constitutes a direct abortion. He held that "this method of operating, if the fetus is alive, is certainly a direct killing, and certainly indefensible. It is one thing to remove the tube containing the fetus; it is another thing to remove the fetus directly .... It is necessary to emphasize the fact that only the first method of operating—the removal of the tube itself, without interfering directly with the fetus—is the only method which is in any way defended in this thesis."[27] Directive # 16 of the Bishops' *Ethical and Religious Directives* also rejects salpingo(s)tomy as immoral, for, as we have seen, it explicitly states that a procedure can not be allowed if it is "just a separation of the embryo or fetus from its site within the part," precisely because this "would be a direct abortion."

Moral Analysis

1. Tubal Ectopic Pregnancies

A. Salpingectomy and Segmental Resection

The review of relevant teaching of the magisterium (and of the work of Bouscaren) in the previous section of this paper is sufficient to show us that one morally proper way to cope with the problems posed by tubal ectopic pregnancies is to remove the entire tube by salpingectomy, inasmuch as when this is done the death of the unborn child is not directly intended but only foreseen as an unavoidable result of the removal of the pathological organ, and the removal of the tube is urgently necessary in order to protect the mother's life. Thus, when a salpingectomy is required, there is no direct abortion. It likewise seems clear that segmental resection is morally justifiable for the same reason and under the same conditions under which a salpingectomy is justifiable. In this procedure the affected part of the fallopian

96

tube (the pathological part) is removed with its contents, and as a result of doing so the threat to the mother's life is removed. The unborn child also dies as a result of this procedure, but its death is surely not intended as either an end or a means. Thus O'Donnell is surely correct when he says that the " 'Bouscaren approach' is legitimately applied in the microsurgical technique of removing the severely damaged segment of the tube with the fetus *in situ*, when this is indicated due to the extent of damage of maternal tissue."[28]

It is, however, important to note that today medical authorities regard salpingectomy as "radical surgical treatment" of tubal pregnancies, necessary only "when a tubal pregnancy has ruptured, causing intraabdominal hemorrhage that must be quickly controlled."[29] Here it is also most important to remember that up until very recent times tubal ectopic pregnancies could not be diagnosed early in pregnancy, as they can be today.[30] In earlier days the possibility of tubal ectopic pregnancy was not considered until the pregnant woman came to her doctor to complain of symptoms leading him to suspect that she indeed might have such a pregnancy. By this time the trophoblastic tissues of the unborn child were already firmly embedded in the fallopian tube, and there was danger of its rupturing. It was precisely for this reason that Bouscaren came to the conclusion that excision of the entire tube (salpingectomy) was morally permissible, and from the way Directive # 16 of the U.S. Bishops' *Ethical and Religious Directives* is worded it is evident that this is the reason why the bishops accepted Bouscaren's thesis.

But today, as we have seen, new diagnostic tools enable a pregnant woman's doctor to discover tubal ectopic pregnancies at an earlier stage of pregnancy. It is precisely for this reason that one of the "therapies" advocated today to cope with tubal ectopic pregnancies is "expectant therapy," to which we will now turn.

B. EXPECTANT THERAPY

There are no moral objections to "expectant" therapy as described by Rock and others, because nothing is done here to bring harm to either the unborn child or the mother. Nature, apparently, runs its course, and the ectopic pregnancy is spontaneously aborted or dies and is absorbed and the threat to the mother's life is removed. Here the moral imperative seems to be to monitor the situation closely in order to protect the mother's life should the pregnancy not be "resolved" of itself.

But I believe that, in the light of scientific evidence, a much more stringent moral imperative is incumbent upon doctors who discover ectopic tubal pregnancies at an early stage of development, when "expectant" therapy is recommended. This is the imperative to seek to transplant the developing young baby from the fallopian tube into the uterus, where it belongs. I say that this is an imperative rooted in scientific evidence. What is this evidence?

O'Donnell refers to a successful transplantation of an unborn child from the fallopian tube into the womb.[31] Remarkably, the article to which he refers, by Dr. C. J. Wallace, was written in 1917! In his article Wallace observed that at that time "early diagnosis of ectopic pregnancy is next to impossible unless it is accidentally discovered." But, he continued,

> when we do find an early case, where the tube is still in healthy condition, not too badly distended, and all things favorable, I think we should make a supreme effort to save the life of the growing child by opening the tube carefully and dissecting out the pregnancy intact and transplanting it into the uterus where nature intended it should go. It can be very quickly done. It does not endanger the life of the mother.[32]

He then reported on a case that occurred in 1915, when he operated on a woman on September 15 for fibroid tissue in the posterior wall of her uterus. When the abdomen was opened, he "found an ectopic gestation in the left tube at the outer part of the isthmus. The tube was very soft and healthy, enlarged to the size of a walnut but not distended." He then transplanted the child from the fallopian tube into the woman's uterus and her pregnancy then continued normally until a healthy boy was born on May 2, 1916. He then said: "I have not the least doubt that many such transplanted ectopic pregnancies will be reported in the near future."[33]

Wallace's hope, unfortunately, was not realized, for no other successful transplants were reported in the years after. However, in a letter published in 1990 in the *American Journal of Obstetrics and Gynecology* Lawrence B. Shettles described the successful transplantation in 1980 of a forty-day old infant from the mother's fallopian tube into her uterus, with subsequent safe delivery of the baby.[34]

Moreover, not only do we now have the means for discovering tubal ectopic pregnancies early in their development, but we also have much more knowledge about the phenomenon of transplantation and technologies for transplanting young unborn children. The technologies that have made it possible to recommend "expectant therapy" for tubal

98

pregnancies (remember, over 64% of them "spontaneously resolve themselves") have likewise made it possible for doctors to discover tubal pregnancies at a time when it is realistically possible to remove the child from the tube and transplant it into the uterus where it belongs. Surely this must be the moral imperative in the future in the management of tubal ectopic pregnancies.

C. SALPINGO(S)TOMY

In our review of relevant magisterial teaching we saw that some decrees of the Holy Office condemned the removal of nonviable ectopic fetuses from the mother. We likewise saw that Bouscaren repudiated this method of handling ectopic pregnancies as direct abortion and that the U.S. Bishops also rejected this method for the same reason.

Nonetheless, some theologians noted for their fidelity to the teaching of the magisterium have argued that this procedure seems to them justifiable on the grounds of the principle of double effect. The most prominent of these theologians is Germain Grisez, who advanced this suggestion in his massive study of abortion published in 1970.[35] The hypothesis he proposed has been accepted by some theologians, most notably by Joseph Boyle and Marcellino Zalba,[36] and I am also of the opinion that Grisez's understanding of the principle of double effect can be applied to the use of salpingo(s)tomy to manage tubal ectopic pregnancies when this type of medical procedure is needed to protect the mother's life.

Unfortunately, Grisez's hypothesis on this matter has not received much attention from theologians. Some, most notably Joseph Dolan, S. J., in a brief review of Grisez's book on abortion, and John Finnis have offered some criticism.[37] But it is still true to say that his view on this matter has not been subjected to the scrutiny that it merits. Moreover, he did not propose his view as a practical policy for Catholics to follow but rather as a hypothesis to be tested by other theologians and, ultimately, to be judged by the magisterium. He himself admitted that his "conclusions about abortion diverge from common theological teachings and also diverge from the official teaching of the Church as it was laid down by the Holy Office." Continuing, he said:

> I cannot as a philosopher limit my conclusions by theological principles. However, I can as a Catholic propose my philosophic conclusions as suggestions for consideration in the light of faith, while not proposing anything contrary to the Church's teaching *as a practical norm of conduct for my fellow*

believers. Those who really believe that there exists on this earth a community whose leaders are appointed and continuously assisted by God to guide those who accept their authority safely through time and eternity would be foolish to direct their lives by some frail fabrication of mere reason instead of conforming to a guidance system designed and maintained by divine wisdom.[38]

I thus think that the possible licitness of salpingo(s)tomy as a way of handling ectopic pregnancies ought to be explored further both by theologians and by the magisterium. But at present it certainly cannot be recommended as a morally proper way to manage such pregnancies.

D. MTX THERAPY

The management of tubal ectopic pregnancies by the use of MTX has not, so far as I know, been discussed by Catholic moral theologians. As we have seen, MTX "works" by attacking the tissue of the trophoblast, a vital organ of the developing unborn child. By doing so it kills the baby and by this means "removes" it from the fallopian tube. This, at any rate, seems to be its mode of operation. It thus seems to me that in its use the death of the unborn child is included in the *means* chosen to save the mother's life and is thus direct abortion. If it can be determined by diagnostic procedures that the unborn child is *already dead,* then obviously MTX can then be used to attack remaining trophoblastic tissue joining the now dead infant to his or her mother.

2. Ovarian Ectopic Pregnancies

These pregnancies are usually managed by an ovarian resection—removing the hemorrhaging part of the ovary (which contains the unborn child)—and resecting the remaining portions of the ovary. This procedure seems analogous to segmental resection of a fallopian tube. If this procedure is used, the abortion would be indirectly intended. O'Donnell claims that "a considerable portion of ovarian pregnancies have gone to term,"[39] but unfortunately he offers no supporting evidence. Obviously, if it is possible to allow the pregnancy to continue to the stage of viability, when the unborn child could be delivered, without endangering the mother's life, then one must do so. But if the mother's life is truly threatened by the continuation of the ovarian

100

pregnancy, the removal of the part of the ovary or of the entire ovary would be morally justifiable for the same reasons that salpingectomies and segmental resections of the fallopian tube are justified.

3. Abdominal Ectopic Pregnancies

Such ectopic pregnancies are frequently of such a nature that the unborn child can develop to the point of viability with no serious danger to the mother's life. If the membranes rupture, the unborn child dies within the peritoneal cavity. After the delivery of the viable unborn child or its death within the abdomen, the procedures outlined by Rock (clamping the cord and leaving the placenta in site, with the possible use of MTX to hasten trophoblastic degeneration) would surely be morally justifiable.

4. Cervical Ectopic Pregnancies

These ectopic pregnancies usually require abdominal hysterectomy. At times the unborn child is removed by a D&C. In my judgment, an abdominal hysterectomy is morally licit since the abortion is indirectly intended. Use of D&C, unless it is known that the unborn child has already died, would be directly intended abortion and hence immoral.

Conclusion

My first conclusion is that today the moral imperative in the management of tubal ectopic pregnancies is to use the means currently available to detect such pregnancies as early as possible and then to make every reasonable effort to transplant the unborn child from the fallopian tube to the womb. Apparently, this idea has not been tried by many doctors. My own view is that now is the time for it to be worked out by the medical community and that it is morally obligatory to do so.

If an ectopic pregnancy is discovered at a time when transplantation is not possible, serious moral consideration must be given to the methods currently advocated for managing such pregnancies.

Some may ask, why bother about the morality of the different procedures used to manage ectopic pregnancies when there is no chance that the unborn child will become viable. It will die no matter what procedure is used. The end result will be a corpse, so what difference does it make whether its death comes about indirectly as a result of a salpingectomy or directly as a result of using MTX, for example?

The difference, a morally relevant one, is that in the one instance the death of the unborn child, although foreseen, is not the object of one's choice; one does not choose to kill an innocent human being, whereas in the other instance its death is not only foreseen but is precisely the object of one's choice (however reluctantly the choice is made). In the one instance the baby's death is not the *means* to the good end of saving the mother's life, but in the other instance its death is the *chosen means* to this end. And it is in and through our choices that we make ourselves to be the persons whom we are; it is through them that we give to ourselves our identity as moral beings. Thus we ought never freely choose, however reluctantly, to kill an innocent human being.

ENDNOTES

1. In 1970, 17,800 such pregnancies were reported in women aged 15–44, but by 1980 the figure had reached 52,000 in women of this age, and today it is estimated that approximately 1 pregnancy in every 60 is ectopic, and the rate is continuing to increase. For data, see John A. Rock, "Ectopic Pregnancy," in *TeLinde's Operative Gynecology* (7th ed.: Philadelphia: J. B. Lippincott Co., 1992), p. 412, Table 18–1. See also Lisa Cannon and Hanna Jesionowska, "Methotraxate treatment of tubal pregnancy," *Fertility and Sterility* 55.6 (June 1991) 1033; R. E. Leach and S. J. Ory, "Modern management of ectopic pregnancy," *Journal of Reproductive Medicine* 34 (1989) 324; B. S. Shapiro, "The nonsurgical treatment of ectopic pregnancy," *Clinical Obstetric Gynecology* 30 (1987) 230; *Suspected Ectopic Pregnancy,* Pamphlet APO31 of the ACOG Patient Education Series, prepared by the American College of Obstetricians and Gynecologists, August, 1992.

2. On this see Rock, "Ectopic Pregnancy," pp. 412–414; Carmen J. Sultana, Kirk Easley, and Robert L. Collins, "Outcome of laparoscopic versus traditional surgery for ectopic pregnancies," *Fertility and Sterility* 57.2 (February 1992) 285.

3. Rock, "Ectopic Pregnancy," pp. 421–427.

4. Ibid., p. 420, with a reference to the study of H. Fernandez, J. D. Rainhorn, E. Papiernik et al., "Spontaneous resolution of ectopic pregnancy," *Obstetrics and Gynecology* 71 (1988) 171.

5. Rock, "Ectopic Pregnancy," p. 421.

6. "Actively proliferating trophoblastic tissue is exquisitely sensitive to this effect of MTX, which forms the rationale for its use in the treatment of EP [ectopic pregnancies]." Cannon and Jesionowska, "Methotraxate treatment of tubal pregnancy," 1034.

7. Rock describes the procedure as follows: "gentle pressure is exerted from the opposite side of the tube [and] the products of gestation are gently expressed from the lumen [the cavity of the tube]. Because a certain amount of separation of the trophoblast has usually occurred, the conceptus generally can be easily removed from the lumen. Gentle traction by forceps without teeth or by suction may be used if necessary" ("Ectopic Pregnancy," pp. 422–423).

102

8. Use of MTX, linear salpingo(s)tomy, and segmental resection are advocated because these procedures to not require the excision of the entire tube. Thus the possibility that the woman may become pregnant later is enhanced. On this cf. Rock, "Ectopic Pregnancy," pp. 421–425.

9. Ibid., p. 425.

10. Ibid., p. 430.

11. Thomas J. O'Donnell, S.J., *Medicine and Christian Morality* (2nd rev. ed.: Staten Island: Alba House, 1991), p. 167. O'Donnell, however, cites no literature to support this claim.

12. Rock, "Ectopic Pregnancy," p. 432.

13. Rock reports an incidence of 1 abdominal pregnancy in 7269 deliveries. Ibid., p. 432. Rock refers to the study of J. C. Stafford and W. D. Ragan, "Abdominal pregnancy: review of current management," *Obstetrics and Gynecology* 50 (1977) 548.

14. Rock, "Ectopic Pregnancy," p. 432.

15. Telephone conversation with John T. Bruchalski, M.D., on August 30, 1992.

16. Rock, "Ectopic Pregnancy," pp. 433–434.

17. Ibid.

18. On this see Germain Grisez, "The Definability of the Proposition: The Intentional Killing of an Innocent Human Being Is Always Grave Matter," *Persona, Verita e Morale: Atti del Congresso Internazionale di Teologia Morale (Roma, 7–12 aprile 1986)* (Roma: Citta Nuova Editrice, 1987), pp. 291–313.

19. On the immorality of directly intended abortion see the following documents of the magisterium: Sixtus V, Constitution *Effraenatam*, October 29, 1588, in *Enchiridion Familiae: Textos del Magisterio Pontificio y Conciliar sobre el Matrimonio y la Familia*, ed. A. Sarmiento and J. Escriva Ivars (Madrid: Ediciones Rialp, 1992) 1.191–199; Innocent XI, Decree of the Holy Office, March 2, 1679, in *Enchiridion Familiae*, 1.216–217; Pius XI, Encyclical *Casti connubii*, December 31, 1930, n. 64, in *Enchiridion Familiae*, 1.747–748; Pius XII, Address *La vostra presenza* to the Italian Medical Biological Union of St. Luke, November 12, 1944, in *Enchiridion Familiae*, 2.1306–1307; Pius XII, Address *Vegliare con sollecitudine* to the Italian Catholic Union of Midwives, October 29, 1951, in *Enchiridion Familiae*, 2.1429–1430; Pius XII, Address *Nell'ordine* to the National Congress of the "Family Front," November 26, 1951, in *Enchiridion Familiae*, 2.1468–1472; John XXIII, Encyclical *Mater et Magistra*, May 15, 1961, n. 190, in *Enchiridion Familiae*, 2.1755; Vatican Council II, Pastoral Constitution *Gaudium et spes*, nn. 27 and 51, in *Enchiridion Familiae*, 3.1827–1828, 1838–1839; Paul VI, Encyclical *Humanae vitae*, July 25, 1968, n. 14, in *Enchiridion Familiae*, 3.1920; Paul VI, Address *Salutiamo con paterna effusione* to the XXIII National Congress of the Union of Italian Catholic Jurists, December 9, 1972, in *Enchiridion Familiae*, 3.2044–2048; Congregation for the Doctrine of the Faith, *Declaration on Procured Abortion*, November 18, 1974, in *Enchiridion Familiae*, 3.2071–2095; John Paul II, Homily during the Mass on the Capitol Mall of Washington, D.C., October 7, 1979, in *Enchiridion Familiae*, 3.2380–2381; Congregation for the Doctrine of the Faith, *Instruction on Respect for Human Life in Its Origin and on the Dignity of Procreation*, February 22, 1987, in *Enchiridion Familiae*, 5.4608.

20. Pius XII, Address *La vostra presenza* to the Italian Medical Biological Union of St. Luke, November 12, 1944, in *Enchiridion Familiae*, 2.1306–1307, n. 25. This text was cited by Paul VI, with reference to the immorality of direct abortion, in *Humanae vitae*, footnote 24 (in *Enchiridion Familiae*, 3.1920); by the Congregation for the Doctrine of the Faith in its *Declaration on Procured Abortion*, November 18, 1974, n. 7, footnote 15 (in *Enchiridion Familiae*, 3.2078); and by the Congregation for the Doctrine of the Faith in its *Instruction on Respect for Human Life in Its Origin and on the Dignity of Procreation*, February 22, 1987, footnote 20 (in *Enchiridion Familiae*, 5.4608).

21. Pius XII, Address *Nell'ordine* to the National Congress of the "Family Front," November 26, 1951, in *Enchiridion Familiae,* 2.1471–1472, n. 15. Emphasis in the original.

22. For a brief presentation of the reasons why it is reasonable to hold that there is a core of Catholic moral teaching, including the teaching on the grave immorality of direct abortion, see my *An Introduction to Moral Theology* (Huntington, IN: Our Sunday Visitor, 1991), pp. 207–215.

23. The relevant decrees are the following: (1) the Decree of the Holy Office of August 19, 1889 and confirmed by Leo XIII regarding the immorality of "craniotomies" and "any other surgical operation which is a direct killing of the fetus or of the pregnant mother" (text in *Enchiridion Symbolorum Definitionum et Declarationum de Rebus Fidei et Morum,* ed. Henricus Denzinger and Adolfus Schoenmetzer (33rd ed.: Barcelona: Herder, 1975), n. 3258; hereafter referred to as DS); (2) the Decree of the Holy Office of May 4, 1898, which stated that in cases "of urgent necessity, laparotomy for the removal of ectopic conceptions is licit, provided serious and opportune provision is made as far as possible for the lives of both the fetus and the mother," a decree also confirmed by Leo XIII (DS, nn. 3336–3338; see also *Enchiridion Familiae,* 1.576); and (3) the Decree of the Holy Office of March 5, 1902 (DS, n. 3358). This Decree was in answer to the question: "Whether it is sometimes licit to remove from the mother ectopic fetuses which are immature, before the expiration of the sixth month after conception." The reply was: "In the negative, according to the Decree of May 4, 1898, which declares that as far as possible serious and opportune provision must be made for the lives of both the fetus and the mother. As regards the time, let the petitioner remember that according to the same decree no hastening of delivery is allowed unless it be done at a time and in a manner which are favorable to the lives of the mother and the child, according to ordinary contingencies." This decree lacked papal approbation.

24. T. Lincoln Bouscaren, S. J., *The Ethics of Ectopic Operations* (2nd rev. ed.: Milwaukee: The Bruce Publishing Company, 1944), p. 59. The second and revised edition of Bouscaren's work, a model of scholarship, was published in 1944. The first edition had been published in 1933, and that edition was a revision of his 1928 Latin dissertation on the subject, presented to the Faculty of Moral Theology of the Gregorian University in Rome in partial fulfillment of the requirements for the degree of Doctor of Sacred Theology (STD).

25. "The removal of a pregnant fallopian tube containing a nonviable living fetus, even before the external rupture of the tube, can be done in such a way that the consequent death of the fetus will be produced only indirectly. Such an operation may be licitly performed if all the circumstances are such that the necessity for the operation is, in moral estimation, proportionate to the evil effect which is permitted. In all such operations, if the fetus is probably alive, care must be taken to baptize the fetus immediately, at least conditionally." Ibid., p. 147.

26. National Conference of Catholic Bishops, *Ethical and Religious Directives for Catholic Health Care Facilities,* Directive # 16 (Washington;, D.C.: United States Catholic Conference, 1971).

27. Bouscaren, *The Ethics of Ectopic Operations,* pp. 101–102.

28. O'Donnell, *Medicine and Christian Morality,* p. 165.

29. Rock, "Ectopic Pregnancy," p. 425.

30. For a description of the diagnostic procedures currently available for detecting ectopic pregnancies early in their development see ibid., pp. 414–420.

31. O 'Donnell, *Medicine and Christian Morality,* p. 166. O'Donnell cites in support of this claim an article by C. J. Wallace, "Transplantations of Ectopic Pregnancy from Fallopian Tube to Cavity of Uterus," *Surgery, Gynecology and Obstetrics* 24 (May 5, 1917) 578–579.

32. Wallace, "Transplantations of Ectopic Pregnancy from Fallopian Tube to Cavity of Uterus," 578. Note that Dr. Wallace refers to the "growing child," not to an embryo or fetus. He surely believed that human life begins with conception/fertilization.

33. Ibid., 579.

34. Landrum B. Shettles, Letter, in *American Journal of Obstetrics and Gynecology* (December 1990) 2026–2027.

35. Germain Grisez, *Abortion: The Myths, the Realities, and the Arguments* (New York/Cleveland: Corpus, 1970), pp. 340–341. See also his "Toward a Consistent Natural Law Ethic of Killing," *American Journal of Jurisprudence* 15 (1970) 64–96.

36. See Joseph M. Boyle, Jr., "Double Effect and a Certain Type of Craniotomy," *Irish Theological Quarterly* 44.4 (1977) 301–318, and Marcellino Zalba, S.J., "Nihil Prohibit Unius Actus Duos Effectus," in *Atti del Congresso Internazionale: Tommaso D'Aquino nel Suo Settimo Centenario*, Vol. 5, *L'Agire Morale* (Naples: Edizioni Dominicane Italiane, 1976) 567–568.

37. Joseph Dolan, S.J., "Review of *Abortion: The Myths, the Realities, and the Arguments*," *Thought* 47 (1972) 143–144; John Finnis, "The Rights and Wrongs of Abortion: A Reply to Judith Jarvis Thompson," *Philosophy and Public Affairs* 2 (1972).

38. Grisez, *Abortion . . .* , pp. 345–346; emphasis added. The attitude Grisez expresses is precisely the attitude that should characterize Catholic scholars engaged in philosophical and theological study *according to the magisterium itself*. For in its May 24, 1990 *Instruction on the Ecclesial Vocation of the Theologian*, the Congregation for the Doctrine of the Faith explicitly recognized that theologians can raise questions even concerning the contents of teaching of the magisterium on matters *per se* not irreformable, so long as they are willing to abide by the judgment of the magisterium (n. 24).

39. O'Donnell, *Medicine and Christian Morality*, p. 167.

Chapter 8

SUCCESS STORIES: NATURAL FAMILY PLANNING

Kay Ek

In 1961, the year Dave and I were married, there were some assumptions about being married in the Catholic Church. For example, engagement should be no longer than six months. And, it was a given that children would follow and that any means of spacing children would be, after permission from a confessor, to use the Rhythm Method or the combination of the Temperature and Rhythm Methods. These were the only known natural methods at that time, the only methods of family planning universally accepted by the Church, as far as I know, other than no method at all.

Child spacing was most always discussed between the wife and her doctor, rarely with any involvement of the husband.

We were anxious to begin our family and yet, there really wasn't any information available to help define the days of potential fertility. For those who were having children in rapid succession, there also wasn't any help except for the rare Catholic physician who took time to explain the Rhythm Method. But, faith was strong back then and couples were, regardless of the hardships, inclined to follow the teaching of the Church and not to do anything contrary to what their confessor deemed appropriate for them.

By 1968, when *Humanae vitae*[1] was published, however, many couples were convinced that it was okay to take the Birth Control Pill. They were told to follow their conscience. It was likened to a cold tablet, taken to just control an illness, in this case fertility.

As you all know, *Humanae vitae*[2] encouraged the scientific community to advance the welfare of marriage and the family by developing a proper regulation of birth "founded on the observance of natural rhythms" of a woman's cycle.

In 1953, Dr. John Billings of Melbourne, Australia, had begun development of a new natural method. Through clinical studies, the basic principles and guidelines of the Method were established. By 1964, Dr. Billings wrote the first edition of *The Ovulation Method*.[3] That same year, his wife Evelyn, also a physician, joined him, continuing research and development of the Ovulation Method.

By the late 1960's, it was clear the Ovulation Method was so simple that even illiterate and blind women could quickly learn it with their husbands, and apply it successfully.

During that same period of time, Dr. Josef Roetzer was perfecting the Sympto-Thermal Method in Austria, and in Sweden, Dr. Erik Odeblad was conducting studies on cervical mucus, collaborating Dr. Billings' findings.

In June of 1972, at the invitation of Bishop George Speltz, Dr. John Billings spoke to local physicians and priests of our Diocese. A smattering of physicians attended, affording Dr. Billings a polite but cool reception. A second presentation was given at St. John's University in Collegeville, Minnesota, just a few miles from our home in St. Cloud, the room was filled to overflowing.

Bishop Speltz saw the potential of the Ovulation Method as answering the call of *Humanae vitae*[4] and as an opportunity to fill a basic need of the Catholic people in the Diocese.

That Fall, Mary Hughes, who was also working in the marriage prep program, and I were asked to attend the first training workshop in the United States for the Billings Ovulation Method, conducted by Mercedes Wilson, in New Orleans.

Before making the commitment, my husband thought he would do a little research on his own. He contacted a family practitioner friend of ours and asked him, father of 8, if he had heard of the Billings Ovulation Method and if so, what he thought of it. He hadn't heard of it and when the words Natural Family Planning entered the conversation, the doctor painted a picture of babies being left at our doorstep with a note suggesting it be named Dave or Kay as a living monument to the ineffectiveness of NFP.

My husband's second source of counsel was an OB/Gyn, a graduate of St. Thomas College (now the University of St. Thomas), my husband's alma mater, where the *Summa* was, at that time anyway, not only required reading, but part of the school's credo. This doctor, a product of St. Thomas College not only pooh-poohed NFP, but strongly discouraged the Billings' Method as an adventure doomed to failure because, as he put it, "all women are different and no single method will work for all, except for the Pill, of course."

In spite of these admonishments, I elected to go and decide for myself. Twenty years ago, I committed one year to the program with the proviso that I would only teach something I felt confident about.

The audiences in the early years in the parishes my husband and I spoke in were mainly women with few men venturing out into the unknown. This is in great contrast to the classes taught now, where the woman unaccompanied by her husband or fiancé is rare.

The need expressed by those attending was for a method that was simple to understand, adaptable to every condition and stage in the reproductive life of the woman, reliable and healthy. It was also and very importantly, a method which did not violate their conscience.

The Rhythm Method, which was based on calculations of past menstrual cycles, did not take into account any variations due to stress, illness, cycle alterations during the time after childbirth, while breastfeeding or during the premenopausal years. Prior to 1920, it was understood that a woman could become pregnant at any time of the cycle. This method worked for a small percentage of couples, consequently, a natural method which Dr. Billings introduced to the U.S. in the 1970's, was met with great skepticism.

This subtle but essential myth that ovulation could occur anytime during the cycle was brought home to me at the very first parish presentation I made in the winter of 1973.

A man who identified himself as a doctor questioned this basic principle of the Ovulation Method: that is, that ovulation can occur only once during a menstrual cycle. He was sure that ovulation could be triggered by sexual arousal any time—like mink can ovulate any time, he said.

It turned out that the doctor was a veterinarian and while he knew of the importance of mucus for the insemination of dairy cows, he was sure there was a closer relationship between the chemistry of women and mink, the misunderstanding continues to this day.

The secular press still refers to Natural Family Planning as the Rhythm Method.

Dave and I were the parents of three young children when we learned the Ovulation Method. We had used the Rhythm Method, my cycles were irregular and I never knew when ovulation was occurring. We will be forever grateful to the Drs. Billings for their work and the other physicians who made it possible to easily identify the fertile and infertile phases of the cycle. For up to the point of learning modern NFP, there was stress because we wanted to space our children and we wanted to breastfeed the children.

Consequently, during breastfeeding, we simply abstained for several months during what we now know as a time when it would have been almost impossible for us to conceive.

NFP was and is counter-cultural with the popularity of the Pill which exists today and without the total support and encouragement of my husband, I would not have been able to survive all of the roadblocks before me. As I reflect back to those days, I have come to realize that only by the Grace of God did we hold strong to the teachings of the Church.

During the past 20 years, our program has taught in excess of 10,000 couples and has participated in a number of studies proving the method's effectiveness and demonstrating an excellent continuation rate.

Several factors contribute to this. The first and most important was Bishop George Speltz's strong support for 15 years and that of Bishop Jerome Hanus for the past five years. Our Vicar General, Father Daniel Taufen recently stated, "we put our money where our morals are. If we do not condone contraception and abortion, it is necessary for us to provide couples with a viable, realistic alternative, that is, Natural Family Planning". It is considered a very important program in the Diocese, worthy of its own office and budget. A very dedicated and paid staff make NFP accessible and affordable.

In 1988, a *Minnesota Common Policy for Marriage Preparation*[5] was issued after several years of meetings of the Task Force, of which I was a member.

Guidelines were developed and the consensus was that with each Bishop's approval, these guidelines would be followed.

The adoption of all or part of this policy, is of course, the decision of the Bishop.

The St. Cloud Diocese has adopted it wholeheartedly and Natural Family Planning instruction is a requirement in the Diocesan Marriage Preparation Course.

NFP is recognized as a topic as worthy of time as communications, finances, or any of the other topics presented.

Young, professional, certified NFP teachers provide the first in the series of classes at all marriage prep courses. Continued classes and individual chart reviews help guide couples to a full understanding of NFP throughout the rest of their reproductive lives.

Prior to this, it was thought by many that by making NFP mandatory, we would "turn couples off" and for a couple of years, before the Common Marriage Policy[6], we offered NFP instruction as an optional part of Marriage Preparation. The very motivated couples came. Now, as part of the entire course, each couple receives the First Instruction in the Ovulation Method. If they agree to return in two weeks for follow-up and continued classes, they are given the charts and stamps and a packet of related reading material which allows them to start charting immediately that evening. This, I believe, is the key to the success. As couples preparing for marriage, there are so many demands on their time other than making arrangements to take the First Instruction class later, they are able to begin charting immediately.

Another key to the acceptance of Natural Family Planning is that these couples become excited about the natural methods when they see another attractive, young teaching couple say to them, "We recall when we took our Marriage Course, we were just like you, we didn't know if this would be a method for us or not and then we decided to try it. We wanted to follow the teachings of the Church, we wanted something that was effective and harmless". So the young couples identify with them. They share the same feelings. And, as more than one couple has said to me, "We want our marriage to be like the couple who taught us." They see a love that is growing and not diminishing, they see the respect the teaching couple has for each other and they see something very special, and they know it is different, and they become excited about NFP and they want to use it.

Couples presenting any aspect of marriage preparation are carefully chosen and they have agreed to uphold the teachings of the Church. This is primary, for if contraceptive birth control is mentioned by any of the speakers as acceptable, there is a whole different attitude. Speakers complement each other in their support of NFP.

During the Sexuality talk, which is given a day prior to the instruction on NFP, a young couple, one of our dozen Witness Couples, gives a 10 to 15 minute presentation witnessing to their use of NFP. They share their own experience and urge the young couples to whom they are speaking, to use NFP in their marriages. They share how they feel NFP has helped their communication and total understanding of each other's sexuality, and importantly, they talk about how good they feel about following the teaching of the Church and why this has been such a wise decision. They affirm the Magisterium. They are living witnesses to the wisdom of *Humanae vitae*[7].

When they hear the instruction, they are open to the whole idea of NFP. They have seen the respect these couples have for each other, a respect that's so very evident. They see something special and exciting about NFP, and they want to make it part of their marriage.

There are times when 50 or 60 percent of the couples during any given weekend commit to further instruction and follow-up. We have, overall, a 33 percent acceptance rate. Hopefully as time goes on, these numbers will continue to increase.

I have heard priests say they don't believe the average young couple is capable of dealing with the periodic abstinence involved with the use of NFP. It's the same attitude we see in the community at large, that it's too much to ask teenagers, or other unmarrieds, to abstain and therefore the major emphasis is not on saving sex for marriage, but rather making sex safe before marriage. Our people are capable of more and in most cases, their expectations are more than we give them credit for.

There seems to be an air of apology on the part of some Catholics, including priests and religious, for the Church's teaching in *Humanae vitae*[8]. Dr. Hanna Klaus, an obstetrician/gynecologist who is also a convert from Judaism and a Medical Missionary Sister, in an interview for our newsletter, the *NFP Quarterly,*[9] stated the reason 80 percent of Catholics reportedly are not following the Church's teaching on family planning is that so many "ordained leaders have not done their jobs or else they actively work against it."

Father Ronald Lawler, in a talk he gave in Los Angeles, a few years ago, called "Marriage: A Call to Greatness,"[10] said, "The cruelest people in the Church, I think, are those, who hoping to be kind to suffering people today, destroy or neglect (or fail to insist on) sacred values that are needed to brace ordinary lives". How often I think of this when I hear of the lack of confidence that a couple or the confessor has in the ability to expect, of our Catholic people, something greater than the use of contraception.

I think one of the problems is that the parish priest does not hear of the successes of the natural methods unless there is a close relationship with the couple or couples using it in his parish. I believe the parish priest is often told NFP won't work because "my cycle is irregular" or "I tried it and it doesn't work for us" or "my husband would never go for that" . . . Women with irregular cycles are those for whom

112

this method is the most beneficial. Husbands will lovingly abstain when they understand and realize how meaningful their cooperation is to their wives. A whole new trust in the relationship often develops.

I feel the parish priest or priest working with engaged and married couples needs to understand NFP, to be able to defend its validity.

If priests would take the time to learn how a woman can very simply identify the fertile and infertile phases of her cycle, he may be convinced that this method can work for any motivated couple, with proper instruction and follow-up.

Priests need to know that a woman is really infertile most of the time while the man is fertile from puberty into old age, but that their combined fertility spans just a few days each cycle and that couples are extremely grateful for this knowledge and they don't have to be shy about recommending it.

A number of women, who coming to NFP after having an out-of-wedlock pregnancy, or coming away from contraceptives, have told me "if I had only known this earlier, I would never have abused my body." We need to realize that our competition, Planned Parenthood, with its millions and millions of dollars is luring our Catholic people and winning their hearts and souls with contraception and abortion.

I am convinced we will have to make NFP happen on the diocesan level. Tremendous contributions to the welfare of families have been made by dedicated physicians working in the field of Natural Family Planning.

The Ovulation Method and the Sympto-Thermal Method have had resounding success. Studies conducted by the World Health Organization conclude the Billings' Ovulation Method and the Sympto-Thermal Methods to be 98 to 99 percent effective when couples are motivated, properly taught and correctly followed by a certified NFP instructor.

Both methods are certainly as reliable as any artificial method on the market today and are without the negative side effects to the health, spiritual and emotional lives of the couples.

We are living in an era where abortion is being used as birth control, where young people are in doubt where the Church stands relative to contraception and we have a whole generation who do not know the basis of *Humanae vitae*[11] and other related documents. It is regretable that parents who are sacrificing to send their children to parochial schools and Catholic colleges and universities are often not getting the basic understanding of the Faith including education on a whole vital area of human sexuality.

If parents are contracepting, we can hardly expect these offspring to abide by any thing other than what a sex-saturated society is telling them. These young people are without clear direction and they want direction. I see it all the time in the young people, when they, who are sexually active, are challenged to reverse the way they are living. They take the challenge. Many couples who had been living together move apart. It is almost like no one has ever mentioned chastity to them before now. I hear from these couples how their relationships have changed and I hear the words of gratitude for the knowledge and understanding that comes with NFP. I see a return to the Faith and a stronger Faith commitment as they choose to go forth and help other people in this apostolate.

In a video we have recently produced for clergy, called "Natural Family Planning, The Spiritual Link",[12] you will hear the support of NFP by physicians and as one states, "Following this precept of the Church with respect to Natural Family Planning really brings a whole abundant life, spiritual life, and makes it possible for more vocations because people are listening and following the Church." In the same video, Scott Hahn, the former Presbyterian Minister now teaching at Franciscan University of Steubenville, urges priests to risk unpopularity and to affirm the teaching of the Church, a teaching that was instrumental in his process of conversion.

Unfortunately, many Catholic physicians and priests are not as supportive as Dr. Virnig and Scott Hahn. Many are sanctioning contraception and sterilization in large numbers.

During the past 20 years, I can number on one hand the couples who have had a marriage breakup who were using NFP or who were using NFP from the beginning of their marriage. It is truly rewarding, in this era, when a large percentage of marriages are not making it beyond a few years, that we continue to see such great success in the NFP marriages.

A priest in our Marriage Tribunal office asks every couple, "Was artificial birth control used in your marriage?" And I asked him, what are the results? Without hesitation, I was told that in 100 cases, only 1 or 2 couples will have used NFP.

In 1932, a Catholic doctor named Leo Latz wrote a book called, *The Rhythm of Sterility and Fertility in Women*.[13] In his introduction, he spoke strongly about the problems contraception would bring. He said, "Someone has remarked that the Church is in danger of disruption because of the heresy of contraception. No other heresy was more generally, more cleverly, more effectively propagated by men and women in authority than contraception; none affects the members of the Church more directly and more intimately . . . contraception has the support of scientists, sociologists and even large religious bodies; the advances it has made within a decade are terrifying."

114

As we reflect today, we realize the profoundness of those words written over 50 years ago and the escalating negative effect contraception has had since that time.

But we have made great progress in recent years and live with the hope of continued acceptance.

Those of us who are working in the dioceses are very grateful to the Knights of Columbus and for what they have contributed in making it possible for us to have the leadership of Bishop James McHugh and the Diocesan Development Program for Natural Family Planning in Washington, D.C. Through that office, we are kept updated with newsletters and meetings and because of that office, we have a connection with NFP offices across the country. Thank you, Knights, for your continued support of that office and for the opportunity for me to be here this week.

Perhaps the most profound and appropriate way I can conclude, is to restate the words of the Holy Father, in his special message to the bishops of the world in *Humanae vitae*.[14]

"At the conclusion of this encyclical, our reverent and affectionate thoughts turn to you. To all of you we extend an urgent invitation . . . work ardently and incessantly for the safeguarding and the holiness of marriage, so that it may always be lived in its entire human and Christian fullness. Consider this mission as one of your most urgent responsibilities at the present time."

NOTES

1. Pope Paul VI, *Humanae vitae*, #24.

2. ibid.

3. Cf. Dr. John J. Billings M.D., *The Ovulation Method* (Melbourne, Australia: Advocate Press Printery, 1964).

4. Pope Paul VI, *Humanae vitae*

5. Cf. Minnesota Catholic Conference, *Minnesota Common Policy for Marriage Preparation* Sept. 1988

6. ibid

7. Pope Paul VI, *Humanae vitae*

8. ibid

9. Cf., *NFP Quarterly,* Diocese of St. Cloud, Office of Natural Family Planning.

10. Rev. Ronald Lawler O.F.M., Cap. *"Marriage: A Call To Greatness"*. Paper given at the Sixth International Ovulation Method Institute, Los Angeles, January 1980

11. Pope Paul VI, *Humanae vitae*

12. Cf., Diocese of St. Cloud, Office of Natural Family Planning Video produced & copywrited 1993, "Natural Family Planning: The Spiritual Link".

13. Leo J. Latz, M.D., LL.D., *The Rhythms of Sterility and Fertility In Women,* (Chicago, Latz Foundation, 1932) Introduction.

14. Pope Paul VI, *Humanae vitae*

Chapter 9

SUCCESS STORIES: TEACHING THE CHRISTIAN VISION OF SEXUALITY TO THE YOUNG

Rose Fuller

Introduction

I come to you today as Executive Director of Northwest Family Services (NWFS) of Portland, Oregon. I have been asked to speak to you about what works in chastity education. During our time together I wish:

—to describe our chastity education program,
—to identity the intrinsic value of chastity,
—to identify what works in practice in teaching chastity,
—including a discussion of the condom issue,

—and to identify the role Catholic schools and religious education programs can take in promoting chastity.

First, our program . . .

Northwest Family Services is a non-sectarian, not-for-profit organization with a policy not to refer for contraception, sterilization, or abortion. Respect life issues, support of marriage and family life, and chastity have always been part of our mission. Our efforts in youth chastity education go back over a decade as a natural spin off from our work in natural family planning. We were often asked to speak as an opposing view to Planned Parenthood. It became clear young people did not have the support or skills to practice premarital abstinence. They saw no benefit in doing so.

Four years ago, we were awarded a federal grant through the Health and Human Services Title XX office. Title XX funding is directed to the demonstration of care and pregnancy prevention programs.[1] It is unique. There is no requirement to refer for contraception or abortion, families are to be involved, premarital abstinence is to be explicitly taught, and adoption is to be presented as a positive option. From the beginning there has been opposition to the Title XX funding. The American Civil Liberties Union and certain legislators have tried to cut funding for these programs because they believe that teaching abstinence is exclusively a religious issue. Clearly the devastation to society and health are compelling reasons alone to teach premarital abstinence. Time will tell what happens with the present administration.

The Northwest Family Services' program is called FACTS, an acronym for Family Accountability Communicating Teen Sexuality. As part of the project a junior, senior, and parent curriculum and support materials were developed. Parental involvement is a unique feature of FACTS. With this project, we are inservicing school staff, and offering parent education and parent-teen programs in schools, churches, and other community settings. During the last three years, over 5,000 teens, parents, and teachers have participated in FACTS programs in Oregon.

Because the FACTS research project is partially federally funded, it is religiously neutral. The fullness of Catholic faith is not presented. But it should not surprise us that a program whose secular objective is to provide reasons for chastity should also fit hand in glove with faith. Teens tells us that "Now I understand why my Church is opposed to premarital sex." And a Catholic priest from California recently wrote

118

saying they used the material "as is" and afterwards supplemented it with explicit Catholic morality. He said the parents and students were able to see the "reasonableness" of the position and then to explore why this rational stance fits with faith.

The Faith Perspective: Chastity as a Critical Virtue

John Paul II writes in *Familiaris consortio* "God created man in his own image and likeness: calling him to existence *through love,* he called him at the same time *for love.*"[2] In biblical perspective, sexuality differentiates us and orients us to selfless interpersonal communion in service to life, not least in transmitting the image of God through procreation and nurture of children.[3] It sets us forth on the path of imaging the communion of love that is within God. This imaging reaches its consummation in the wedding banquet of heaven, foreshadowed by marriage upon earth, and in the Church's spousal union with Christ (Eph 5:32, 1:9–10; Rev 21). From start to finish in Scripture, chaste love in monogamous marriage is increasingly identified as the sacramental embodiment of faith and salvation.

Education for chastity is therefore ultimately an education in the grammar of our humanity by which God wishes to reveal to us in the flesh his final hope for us. In other words, what we do with our bodies reflects who we are as spiritual persons. And the virtue of chastity, by which our sexuality, masculine and feminine, is actualized in accord with our vocation in life, is no trivial matter.

Because chastity "signifies spiritual energy capable of defending love from the perils of selfishness and aggressiveness, and able to advance it towards its full realization,"[4] it is closely linked with succeeding in our vocation as persons. The virtue of chastity is intrinsic to a person's authentic maturity. It is the gateway to respecting and fostering the "nuptial meaning" of the body: namely, that we achieve the truth of our being only through a sincere gift of self.[5] Chastity, properly understood, is not repressive, but a freedom enabling persons to fully love in a profoundly personal way.

Sexuality and chastity are therefore not just about sex and pleasure, but rather about preventing the reduction of our life to that. For sexuality by nature draws us out from our self-centeredness to interaction and true human intimacy on all levels. Sexual attraction is not, at root, a longing for mere physical pleasure, but for completion of self through relationships with others. Rollo May sums it up well "[F]or human beings the more powerful need is not for sex, per se, but for relationships, intimacy, acceptance, and affirmation."[6]

Philosopher Joyce Little succinctly describes our mission as Christians in the modern world: "The most urgent task facing Christians in society today is to be a visible image, a living sacrament, and thus a prophetic witness to the reality of divine love, to the reality that we have been chosen, to the reality that the burdens of love can be embraced and sustained. Only when Christians are willing to do this will we see a genuine renewal both of the Church and of the world."[7]

Chastity education—What is it?

Good chastity education is a course in life. It teaches the students how to become loving, emotionally mature people. Marriage is presented as the norm for sexual expression. Sexuality and fertility are viewed as wonderful gifts to be cherished. Chastity is made real as a way of respecting and protecting the dignity of others as persons called to give love and life. Good chastity education contains four key elements.

1. Personal Love. Love of oneself and others is critical in chastity education. Love is presented as benevolence: a decision to accept all other persons as equal; to do everything to help them to be the best they can be; to do nothing which will make them less than they are. The sacrificial elements as well as the joys are understood as part of love. This is a tall order for all of us to follow.

2. Emotional Maturity. Emotional maturity is part of love: the ability to cope with life's normal pains and pleasures; to take responsibility for one's actions; and to accept feelings, but to base actions on principles. Teens need to know they will experience sexual feelings, but that these feelings will frequently be indiscriminate, that is, essentially impersonal, whereas love must be personal. Maturity requires that we not simply act on feelings, but rather think about the consequences of acting.[8] Two hours from now, will the feelings still warrant the action?

3. Sexual Intercourse Full of Meaning. Sexual intercourse is presented as part of a beautiful body language which is meant to communicate all the commitment, future, forgiveness, caring, and hope which married couples should have. A context less than marriage is a betrayal of this meaning. It robs sex of something of its "sacramentality" for that individual or couple, like an overused word that begins to mean nothing when it means anything and everything. Conventional sex education courses find it almost impossible to present the procreative aspect of human sexuality in a positive manner. Good chastity

120

education, by contrast, communicates that children are a gift to be received with reverence, that only in marriage can a child truly have the security he or she deserves, and therefore only in marriage can sex be honest.

4. The Freedom of a Chaste Life. Finally, good chastity education must emphasize the benefits, and not just the difficulties of remaining abstinent. Teens need to know: What do they gain with the practice of chastity? In a word: Freedom.

Freedom from fear of . . .	Freedom to develop . . .
•Sexually transmitted diseases.	•Friendships.
•Cervical cancer.	•A value system.
•Unintended pregnancy.	•Socially.
•Abortion.	•Intellectually.
•Birth control side effects.	•Self-control.
•Out-of-wedlock pregnancy.	•At your own pace.
•Parents' finding out.	•Future plans.
•Ruining one's reputation.	•Spiritually.
•Ruining one's future.	•Personally for your vocation

The Culture's Challenge

If we are going to teach chastity, we need to know about the social and sexual culture of today's teens. Abortion has been legal on demand their entire lives. Sex between any two people of any sex for any reason is considered the norm. If their parents aren't divorced, many of their friends' parents are and they are worried about it. Their friends talk about suicide and some of them follow through. Classmates carry guns and knives. Peers come to school regularly drunk or high on drugs. For many of them, life is literally a war zone. In this context, educating for chastity is difficult, but not impossible. Teens respond to a witness of hope, a "can do" attitude. Jesus does call us to live exceptional lives. Teens are up to the challenge, if only we offer it.

Unfortunately, as a society we have been trying to address symptoms of the sexual revolution and not its cause. The present social expectation is that teens will be sexually active. From that assumption follows the faulty conclusion that there is little to do but inform them about contraceptives and sexually transmitted diseases (STDs) in the hopes of minimizing unintended pregnancy and disease. Pedagogically we have abused a fundamental principle: *the self-fulfilling prophecy*; that is, young people will conform to the expectations we hold for them.

There is no need to lower expectation levels. A study by the Rand Institute on effective educational institutions found that when compared to similar populations, private and parochial schools were much more successful than their public counterparts. Part of the success was credited to expectation. These institutions did not tolerate truancy, they set higher levels of scholastic achievement; in a word, they expected more and they got more.[9]

If we expect teens to be sexually active, and teach them as if they were, then they will be. Might that not be a factor in the statistics we now have regarding teen sexual activity? Bearing in mind that generally, boys initiate intercourse younger and in greater numbers than girls, we note that in 1970, only 4.6% of ninth grade girls had experienced intercourse, but that number steadily rose to almost 32% in 1991—a seven-fold increase. In 1991, the about two-thirds of twelfth grade girls and three-fourths of the boys were sexually active.[10] Each year the rate has risen. Teens themselves acknowledge the problem: when sexually active teen boys were asked what the right age was to begin sexual activity, 80% of these boys indicated an age older than that at which they themselves first experienced intercourse.[11]

Despite almost universal availability of contraceptives, explicit sex education, use of health clinics, and a heightened awareness of STDs and AIDS, the pregnancy rate among sexually active teens has only fallen slightly.[12—13] The birth rate, however, has not remained the same, but dropped! Why? Abortion has taken up the slack where promiscuity has grown epidemic.

The practice of unchastity spawns numerous social, physical, emotional, and spiritual consequences too.[14—16] AIDS is also a real possibility for those who are not chaste, but teens believe they are invulnerable. They don't really believe they will get AIDS (they don't see their immediate peers with AIDS). Superman may have been retired, but not the syndrome.[17]

What we are learning from the research is that teens simply do not have the personal or social maturity to get involved with sex or practice contraception effectively.[18—20] And readily available abortion removes incentives for caution. In today's culture many believe they have a right to be sexually active without pregnancy. What we see is a social expectation of contraception leading to backup abortion. Conventional sex education has failed to help our teens. It assumes they have the emotional, social, and ethical skills to negotiate a sexual relationship; they do not. Developmentally, however, teens can handle premarital abstinence.

Predictors of Abstinence

Our goal is to educate for chastity. High expectations are right and just. And we have come to recognize that education for contraception is a betrayal of youth; it feeds into a self-fulfilling prophecy based on low expectations; in short, it does not work. What then should we teach, and how should we go about it?

We need first to realize that the research identifies several converging factors predictive of abstinence.[21] To be successful a chastity education program needs to build its components in such a way as to bring these factors into synergy with one another. Let me mention these factors. With respect to each the focus of the FACTS program will be noted.

1. Religious Affiliation. The first predictor is religious affiliation. Teens with a *religious affiliation* and regular church attendance are more chaste than their non-attending peers. Conversely, church attendance drops when teens become sexually active.[22]

Churches, however, could do more, to be a stronger factor for abstinence. In a survey of 46,000 youth, 43% reported two or fewer hours in their lifetime spent at church discussing sex.[23] If our goal is to develop chastity, and if every virtue is a good habit to be cultivated over time, we must ask: Is adequate time given to chastity education in our churches?

2. Approachable, Respected, Credible Parents. A second predictor of abstinence: If teens perceive their parents as *approachable, respected* and *credible* in the area of sexuality, then the teens are more apt to abstain.

FACTS was designed to test parental involvement levels. We have been very successful in educating them. Participating parents have felt an increased sense of responsibility, of confidence and competence in fulfilling that responsibility, and of the level and quality of interaction with their teen on sexual matters. The teens have reported an increase in parent-teen communication.[24]

3. Abstinent Values. Third, teaching the advantages of abstinence not only benefits virgins, but also those who have been sexually active. Secondary virginity is taught. Scientific studies show that these young people make dramatic changes when *abstinent values* are presented.[25]

4. Future Orientation. Fourth in our list of predictors: Teens who have a *future orientation* are less apt to be sexually involved. My freshman daughter said to me after we attended a FACTS class, "I'm going to be a kindergarten teacher. So I have to get good grades and finish college. Besides I want to be married and have a bunch of kids. I don't want to mess up my life by having sex before marriage." That is a solid future orientation.

5. Positive Peer Support. A fifth predictor of abstinence is: peer pressure, in the right direction. Studies show that of teens whose peers are sexually active, 57% said they also were sexually active. But of teens who said their friends were *not* sexually active, only 2% said they were sexually involved.[26] *Positive peer support* is of striking importance.

While a teacher cannot pick a student's friends, the teacher does relate to teens as a group and can influence the peer environment by motivating the group. A teacher's acceptance of abstinence can result in a positive peer environment.[27] This is one area in which the school can play a critical role, either by supporting unchastity or chastity.

Northwest Family Services sponsors a group of teens and young adults who are committed to living chaste lives and are willing to help others. They call themselves "The Bod Squad." They help at FACTS classes, telling stories and leading small group discussions. The Squad also assists at other programs that we call "one night-stands," evening programs with youth groups. We also offer a Christian-based program entitled "Keys to Sexual Freedom" where Christian beliefs are clearly incorporated into the discussion.

6. Dating Later and Not Dating Steady. A sixth predictor of abstinence: delayed dating, and avoiding steady dating. Research has shown that teens who *date early* and who *date steadily* are more apt to be sexually active. Social activities, parties, and dating are presented in FACTS as privileges which require responsibility, structure, and standards that are internalized by teens. Too often premarital sex happens because there is nothing else to do.

Conventional wisdom shies away from structure and rules, on the assumption teens are opposed to it. They love it—there is something to challenge! It gives them bearings. They need effective discipline and control strategies. Clear rules and limits, reasonable consequences for rule breaking, and reinforcement for positive behavior are important.[28]

What's involved in programs that work?

1. Successful Programs Know that Knowledge Does Not Equal Virtue. Knowledge based programs have not been effective.

Study after study demonstrates that mere knowledge of contraception and disease does not change attitudes or behavior.[29—38] From the research, another picture emerges. A report from a Georgia program, which at least begins with the supposition of abstinence states "A knowledgeable 13-year-old is no more likely to use contraceptives than is an uninformed 13-year-old."[39] We know, then, that conventional contraceptives-and-disease oriented sex education and AIDS education are not changing attitudes or behavior. Good research, however, is showing chastity education works when done right.[40—47] Good curricula based on solid research are part of the solution.

2. A Focus on Relationships, not Physiology. While even pre-teens often know all about STDs, AIDS, abortion, homosexuality, and contraception, at least the technical information, they don't really listen to the litany of physical complications. They do, however, respond to the emotional ones. They do pick up on the idea that pills and condoms won't protect them from emotional trauma. Emotional pain is often hard to quantify, but there is some data. Imagine the emotional pain a young woman experiences. The world is telling her sex is love, yet in her experiences she finds rejection, fear, and emptiness. One 16-year-old woman wrote, "Since that first night, he expects sex on every date. . . . Our whole relationship seems to revolve around going to bed . . . I don't think this guy is in love with me—at least he's never said so. I know deep down that I am not in love with him either and this makes me feel sort of cheap."[48] Not surprisingly sexually active girls have lower self-esteem than virgins.[49]

Why do teens become sexually active? If you ask teens, they will respond in the following ways. "I wanted to feel loved." "I was curious." "My friends were doing it." "I was drunk and I didn't know what I was doing." "I didn't know how to stop." As family life continues to break up, teens feel more lost, confused, and lonely than ever.

3. Concreteness. Concreteness is essential when educating for chastity. Take, for instance, the term "monogamy." From a Christian perspective, "monogamy" means faithful marriage. But a teenage boy may consider himself "monogamous" because he only has sexual relations with his current girlfriend: that is, to him, "monogamy" means serial promiscuity.

"Abstinence" illustrates the issue too. Teens prefer to operate as minimal literalists (just ask any parent who has suggested a daughter "clean" her room). If a parent says to a daughter, "Don't have sex." She might agree, but then engage in every type of sexual behavior except vaginal intercourse, sincerely believing she is "abstaining from sex." Teens needs clear messages.

An example of the effective "concreteness" used in our FACTS program, that speaks to the kids, is the "3 All's, 3 Any's, 3 Avoid's": "Keep **all** your clothes **all** the way on, **all** the time. Don't let **any** part of **any**one else's body get **any**where between you and your clothes. **Avoid** arousal, **avoid** domineering relationships, and **avoid** dangerous situations." There is no doubt about the message.

4. High Expectations . . . and the Condom Issue. It may be tempting for a given teacher or counselor to recommend contraceptive devices or condoms to a sexually active student, in the hopes that pregnancy would be averted or disease would be prevented, but it would be misguided and wrong to do so. There is no such thing as "safe" or "moral" premarital sex. Every time an authority figure says "abstinence is best, but if you're going to have sex, protect yourself," the inevitable result is that in the mind of the teenager, abstinence and premarital sex appear to be morally equivalent. Teenagers also have great difficulty realistically assessing the relative safety and danger factors of various birth control devices. A teenager reasons, "If condoms aren't effective, my teachers wouldn't be recommending them" (even if the teacher has given statistical information regarding them). The "Don't, but protect yourself" message is translated as a "justifiable risk." The student naturally assumes the teacher or counselor won't harm him or her, relying, quite naturally, on information from persons perceived as friendly, however faulty the information may be.[50—51]

Ultimately, schools taking the "contraceptive" approach to spare their teens from the devastation of AIDS only contribute to a tragic self-fulfilling prophecy based on low expectation. If you, your religious education department, or Catholic schools are tempted in any way to support condom education, "Just Say 'No'."

What is the Role for Catholic Schools and Religious Education Programs?

Just as some in the public sector are recognizing the failures of the conventional secular approach, Catholics educators are implementing a similar type of sex education. In general, these programs are offered to children too young and the information is too explicitly related to reproduction and even contraception. I receive many phone calls about the issue.

I always ask the callers the same questions. Why is the school offering sex ed? Is it to prevent pregnancy and disease or to teach chastity? In what way are parents being involved? Is the young child's

126

modesty protected? Is it really age appropriate? Is reproduction being taught in the early years? Is sexual intercourse presented within marriage? Is contraceptive intercourse subtly promoted? Are Catholic moral teachings clearly taught by the magisterium presented as ambiguous or imminently changing? Is the gospel message presented?

Frequently the caller is a concerned parent saying their parochial school is instituting a sex education program from kindergarten through eighth grade. The typical scenario: the decision to go ahead with the program is made prior to parental input. Lip service is given to parent participation by the school. Parents are ridiculed or intimidated if they ask basic questions. They are instantly labeled "trouble maker" and "sexually repressed." Practical and respectful provision for children opting out of the sex education program is not made.

There are only a few Catholic programs available and are all basically the same. To illustrate the questions some parents have, here is an excerpt from one of the most popular Catholic sex education programs. In the sixth grade student text the woman's fertile time is referred to as "that time of the month when she can become pregnant if sperm are present. Contraceptives prevent sperm from reaching or fertilizing the egg. If the ovum is not fertilized, it will die in a few days and be absorbed into the body."[52] Is there any need to present fertility to eleven-year-old children within the context of contraceptive sexual activity or to imply that contraceptives are the means to prevent pregnancy rather than periodic abstinence within marriage and abstinence outside it?

Allow me to make a few final recommendations for chastity education:

1. *Focus on the Family.* Offer sex education, but offer it within the context of chastity education that respects and enhances the priority of the family called for in *Educational Guidance and Human Love* and *Gaudium et spes* 49. We must explicitly and concretely talk about chastity, at the right time and in the right way, without violating the family and whatever innocence our youth still have.

    a) *Kindergarten-Fourth Grade.* Offer parent education for kindergarten through fourth grade parents. Parents are eager for support and guidance. Sexuality education doesn't happen over a two-hour or four-week course, it happens gradually over time. Parents are rightly called the primary educators, the schools should be supporting this dialogue.

b) *Fifth-Sixth Grade.* Mother-Daughter and Father-Son basic growth and development classes are excellent for fifth and sixth grade students and their parents. By offering such programs, the schools can be vehicles which foster parent-child communication.

c) *Seventh-Eighth Grade.* Seventh or eighth grade onward is the time to deal with issues of chastity. Again, parents should be involved in a way that makes clear to the youth the institution's respect for the parents, and makes it possible to find the parents approachable and credible. The ground work should have been laid with solid, concrete religious education in faith and morals in the earlier grades.

d) *High school and beyond.* The focus of chastity education should be on relationships, discernment of vocation, the meaning of love, and the development of the virtues. Teens need to be challenged to be a sign of contradiction to the world and role models to their peers.

2. *Select Comprehensive Catechetical Materials.* Chastity programs should not have to carry the entire load of moral education, in effect covering for otherwise defective catechetical materials. Religious education programs are insufficient if they offer little clear support for our young people on basic moral issues. By clear support is meant "confident truth telling" or witness to the moral imperatives of being human in the image of God. Balance must be restored in our texts, in our programs, and most importantly in the selection and formation of those teaching our youth.

3. *Screen Faculty Carefully.* What about the teachers of chastity? We need to know: Do they believe in premarital chastity? Do they believe that high schoolers should avoid sex, but that sex is O.K. for single adults? Strange, but true: One director of religious education honestly asked, "You mean to tell me the Church says premarital sex is a sin?" Teachers of chastity need proper formation and supervision.

4. *Use Natural Family Planning Ministry Personnel.* The people around the country who fully understand the issues involved in chastity education are those involved in natural family planning. When establishing bodies to set sexuality education policies and review, include natural family planning instructors and parents, not just chancery and school personnel.

5. *Do What the Research Supports.* I often am asked by schools with contraceptive programs to demonstrate that FACTS is effective. It is a fair question, yet rarely asked of contraceptive education programs, a fact readily acknowledged when I return the question in

128

kind. When setting diocesan policy, compare programs in light of data about what is working with regard to real, committed "chastity education." The old adage that you can't judge a book by its cover applies here. The nicest graphics packaging cannot be the primary criterion.

6. *Support Married Couples.* If chastity is to flourish, we must support married couples. The traditional family is the nucleus of the Church. It is where children thrive, where vocations come from, and where right ways are learned through long years of watching and coaching. Natural family planning for engaged and married couples is an important way for them to learn about and live out chastity and become articulate witnesses to their own children.

7. *Be and Support Good Role Models.* Education in chastity as a part of that support is both about teaching curriculum and role modeling. Be good role models yourselves—expect chastity of everyone. Don't be afraid to speak and support the truth in love. Even as the world scorns us, it knows we bear the truth; we just need to show how to live it. Every time an admired athlete is faithful to his wife, every day a celibate priest keeps his promise, every time a married person turns away from the many temptations to be unfaithful, every time a single person refrains from sexual activity, the kingdom is built up. Positive role models from all walks of life are needed today.

Living a chaste life is not merely an ideal (*Familiaris consortio* 34). It is an integral part of holiness to which all, religious and laity, married and single, are called. We must, then, form our youth in this virtue, not only for the sake of their earthly happiness, but for their eternal happiness as well. Thank you.

NOTES

1. Relatively speaking, it is a small federal program, only about 8% the size of Title X family planning program.

2. John Paul II, *Familiaris consortio,* 11. November 22, 1981. St. Paul Books and Media, Boston, Mass.

3. Traditional sacred scripture citations include "God created man in his image . . . male and female he created them" (Gen 1:27)—sexual differentiation was part and parcel of the original image. There were reasons for it: "Be fruitful, multiply" (Gen 1:28); and "It is not good that man should be alone. I will make him a helpmate" (Gen 2:18–19).

4. John Paul II, *Familiaris consortio,* 33. November 22, 1981. St. Paul Books and Media, Boston, Mass.

5. For a complete discussion of the nuptial meaning of the body read, Wojtyla, K., *Love and Responsibility* (1962), and John Paul II's *Original Unity of Man and Woman, Blessed Are the Pure of Heart, Reflections on Humanae Vitae,* and *The Theology of Marriage and Celibacy* (1980–86).

6. May, Rollo, *Love and Will,* Norton, New York, New York, 1969.

7. Little, Joyce, "Naming Good and Evil," *First Things,* May 1992.

8. McGoey, John, S.F.M., *Through Sex to Love,* Gall Publications, Toronto, 1976. This book contains a complete discussion of emotional maturity and issues of sexuality.

9. Hill, P. T., Foster, G. E., Gendler, T., *High Schools with Character,* Rand Publications Series, Santa Monica, August 1990.

10. *Morbidity and Mortality Weekly Report,* January 3, 1992, Vol. 40, Nos. 51 & 52, U.S. Department of Health and Human Services, Public Health Service.

11. Zabin, Hirsch, Smith, and Hardy, "Adolescent Sexual Attitudes and Behavior: Are They Consistent? *Family Planning Perspectives,* Jul/Aug 1984.

12. Hays, Cheryl (ed.). *Risking the Future: Adolescent Sexuality, Pregnancy and Childbearing.* Washington, D.C.: National Academy Press, 1987.

13. Kirby, D., Waszak, C., Ziegler, J., "Six School-Based Clinics: Their Reproductive Health Services and Impact on Sexual Behavior," *Family Planning Perspectives,* Jan/Feb. 1991.

14. In Oregon, 80% of abortions occur among unwed mothers. If that number holds true for the rest of the country, it accounts for 1.3 million abortions annually. Dignity for the unborn child clearly depends upon respect for the family and the meaning of sexual intercourse. *Oregon Vital Statistics Report, 1990, Health Reports,* Department of Human Resources, July 1992.

15. Each year, one in every eight teenagers contracts a reportable sexually transmitted disease (STD). According to the 1990 Census there are 25 million teens in the U.S. The Center for Prevention Services, "1990 Division of STD/HIV Prevention Annual Report," Centers for Disease Control, Atlanta, 1991, p. 3, reported 3 million new cases of reportable STDs among teenagers each year. Eighty-six percent of all STDs occur among persons aged 15–29. *Morbidity and Mortality Weekly Report,* January 3, 1992, Vol. 40/ Nos./ 51 & 52, U.S. Department of Health and Human Services, Public Health Service.

16. Orr, D., MD, et al, "Premature Sexual Activity as an Indicator of Psychosocial Risk," *Pediatrics,* Feb 1991. Nonvirginal boys and girls are significantly more likely than their virginal cohorts to engage in other activities considered risky including drugs, alcohol, delinquency and other school problems, and attempted suicide. Orr, D.P., Beiter, M., Ingersol, G., "Premature Sexual Activity as an Indicator of Psycho-social Risk," *Pediatrics,* February 1991. One study found that sexually active girls were 6.3 times more likely to attempt suicide than their virgin peers.

17. Boyer, D., Fine, D., "Sexual Abuse as a Factor in Adolescent Pregnancy and Child Maltreatment," *Family Planning Perspectives,* Jan/Feb 1992. There is a self-perpetuating legacy of abuse. A recent study found that two-thirds of unwed teen mothers had been sexually abused. These women were more apt to be physically assaulted by their sexual partner.

18. Bardwick, J., *Psychodynamics of Contraception with Particular Reference to Rhythm,* Proceedings of a Research Conference on Natural Family Planning, The Human Life Foundation, 1973.

19. Elkind, D., *All Grown Up & No Place to Go, Teenagers in Crisis,* Addison-Wesley Publishing Company, 1984.

20. Elkind, D., *The Hurried Child, Growing Up Too Fast Too Soon,* Addison-Wesley Publishing Company, Inc., 1988.

21. Weed, S., Olsen, J., "Working Model," Institute for Research and Evaluation, June 7, 1989.

22. Thornton, A., Camburn, D., "Religious Participation and Adolescent Sexual Behavior and Attitudes," *Journal of Marriage and the Family,* 51:641, 1989.

23. "The Faith Factor," *Source,* Search Institute, Minneapolis, February 1992.

130

24. Weed, S., Plewe, S., "FACTS Project, Year-End Evaluation Report, 1990–1991," prepared for the Office of Adolescent Pregnancy Programs by the Institute for Research and Evaluation.

25. Weed, S., Plewe, S., "Preventing Teen Pregnancy In Utah, Final Report, Governor's Task Force on Teen Pregnancy Prevention," by the Institute for Research and Evaluation, November 1988.

26. Weed, S., Olson, J., "Preventing Teen Pregnancy in Utah, Final Report, Governor's Task Force on teen Pregnancy Prevention," November 1988. Personal communication with Stan Weed, PhD, revealed this finding has been corroborated in the evaluation of Teen Aid, Sex Respect, and FACTS which are all federal Office of Adolescent Pregnancy Programs demonstration sites.

27. Weed, S., "The Teen Aid Family Life Education Project, Year End Report 1991" for the Office of Adolescent Pregnancy Programs by the Institute for Research and Evaluation.

28. Benson, P. L., "The Troubled Journey: A Portrait of 6th–12th Grade Youth," a research report conducted and published by the Search Institute, Minneapolis, MN, 1990.

29. Kirby, D., Barth, R. P., Leland, N., Fetro, J. V., "Reducing the Risk: Impact of a New Curriculum on Sexual Risk-Taking," *Family Planning Perspective,* Nov/Dec 1991.

30. Weed, S., Olsen, J., "Policy and Program Considerations for Teenage Pregnancy Prevention: A Summary for Policymakers," *Family Perspective,* Vol. 2, No. 3.

31. Rind, P. (assistant editor to Family Planning Perspectives), "Peer Support to Keep Teenagers Alive and Well," *Family Planning Perspectives,* Jan/Feb 1992.

32. MacDonald, NE, et al, "High Risk STD/HIV Behavior Among College Students," *Journal of American Medical Association,* June 20, 1990, Vol 263., No. 23 pp. 3155–3159.

33. Stiffman, A., et al, "Changes in Acquired Immunodeficiency Syndrome-Related Risk Behavior After Adolescence: Relationships to Knowledge and Experience Concerning Human Immunodeficiency Virus Infection," *Pediatrics,* May 1992.

34. Kirby, D., Waszak, C., Ziegler, J., "An Assessment of Six School-Based Clinics: Services, Impact and Potential," Center for Population Options, October 1989.

35. Kirby, D., "Sexuality Education: An Evaluation of Programs and Their Effects," Santa Cruz: Network Publishing, 1984.

36. Furstenberg, F., Moore, K., Peterson, J., "Sex Education and Sexual Experience among Adolescents," *American Journal of Public Health,* November 1985.

37. Kegeles, S., Adler, N., Irwin, C., "Sexually Active Adolescents and Condoms: Changes Over One Year in Knowledge, Attitudes and Use," *American Journal of Public Health,* April 1988.

38. Stout, J., Rivara, F., "Schools and Sex Education: Does it Work?" *Pediatric,* March 1989.

39. Howard, M., McCage, J. B., "Helping Teenagers Postpone Sexual Involvement," *Family Planning Perspectives,* Jan/Feb 1990. *Postponing Sexual Involvement,* the program reported on, does have a reproduction, contraceptive, and sexually transmitted disease component though the primary focus is on refusal skills. This program is not a chastity program.

40. Weed, S., Olsen, J., DeGaston, J., Prigmore, J., "Predicting and Changing Teen Sexual Activity Rates: A Comparison of Three Title XX Programs," by the Institute for Research and Evaluation, submitted to Office of Adolescent Pregnancy Programs and Utah Department of Education, December 1992.

41. Richard, D., *Has Sex Education Failed Our Teenagers, A Research Report?* Focus on the Family Publishing, Colorado Springs, CO, 1990.

42. Newman, A., Richard, D., *Healthy Sex Education in Your Schools,* Focus on the Family Publishing, Pomona, CA, 1990.

43. Whitehead, M., McGraw, O., *Foundations for Family Life Education, A Guidebook for Professionals & Parents,* Educational Guidance Institute, 1990.

44. Weed, S., Plewe, S., "FACTS Project Year-End Evaluation Report, 1990–1991," prepared for the Office of Adolescent Pregnancy Programs by The Institute for Research and Evaluation.

45. Weed, S., DeGaston, J., Prigmore, J., Tanas, R., "The Teen Aid Family Life Education Project, Fourth Year Evaluation Report" prepared for the Office of Adolescent Pregnancy Programs, 1991 by The Institute for Research and Evaluation.

46. Weed, S., Plewe, S., "First Year Evaluation of Facing Reality Program, Results for the 1990–91 School Year" prepared for the Office of Adolescent Pregnancy Programs by The Institute for Research and Evaluation.

47. Weed, S., Olsen, J., "Evaluation Report of the Sex Respect Program; Results for the 1989–1990 School Year," submitted to the Office of Adolescent Pregnancy Programs by The Institute for Research and Evaluation.

48. Yoest, C. C. (ed.), *Free to Be Family, Helping Mothers and Fathers Meet the Needs of the Next Generation of American Children,* Family Research Council, 1992.

49. Orr, D., et al, "Reported Sexual Behaviors and Self-Esteem Among Young Adolescents," *American Journal of Disease of Children,* Jan 1989.

50. The pregnancy rate for the condom for unmarried teenagers ranges between 13 and 27%, Jones, E. J., Forrest, J. D. "Contraceptive Failure Based on the 1988 National Survey of Family Growth," *Family Planning Perspectives,* Vol 24, No 1, January/February 1992. There is no data on the condoms efficacy in preventing the transmission of HIV.

51. *Population Reports,* The Johns Hopkins University, September 1990. The actual size of a sperm compared to an HIV organism is roughly that of a football field to a football.

52. Reichert, R., *Growing Within, Changing Without,* Grade 6. The New Creation Series, Religious Education Division, Wm. C. Brown Company Publishers, Dubuque, Iowa, revised printing 1987.

PART TWO

END OF LIFE ISSUES

Chapter 10

CONTEMPORARY ATTITUDES TOWARD DEATH AND DYING

Arthur Dyck, Ph.D.

Nothing that we do should serve to separate someone who is dying from his family. There may be moments of difficulty or even despair but it is of first importance that they should come through to the end together. The journey itself may ease the next stages for those who have to go on living afterwards.[1]

This eloquent statement comes to us from Cicely Saunders. It expresses her philosophy of care, the kind of care intended to rescue individuals and families from any resort to suicide or euthanasia. To illustrate the efficacy of such care, she describes the experiences of one family under such care:

A family doctor asked our clinic staff to visit one young woman in her forties whose pain and vomiting had become uncontrollable. We discovered later that by this time her distress was so great that not only had she attempted suicide but when she failed the family had discussed whether they should not add together all the pills in the house and try to end her life. We were not told this until a year later. Instead she spent most of that year at home with her family, able once again to enjoy life, to work and even to shop and to care for the three children. She overcame her fear of hospitals, attended our Out-Patients, came for one short stay to re-establish control of her vomiting and finally came in peacefully for her last two weeks. One of the things she said to us at [this] stage was, "The children are a year older." It was when she was dying that we were told of the despairing attempt of a year before. We asked if she had ever again demanded for her life to be ended. We were told, "Never. Not after the Sister came, because [I] never had any more pain." We know that this family has really begun to live once more, as her husband calls frequently at a social club at the Hospice designed for such informal "follow-up." How different it would have been if they had remembered only the bewilderment and guilt that follow a suicide or the course they had discussed. And they all needed that extra year.[2]

I begin with Cicely Saunders and I will return to her in conclusion because she represents, certainly for me, and I trust for all of us, an important mode of the Catholic Vision of Life, as embodied in the care for the dying she has championed.

Alas, I need not even bother to say that the kind of care I have briefly illustrated does not make the daily headlines. And it is a gross understatement to say that such care does not dominate special features and movies on TV. Instead, we are facing a veritable barrage of literature, media coverage, polls, conferences, and the beginning of referenda urging the moral approval and legalization of physician-assisted suicide and euthanasia. So massive is the scholarly literature alone that my preparation for this gathering was quite inhibited for a period as I read still more, with still more crossing my desk.

On the face of it, we appear to be in the midst of rapidly changing attitudes toward death and dying, and toward the kind of care appropriate for the dying. Whereas in 1982 the percentage of all Americans polled who believed the law should allow doctors to honor patients' wishes, even if that means allowing such patients to die, was 68 percent; in 1991 it was 81 percent. Furthermore, three out of four individuals support withdrawing life-support systems, including food and water, from patients declared to be "hopelessly ill" or from irreversibly comatose patients whose families request such a step. Commenting on currently expressed attitudes, George Annas, a lawyer at Boston University, declares that "the issue of refusing treatment has become a non-issue. Just a couple of years ago that was hotly debated, and only last year [in 1990] withdrawing food and water was a hot issue. But not anymore."[3] And so Annas swiftly gives the back of his hand to any call for urgent attention to such carefully nuanced perspectives on withdrawing nutrition and hydration as in the statement issued by the National Conference of Catholic Bishops or in the statement superbly crafted by William E. May and his colleagues.[4]

But if withdrawing food and water from patients is not a "hot issue," what is? The *Boston Sunday Globe*'s headline on November 3, 1991, two days before Washington State's referendum on so-called "aid-in-dying,"[5] is clear about what is supposed to be "hot." The headline reads, "Poll: Americans favor mercy-killing." The headline refers to a poll sponsored by the *Globe* and the Harvard School of Public Health that recorded 64 percent of the American population as favoring physician-assisted suicide and euthanasia. Furthermore, this same poll asked whether individual Americans would vote for the Washington initiative if it were on the ballot in their state: sixty-one percent said they would. Polls in Washington State conducted in October yielded the very same percentage ready to vote for its "aid-in-dying" initiative. Of course, as we know, this alleged support was not there when the secret ballot votes were counted; it had dwindled to 46 percent as it also did in California. Interestingly, and I would venture to say predictably, the Roman Catholic church is cited in this same *Globe* article for helping to lower support for the Washington initiative through its "all-out opposition," while at the same time the churches generally, and the Roman Catholic church in particular, are said to be no barrier to support for physician-assisted suicide and euthanasia: Seventy-one percent of all Catholics say they would vote for the Washington initiative; for Jews, the percentage is 69; for Protestants, it is 57. The *Globe* quotes Father John J. Paris, a Jesuit teaching medical ethics at Boston College, as being "disturbed" by the results but not in doubt about their validity. Noting that the church's "theological framework" on suicide has "eroded," he asserts that "It's quite clear: two-thirds of the Catholics don't believe what the bishops are teaching."

With all due respect for Father Paris, I do not know how to interpret the poll data, nor do I know how seriously to take the numbers. I am intensely curious as to why there is this definite discrepancy between what people allegedly say to pollsters before they vote in secret, and what they say on their secret ballots. And I would like to know why, both in California and Washington, the polls began by showing large majorities favoring physician-assisted suicide and euthanasia, a majority which shrank to the vanishing point by the time the ballots were cast. The *Boston Sunday Globe*'s article of November 3, 1991, and the *Globe*/Harvard poll shed no light on either of these questions, and certainly provide no data. At this point, the nature and depth of currently polled attitudes on physician-assisted suicide and euthanasia are largely unknown. The same can be said about the extent to which individual beliefs are and will be shaped by church teachings, including what Catholic bishops are and will be teaching. Who knows?

What we do know is that there are good reasons to teach the errors of any policy legalizing the intentional killing of innocent human beings, including those who are dying and under the care of physicians. And we know that for the dying and seriously ill, there are humane and inspiring ways to live and be cared for.

And so I devote the rest of my attention to those current perspectives on death and dying about which we do know something. These inform the present debate over how best to care for the dying, and will inform us as we seek to sketch a vision faithful to our Christian heritage and our common humanity.

Divergent Perspectives on Death and Dying

Opinions in American courts appear to be changing as rapidly as public opinion. In a mere fifteen years, our courts have moved from the Karen Ann Quinlan case, from permitting the withdrawal of a ventilator from an unconscious brain-damaged patient, to the Jobes case, approving the removal of food and water from an alert, mentally handicapped individual. Although this represents a rapid shift from using the American courts largely to gain permission for life-saving therapies, the perspectives present and still vying with one another in the courts have been there throughout most of this century. There has been a considerable shift over time with respect to which of these perspectives dominates decisions. A single court case will serve nicely to identify the three major perspectives that vie with one another in American constitutional courts. Their presence is, however, quite pervasive.

Consider the Brophy decision, handed down by the Massachusetts Supreme Judicial Court in 1986.[6] Paul Brophy was deemed to be in a semi-vegetative state since being diagnosed in April of 1983. He was breathing on his own and his care was aimed at "comfort only." He was free of bed sores; and his G-tube, for purposes of nutrition and hydration, was not having any adverse side effects. Brophy was regarded as one who could live this way for a number of years, perhaps for more than twenty. The majority of the court, four of seven justices, were convinced that Brophy did not wish to live in his present situation and that certain previous comments of his should be construed as evidence to that effect. To implement that wish, Paul Brophy's wife, Patricia, was asking that her husband no longer be given food and water. Four of the seven justices decided that there was a state interest to implement this wish, since they saw it was superseding any other possible state interest to the contrary, including the state's interest in protecting life and preventing suicide; the other three justices dissented.

1. A Millian Perspective: Life as a calculated right. Writing for the majority, Judge Liacos asserts a right of self determination as the state's interest in granting Brophy's alleged wish to cease receiving food and water. He regards this right as having deep roots in the history of the United States. To make his argument, he quotes John Stuart Mill:

> The only purpose for which power can be rightfully exercized over any member of a civilized community, against his will, is to prevent harms to others. His own good, either physical or moral, is not a significant warrant. He cannot rightfully be compelled to do or forbear because it will be better for him to do so, because it will make him happier, because in the opinion of others to do so would be wise or even right.[7]

Accepting Mill's case for non-interference does not by itself guide Liacos as to what to do about the state's interest in preventing suicide and protecting life. Liacos, therefore, feels compelled to comment on Brophy's quality of life and his prognosis. He depicts Brophy as in some kind of twilight zone in which the body is in some sense alive but a significant part of the brain is not. And for that reason, he regards procedures that sustain life in such circumstances as "prolonging the dying process" rather than "a means of continuing life." And, although Brophy is presumably without conscious awareness, Judge Liacos speaks of his "agony" and wish to "die with dignity." Ignoring the facts in the case, namely that Brophy could live a number of years if supplied with food and water, Judge Liacos views his death, when food and water are not supplied, as "natural," a result of his inability to swallow on his own. Liacos construes the court's decision as one of letting Brophy die, refusing treatment in accord with his wishes, and reasonably so, under the circumstances.

In the perspective taken by Judge Liacos, we detect no natural inalienable right to life. On the contrary, the value of having one's life protected can reasonably be wished away under certain circumstances. And, under such circumstances, the state should not invoke its interest in protecting life. The state, therefore, calculates when it will protect innocent life. These premises also underlie the ease for physician-assisted suicide and euthanasia, as we shall see shortly.

2. A Hobbesian Perspective: Life as a natural right. Justice Lynch dissented from the decision and opinion of the majority. He did consider the law against suicide to be at least partially nullified. In his view, the majority failed to weigh sufficiently Brophy's right to life and the state's interest in protecting it. To support his contention, he cites Hobbes who saw the justification of government power and law as that of protecting life. Indeed, for Lynch, society invests the state with sovereign authority in order to maintain the sanctity of life.

Hobbes does affirm life as a natural and inalienable right, one that a sovereign cannot and should not try to take away, and one which an individual cannot and should not try to surrender to a sovereign. For Hobbes, individuals naturally seek to preserve their own lives. It is irrational, contrary to natural drives, to seek to kill oneself, or have oneself killed. Judge Lynch explicitly depicts the state's interest in preventing suicide as an interest in preventing "irrational self-destruction." We can see the direct clash between the perspectives of Judge Lynch and Judge Liacos regarding the moral and legal status of the right to life.

Despite the fact that a Hobbesian perspective retains a natural right to life, the rejection by Hobbes of what he calls "natural duties" and the social nature of human beings, does, as we shall note shortly, undermine the actualization of the right to life.

3. A Christian Perspective: Life as a natural moral responsibility and right. Judge Nolan also dissented and also wrote an opinion. Like Judge Lynch, he views the removal of food and water as the proximate cause of Brophy's death, and, hence, the court has failed sufficiently to assert its interest in protecting life. He regards the court decision as a "triumph for the forces of secular humanism (modern paganism)." Judge Nolan explicitly asserts that the Jewish and Christian traditions are the foundations of American law.

Judge Nolan is quite willing to accept patient decisions to refuse treatments which are burdensome rather than beneficial given their medical condition. He explicitly appeals to the principle of double effect to argue that patients may opt for comfort, even if death is hastened thereby. But, in Judge Nolan's opinion, the principle of double effect does not apply to Brophy's situation. Since the G-tube was in place, food and water were simply being provided and the provision of

140

these did not constitute a medical treatment but only ordinary care. Following the decision of the majority of the court, Brophy's death would be due to starvation, and in approving his death as allegedly wished for by Brophy, the court is sanctioning euthanasia and suicide. And, says Judge Nolan: "Suicide is direct self-destruction and is intrinsically evil. No set of circumstances can make it moral."

It is important to notice that in Judge Nolan's opinion moral responsibilities are the bases of law, of the protection of life, and of human rights: Individuals have the responsibility to refrain from taking their own lives, as well as those of others. The law and the courts are there to teach and enforce, when necessary, such restraints against killing innocent individuals. This view of how the right to life is actualized and protected has its origins, for Judge Nolan, in Jewish and Christian traditions. But the view that the reality and actualization of human rights are grounded in and identified by humanity's shared moral responsibilities is one found in all of the major, longstanding religious traditions of the world.[8]

By examining American court decisions, using the Brophy case as illustrative, we find three competing perspectives which underlie and inform the current debate surrounding physician-assisted suicide and euthanasia. The apparently rapid shift in the courts can be traced to the current, more recent dominance of a Millian perspective, a perspective that has competed, throughout this century, with the older Hobbesian, Jewish, and Christian traditions. This struggle is also occurring within American culture. Whatever separation between church and state exists in the United States it has never been possible, nor is it realistic, to attempt to exclude theological perspectives and quarrels from the arenas in which laws and public policy are formulated and enforced, and in which professionals, including physicians, render their respective services to their communities. Why I call these perspectives theological will soon be clarified. I turn now to the arguments for choosing and developing one of these perspectives, drawing out what these arguments imply for the debate over physician-assisted suicide and euthanasia, and for a Christian vision of care for the dying.

Our Common Humanity: Shared Responsibilities as the Requisites for Shared Human Rights

One might oppose physician-assisted suicide and euthanasia from a Hobbesian perspective. Indeed, many do. After all, a natural and inalienable right to life was asserted as a self-evident truth at the very inception of the United States in the Declaration of Independence. Surely Americans will recognize their obligations to protect and secure this right in all their laws and public policies. But this cannot presently be assumed. Why is that?

In a document designed to provide ethical guidance for decisions to forego life-sustaining medical treatment, a presidential commission on bioethics spoke of the "right to life" as "empty rhetoric, the meaning of which is "hopelessly blurred."[9] This commission designated certain values as dominant values. Life was not among them because the value of life depended on all the dominant values, especially self-determination and well-being.[10] That explains why the "right to life" is an ambiguous concept for the commission. Whether there is an obligation to protect or sustain someone's life depends upon whether that individual wishes to live, and whether that individual's life is such that continuing to live is worthwhile. This is the Millian perspective on the right to life and precisely the basis on which the Massachusetts Supreme Judicial Court decided to order that Brophy no longer receive food and water, and that he be moved to a hospital willing to carry out that order. Proponents of physician-assisted suicide and euthanasia use these same arguments. Increasingly, they make no distinction between "allowing to die," which they call passive euthanasia, and active euthanasia, which they advocate as more merciful:[11] Both intend death and result in death. Indeed, some argue that killing an individual who is not physically or mentally able to choose death is voluntary euthanasia so long as someone acting on that person's behalf gives consent: The very definition of euthanasia begins to specify that death be caused painlessly and quickly, not only to end suffering, but also to end "an undesirable existence."[12] Add to this discussion moral theologians distinguishing life as "mere biological existence" and "personal life," a life with certain desirable qualities, and one can understand why the presidential commission described the meaning of "right to life" as "hopelessly blurred."

At this point, the idea of the "slippery slope" would seem to apply. It does. However, it should not be stated in its usual form, namely that the practice of voluntary euthanasia will lead to abuses and involuntary euthanasia will occur. People hearing this argument simply cite the need for safeguards and tolerance for mistakes which happen now with respect to withdrawing and withholding treatment. Rather the point is this. When you involve physicians, you will have involuntary euthanasia if you have euthanasia at all. Any physician assisting in a suicide or in euthanasia has to decide whether that is the right course of action relative to that physician's assessment of that patient's condition. That judgment is what is conveyed to the patient, if indeed the patient is fully informed or informed at all. That is why in the Netherlands there are, in addition to 2,300 instances of voluntary euthanasia per year, 1,000 instances of involuntary euthanasia, as well as 13,691 instances which should also be called involuntary euthanasia.[13] These 13,691 instances consist of intentionally caused death, in 4,941 cases through excessive doses of morphine, and in 8,750 cases by withholding or withdrawing life sustaining interventions. All of this happened even though euthanasia is only officially permitted on the basis of a patient's persistent and repeated requests for it. In 14 percent of the cases of involuntary euthanasia the patients were fully competent yet uninformed. And in 45 percent of the cases in which the lives of hospital patients were terminated without their consent, the families were not informed.

The so-called "right to die" is at least as hopelessly blurred with this Millian perspective as the right to life. And the Dutch physicians did have a Millian perspective. When asked how they could act to end the lives of patients without their consent, in violation of the official guidelines and the law, they most frequently gave the reasons "low quality of life," "no prospect of improvement," and "the family could not take it anymore." In short the physicians judged that it was best that their patients die, and that patients die when they judge death to be desirable for them or for others. As for Mill, the ultimate criterion for what is right consists of obtaining the most desirable consequences, the best balance of pleasure over pain or the least pain possible, given the options.

Mill's proof for utility as the criterion of rightness was that individuals seek pleasure and avoid pain for themselves.[14] This means that what is right is based on non-moral goods, goods understood as what individuals regard as worth striving for and obtaining for themselves. Mill valued individual freedom highly, yet given the naturally egoistic expressions of it, required a calculus for curbing these. This calculus, in the form of minimizing pain, can be and now is used to justify intentionally causing the death of one who is in pain, or in the otherwise allegedly unhappy state of having a low quality of life, or of somehow merely existing. From this perspective also it makes no difference whether death results from directly inducing it or from withholding or withdrawing life-sustaining measures. There is now a strong tendency to reject the principle of double effect.[15] Results only are to count, not intentions.

As long as the debate is carried on at this level of analysis, an increasing number of people will tend to assert a right to die, that is, a right to specify what should happen to them in various conditions of serious illness. I say this because for a long time now individuals have been taught the Hobbesian theological perspective shared also by Locke, Bentham, and Mill, and behavioral psychology, that we as human beings seek pleasure and avoid pain for ourselves. Hobbes and Locke saw in this also a striving to preserve our own lives, but this has been largely superseded by the logic of maximizing pleasure and minimizing pain to include calculating whether life itself has any pleasure left to it, or whether life is too painful to make its further pursuit worthwhile. This theological or metaphysical doctrine of our nature is used as the basis for determining what is moral and for calculating rights. This doctrine cannot account for community and it cannot account for morality. If we were naturally only out for ourselves and for the preservation of our own lives, no community would result. Hobbes maintained that we would surrender some of our liberty to a sovereign out of fear for our lives, so that force could be employed to secure peace and protect us from one another's greedy self-striving. But this will only work if enough people are moral enough to submit as promised. And such communities will only exist if in addition to acting to preserve our own lives, we also act to procreate and nurture other lives. In short, the Hobbesian and Millian theological or metaphysical perspective gives us no basis in reality for the moral responsibilities without which no right to life can exist or be protected.

Where then should we look for the basis of human rights? We will need to look at what makes human life possible at all.

For human life to exist, it is necessary that human beings have the proclivities to procreate and nurture. These are at once cooperative, communal acts, and acts which are requisite for forming and sustaining communities. Another requisite of the existence of communities and individuals is that individuals are sufficiently inhibited about killing one another. And so a right to life can exist and be actualized; proclivities to procreate and nurture, and inhibitions about killing must exist. Human communities are naturally occurring phenomena made possible by the requisite natural proclivities and inhibitions that bring about, nurture, and protect human life and property. Truth-telling, sexual fidelity, and caring for one's parents are also requisites of community. These requisites of community have been recognized in all of the major religious traditions as moral responsibilities. Rights are expectations that people will naturally act in these ways, and when they do not, rights can take the form of claims to be treated responsibly. Hence, for example, children who are not being adequately nurtured have a right to such nurture. Caring for the malnourished and the sick is one form that our natural proclivity to nurture life takes. This right to life and its nurture is a natural right, based as it is on the natural responsibility to spawn, nurture, and pro-

144

tect life. Our fundamental proclivities and inhibitions as human beings are those of a social being, seeking life not only for ourselves but also for others.

The Hobbesian theological anthropology, accepted also by Locke, Bentham, and Mill, is not a realistic picture of human nature. Human beings live in communities and sustain them through procreation, nurture, and restraints against killing, stealing, lying, sexual infidelity, and envy. The social contract which Hobbes claims is the basis of government, society, and moral behavior as such, is only possible because of the natural proclivities and inhibitions which actualize cooperative, communal behaviors. Moral structures have to be a prior reality to make possible the social structures necessary to enforce and teach the moral virtues. We know what are moral rights, our claims on others, and moral virtues, our dispositions to do what is right, because we know what our basic moral responsibilities are: These are behaviors logically and functionally necessary to form and sustain human communities and institutions.

It is true that human beings exhibit egoistic striving for their own pleasure and the avoidance of pain to themselves. But these are ambiguously related to our moral responsibilities. Individuals can and do take pleasure in being responsible, but even the individual who does may also take pleasure from what is irresponsible or evil. Small wonder, then, that those who accept, implicitly or explicitly, the perspective on human nature found in Hobbes and Mill find the meaning of a right to life ambiguous: When that right is justified because it is based on our egoistic desires to maximize pleasure and minimize pain, what we can expect from others driven by similar egoistic desires is unclear, to say the least. What we claim, and what we receive, if driven by egoistic desires, may be good or it may be evil.

Actually asserting a right to die, and demanding that someone else help secure our death, is a direct attack on the very foundations of morality, an attack on its realization, and the realization of communal life. When Aristotle attempted to define true friendship, he argued that it was a relation based on a right relationship to ourselves.[16] Among the characteristics of a true friendship is that we wish that our friend exists and lives, like the wish of a mother for her child. And again, like a mother in relation to her child, we grieve and rejoice with our friend. Also, friends build one another up in virtue and share all things. The wish that the self and others live, the willingness to grieve and rejoice with our human companions, and the quest to grow together in virtue, are essential presuppositions of the whole moral structure. If we do not wish to live, there are no limits to what we may do. Murders followed by suicide are one extreme example of what is entailed by losing a positive disposition toward one's own life. And the disinclination to grieve as well as rejoice with others is a failure of the very dispositions that can sustain care for those who are desperately ill and dying.

When Jesus declared that "whatever you wish that men would do to you, do so to them," he, like Aristotle, placed these wishes in the context of what parents, despite being capable of evil, wish in nurturing their children.[17] He also notes that this golden rule, if it is to work, is an expression of the law and the prophets, what I have been calling the requisites of community, and the prophets called the law written on the heart. Furthermore, from a Jewish and Christian perspective, these proclivities and inhibitions, which are the natural basis of the moral law, reflect the image of God in human beings. All of the major religions affirm the Golden Rule. In identifying the requisites of community, we are identifying the most fundamental characteristics of our common humanity. What I have endeavored to do, then, is locate the very difficult moral questions regarding how best to treat dying or grievously ill individuals within a perspective that realistically affirms our social nature as human beings. This social nature expresses itself as proclivities and inhibitions which fuel the responsible behaviors absolutely requisite, logically and functionally, to form and sustain the lives of communities and individuals. I turn now, all too briefly, to a Christian vision of care for the dying which is grounded on these shared human moral responsibilities.

A Christian Vision of Care for the Dying

The Hospice of the Good Shepherd, located in Newton, Massachusetts, has a motto that articulates well the effort to care well for the dying: "Healing a person does not always mean curing a disease." There is such a thing as dying well, and whether that happens may well depend upon the care an individual receives. It certainly depends in every sense on how that individual lives while dying. Hospice, with its focus on the whole family and home care, whenever that is best, has been at the forefront in managing pain and relieving suffering. Hospice has as one of its express purposes the avoidance of death through suicide or euthanasia that is intentionally acting to end an individual's life for the sake of what is regarded as merciful. It is important to sharpen the moral and spiritual distinctions between comfort care and mercy-killing.

Comfort Care vs. Mercy Killing. Aiming at the relief of pain and suffering is not the same as aiming at death. It is utterly confusing to equate treatment aimed at comfort with "letting die," "allowing to die," or "withdrawing and withholding treatment." Choosing comfort while dying can and should be a morally responsible decision for a certain kind of care, such as aggressive pain management, or even activities outside a hospital setting. Such choices about how to live while dying may or may not shorten life, and they may or may not involve the rejection of any, and certainly not all, life-sustaining interventions or circumstances, such as the very air we breathe. The relief of pain and suffering is care, and it can aid physical and spiritual healing even if and when it cannot prevent death or cure what will cause death for a given individual.

I need not belabor instances when failing to use or retain the use of life-sustaining measures is morally equivalent to killing someone directly and intentionally. I wish rather to emphasize what makes comfort treatment for someone who is dying different from mercy-killing, whether as assisted suicide or euthanasia. First of all, comfort care maintains the moral bonds of community. The affirmations of one's life and those of others remain; and the inhibitions against killing remain. Mercy-killing violates all of these proclivities and inhibitions, and these relations. A person who chooses comfort care rather than death symbolizes and witnesses to the preciousness of these moral bonds and of the freedom and responsibility to make moral choices to the very end of life. Dying well is living well in the moral and spiritual senses, and with good pain management in the physical sense.

There is an alternative to mercy killing, a very good one even for those who ask; they can instead cultivate the moral bonds of community. Saunders discusses such an experience of a young man who said he would ask for euthanasia if it were available:

> Yet he always demanded antibiotics if he had an incipient chest infection and he well knew how inconsistent were his feelings and his wishes. Finally he said, "Yes, I would have asked but now I see the snags." Weighed against all his problems were his deepening relationship with his wife and his growing confidence that we would never let him choke. He died quietly in his sleep. . . . The two of them had shared the hardness throughout and there were no guilts or hang-ups as his wife began her life.[18]

Here is a young man who could very well have been dead had a policy of mercy killing been in place, and who would have missed out on the virtuous gratification of a strengthening relationship to his wife, one of the most fundamental moral kinds of bonds of friendship and community. He died well, but he could only do so by living well while dying, by receiving exquisite care, and by the support of a larger community protecting him and his wife against mercy-killing and its effects.

This leads directly to another clear distinction between comfort care and mercy-killing: Comfort care allows for and encourages moral and spiritual development; mercy-killing cuts off this process. Saunders tells us about another of her patients, also a young man who had professed a wish for mercy-killing. He had watched with some apprehension the stage of physical helplessness expressed by the other young man depicted above, but found that this stage, when he himself reached it, was totally different from what he had imagined: "He maintained his essential independence, never giving in to anything and fought his way into a peace in which he could say, 'I can't see round the next bend but I know it will be all right.' "[19] Again, this is a young man who would have likely died much sooner, most likely without reaching inner peace as he did, if euthanasia had been regarded as his right. It is disturbing but not surprising to learn that in the Netherlands eight percent of patients dying by active, voluntary euthanasia were expected to live longer than six months.

From a Christian perspective, the last months of life for the dying present many important possibilities, certainly for those deemed competent to make choices about how to live and be cared for. There is so often a need to forgive and to seek forgiveness. Certainly there is a need to consider one's relationships, especially with God. There is always a need to thank those who benefit us, again especially God who in Christ suffered, died, and rose from the dead so that death need not be our ultimate end. Our sorrows and sins need be remembered no more. That is an incomparable source of comfort, not only in our dying days, but also in all our days. Mercy-killing can rob us of more than our physical life; it can rob us of some precious opportunities to experience God's grace and human love on this earth.

But what about those who are unconscious and who do not appear to have the possibilities open to others provided with comfort care? Should comfort care for them at some point include the withdrawal or withholding of food and water? These questions have been dealt with extremely well by William E. May and his co-authors, and most recently by the Committee for Pro-Life Activities of the National Conference of Catholic Bishops.[20] I am essentially in agreement with what I see as erring on the side of life. I wish to underline the importance of the attention given in this most recent statement by the National Conference of Catholic Bishops, to the fact that patients who are firmly diagnosed as permanently unconscious do recover, as many as 41 percent within the first six months in the study cited. These phenomena deserve a great deal more research.

I wish to conclude by highlighting one more highly significant way in which comfort care should be morally distinguished from mercy-killing. Choosing how to live while dying symbolizes and gives clear witness to the incalculable worth of the lives of those who are fatally ill; mercy-killing symbolizes and witnesses to a calculus that puts a value on the life of those who are ill and it is that their lives are of insufficient worth. Those of us who oppose physician-assisted suicide and euthanasia cannot stress enough how excellent comfort care and the choice to live out one's days are among the ways in which individuals, patients, and caregivers can encourage and inspire others to live. Symbolizing the preciousness of our lives is a noble purpose for all of us in our dying days. We uphold the moral bonds of community. We witness to our shared responsibilities and our solidarity with the whole human community. Comfort care does that; mercy-killing does not.

The Roman Catholic church has contributed greatly to comfort care. When Elizabeth Kubler Ross, who did so much to foster good care for the dying, was asked what she was doing for her dying mother, she told her interviewers that she had placed her in a Catholic hospital. She added that Catholic hospitals, unlike many others, were generally good places in which to die. This conference in Dallas represents the continuation of the sincere efforts to keep up and strengthen a praiseworthy tradition of caring for the dying, especially for those severely disabled. Our equal worth before God is honored in the Roman Catholic tradition of medical care.

I end with some further reflections by Cicely Saunders:

> A young man said to me as he faced leaving life and his strong family ties and responsibilities, "I've fought and I've fought— but now I've accepted." We, too, have to learn to accept as well as to fight and to realize that part of our work can have nothing to do with cure but only with the giving of relief and comfort. . . . We need him as much and more than he needs us. Anything which says to the very ill or the very old that there is no longer anything that matters in their life would be a deep impoverishment of the whole society.[21]

That's it exactly.

ENDNOTES

1. Cicely Saunders, "The Care of the Dying Patient and His Family," in Stanley Reiser, Arthur Dyck, and William Curran, eds., *Ethics in Medicine* (Cambridge, Ma.: M.I.T., 1977), p. 511.

2. Ibid.

3. Richard Knox, "Poll: Americans Favor Mercy Killing," *Boston Sunday Globe* (November 3, 1991), p. 22.

4. National Conference of Catholic Bishops Committee for Pro-Life Activities, "Nutrition and Hydration: Moral and Pastoral Reflections" (April 1992), *Issues in Law and Medicine* 3:3 (Winter 1987), pp. 203–11.

5. The Washington State Referendum (Initiative 119), if it had passed, would have made it legal for doctors to give patients who wish it a lethal injection or a lethal dose of drugs. At least two physicians must have diagnosed the patient as terminally ill, with six months or less to live, or as in a persistent vegetative state. Also, it would be legal for patients to request in advance that life-sustaining care, including tube feeding and intravenous fluids, be withheld in the event they are hopelessly ill or injured.

6. Massachusetts Supreme Judicial Court, *Patricia E. Brophy vs. New England Sinai Hospital, Inc.* (1986).

7. Ibid (the citation is to Mill, *On Liberty,* as quoted in *In re Caulk,* 125 N.H. 226, 236 (1984) [J. Douglas, dissenting]).

8. See, for example, Arlene Swidler, ed., *Human Rights in Religious Traditions* (New York: Pilgrim Press, 1982).

9. President's Commission for the Study of Ethical Problems in Medicine and Biomedical and Behavioral Research, *Deciding to Forego Life-Sustaining Treatment: Ethical, Medical, and Legal Issues in Treatment Decisions* (Washington, D.C.: U.S. Government Printing Office, 1983).

10. Dr. Joanne Lynn in a letter in reply to one from me, dated November 1, 1982. Dr. Lynn was writing in her capacity as a member of the commission.

11. See, for example, Michael D. Bayles, "Euthanasia and the Quality of Life," in James Walter and Thomas Shannon, eds., *Quality of Life: The New Medical Dilemma* (New York: Paulist Press, 1990), 265–81.

12. Marvin Kohl, "Altruistic Humanism and Voluntary Beneficent Euthanasia," *Issues in Law and Medicine* 8:3 (Winter 1992), pp. 331–41.

13. Arthur Dyck, "Physician-Assisted Suicide: Is It Ethical?" *Trends in Health Care, Law and Ethics* 7:2 (Winter, 1992), pp. 19–22.

14. John Stuart Mill, *Utilitarianism,* chap. 4.

15. Michael D. Bayles, "Euthanasia and the Quality of Life."

16. Aristotle, *Nicomachean Ethics,* Book IX: chap. 4.

17. *Holy Bible,* Revised Standard Version, Matthew 7:7–12.

18. Cicely Saunders, "The Care of the Dying Patient and His Family," p. 513.

19. Ibid.

20. William E. May et al., "Feeding and Hydrating the Permanently Unconscious Vulnerable Persons," and National Conference of Catholic Bishops Committee for Pro-Life Activities, "Nutrition and Hydration." For another excellent discussion, see New Jersey Catholic Conference, "Providing Food and Fluids to Severely Brain Damaged Patients," *Origins* 16 (January 22, 1987), pp. 582–84.

21. Cicely Saunders, "The Care of the Dying Patient and His Family," p. 513.

Chapter 11

THE CATHOLIC VISION OF DEATH AND DYING

The Reverend Monsignor James J. Mulligan

Catholic Approaches to Issues Surrounding Death

1. Ain't Death Grand?

I once heard a definition of a diplomat as a person who can tell you to go to hell in such a nice way that you can hardly wait to get started. We can expect a lot of dubious diplomacy on behalf of death, as society proposes it as the solution to its problems. Crime in the streets? Give the police better guns. The best deterrent? Capital punishment. An unwanted pregnancy? Abortion. Pain and suffering? Send for that angel of mercy, Dr. Jack Kevorkian—an experienced pathologist perfectly at home with already dead patients.

In the *Journal of the American Medical Association* I read an article called "It's Over, Debbie,"[1] written by a gynecology resident in a large hospital. He was called one night to tend a 20 year-old woman in the last stages of cancer. She had severe vomiting and "had not eaten or slept in two days." She said to the doctor, "Let's get this over with." Now, he had never seen her before and was not her doctor, but he went to the nurses' station and drew 20 mg of morphine sulfate into a syringe. He told the patient and a woman who was there with her that he was going to give her something that would let her rest, and that they should say goodbye. He injected the morphine intravenously and within four minutes she was dead.

Neither author nor editor offer further comment. The doctor had killed a patient he had never even seen before, taking her desire to "get this over with" as a request for assisted suicide. Was it a request? Who knows? In any case, *he* thought that she was better off dead, so he killed her; and he finds that laudable. His article is but one example of the death-diplomacy designed to make us see death as the great answer.

2. Paganism: Death, the Gateway to Oblivion

All sorts of things can influence our attitudes toward death, not least of which is our concept of God and our relationship to Him. What I am characterizing here as "paganism" is the outlook which sees life as here and now, in this world only. The concept of God or any real relationship to Him never enters into it.

The ancient Romans had an idea of afterlife in which the dead entered into a shadowy, vague sort of life in a subterranean realm from which they might still return if not properly propitiated by the living. The afterlife was not nearly so desirable as was life in this world.[2] To keep them at bay, it was necessary to give them a tomb as a home along with clothing, furniture and food offerings. All of this was expressed in a mythology based on a pantheon of gods and goddesses who were gradually perceived as no more than childishly petulant and overly powerful despots. By the end of the period of the Republic disillusionment had set in, and little credence was given to any reality of afterlife at all. Callimachus wrote:

Charidas, what is there down below? Deep darkness.
But what of the journey upwards? All lies.
And Pluto? A fable. Then we are lost![3]

His sentiments are no different than those we find in the love poetry of Catullus:

Suns can set and rise once more,
While we, our brief light quenched forever,
Are forced to sleep for everlasting night.[4]

The development from belief in an afterlife to such a despondent repudiation of it had come about in stages. Plato demythologized the pagan myths, but they were never replaced by anything to fulfill the deepest needs of humanity. Instead, there was a variety of rational philosophies that soon left people with nothing but this world. The ancient traditions were still held out as an ideal, but the aristocracy preached that ideal as a political expedient rather than a reality. Religion was a state function designed to hold the common people to their duty.[5]

The "science" of the day supported this rejection of afterlife. Aristotle had focussed on rationality to the extent that after death all that was left was human reason. The pure intelligence which remained was without either personality or sensibility, and this led others to deny even the existence of the rational soul without the body. Philosophies, however, must be popularized if they are to carry weight with the masses, and that task was left to the Epicureans and the Stoics.

Epicurus (341–270 BC) saw the soul as no more lasting than the body. Life ends in annihilation, when body and soul alike are resolved into their component atoms. He offered enjoyment of this life as an alternative, and put a happy face on what was to come. He said:

Death is nothing to us, since when we are, death has not come, and when death has come, we are not.[6]

The fact of oblivion after death should remove all fear of it. One popular epitaph was the following:

I was not; I was; I am not; I do not care.[7]

The Stoics saw the individual as a detached spark of the Divine Fire. In the end, that spark returns to the Fire, and all is reduced to One. Then the cycle begins again in endless repetition. What happens to us after death is not a moral question at all, it is simply a matter of physics. Individual immortality is no more than a beautiful fiction. We escape life at death and will return to go through it all again. It is a bleak outlook and offers more gloom than hope. One of the ancient epitaphs reads:

> I have fled, I have escaped. Goodbye, Hope and Fortune.
> I have nothing more to do with you. Go play with somebody else.[8]

Another author wrote:

> The best of all things for earthly men is not to be born and not to see the beams of the bright sun; but, if born, then as quickly as possible to pass the gates of Hades, and to lie deep buried.[9]

The same sentiment underlies the bravado of the gladiators: "Hail, Caesar, we who are about to die salute you!"[10]

These pagan sentiments are not so far from the minds of many in our own day. We, too, have been infected with rationalism and a popularized demythologizing which encourage the same fatalistic view of death. Many view death as the final end—an end which makes no sense unless preceded by the search for pleasure. "Grab the gusto . . . You only go around once. . ." The vaguely beautiful hope of another world is too flimsy to support us and so we learn to ignore it.

Science is our friend and can explain everything. Think of the pitiable hope of "cosmic" immorality offered by Carl Sagan near the end of his famous *Cosmos* series on television. He spoke lovely words, all full of hot air, offering hope to an abstract humanity which does not exist, and annihilation to each individual who does. Death is welcome, not as the gateway to another life, but as final oblivion when this life has become too painful to endure. It is even imposed on those not yet born, on the off-chance that they might otherwise find life too painful. It is a rationalism which aims at total autonomy, and what it cannot control or does not want to face, it destroys.

3. Gnosticism: Death, the Gateway to Liberation

Both Epicureanism and Stoicism were materialistic. The soul was as mortal as was the body, so happiness had to be within this life. Once that life became unbearable, there was little point in continuing it. The individual was autonomous and suicide was logical. Zeno, the

154

founder of Stoicism, was faithful to his principles and, at the end of a long life, killed himself.

Although early Christianity was open to some of the moral norms of Stoicism, it was not really in danger of itself becoming Stoic. However, there was a movement in the ancient world which was far more dangerous to Christianity. It appealed to the desire for something more than a material world whose promises of happiness were always doomed to failure. That movement was Gnosticism.[11]

"Gnosticism" is a generic term, and encompasses a number of vague tendencies and more or less developed schools of thought. Since I don't really have a vast knowledge of Gnosticism, you can rest assured I will not torture you with a complete exposition of all its varieties. But I do want to look at some of the elements which made it so important to the pagans, and such a challenge to the first Christians.

The Romans were great legislators and soldiers. But they were intimidated by the culture of the Greeks, with their philosophy and their attitude that all who were not Greek must be barbarian. Greek ideas spread quickly among the Romans and this included religious attitudes. Demythologizing and the "scientific" view of the world had undermined religion, but this did not destroy the religious *needs* that all peoples feel in one way or another. The pessimistic outlook of the Epicureans and Stoics was intellectually satisfying to some, but it was no answer to humanity's deepest longings for real and lasting happiness. Christianity had enormous appeal to the pagans. Paul was certainly aware of this when he wrote his *Epistle to the Romans*:

> All that can be known of God is clearly before them; God has shown it to them. Ever since the creation of the world, his invisible nature—his eternal power and divine character—have been clearly perceptible through what he has made.[12]

The Gnostics felt the need, but they tried to fulfill it on their own terms, just as many do today.

Christianity preaches a faith that challenges our autonomy. We are called to trust in a God who loves us. We can never save ourselves. Salvation comes, not from knowing the rules and playing the game, but from a total giving of oneself into God's hands. That offers the consolation of fulfillment, but it also offers the discomfort of total dependence and gratitude. It demands a faith that is far more than simple consent to the truth of a set of dogmas. It is a faith which permeates every facet of our lives. The closer we come to God, the more darkness we find in our own power to act and to know—realizations that are

155

clearly expressed in the classical mysticism of Saint John of the Cross, the author of *The Cloud of Unknowing,* and even the letters of Saint Paul himself.

Gnosticism appealed to Christians because it seemed so "spiritual." It started from the problem of evil. Christianity taught that God had created the world from nothing and that He made it good. It was humanity's misuse of freedom which brought evil into the world. The gnostics found this entirely too simple.[13] Instead, they proposed one God who was responsible for creation, but creation involved a whole series of "mediators," each one slightly less perfect than the one before. Finally there came one who was evil, and it was he who created this world and mankind. He was the "Demiurge," the God of the Old Testament. The spark of the goodness of God in man could still be salvaged, provided that a person came to the truth. That truth was not "faith," but a secret "knowledge" (γνωσις). They come back to exactly what Saint Paul had rejected—knowledge provides the rules, and you then make your own salvation.

They were filled with dualistic contradictions. Matter was evil and spirit was good. This led to a thoroughly divided philosophy. Its practical effects can be clearly seen in its ambivalence to sexuality. Matter is bad and sexual activity is obviously material since it always involves the body. Since it is so evil, all sexual activity is to be avoided. Others began with the same premise and concluded that since the body is already so bad, it doesn't much matter what you do with it. Any sort of sexual activity is allowable. Those who held that all sex was bad were caught in still another practical contradiction. A philosophy which truly rejects sex should not have a second generation, but the fact is that it went on for quite a long time.

For the Gnostics, salvation could not possibly be a matter of the resurrection of the body. The body is evil and cannot take part in a salvation which consists in making us entirely spiritual. Therefore, salvation consists in "liberation." The prisoner is finally freed from the body to go forth into another realm entirely.

What do we find in our own times? There is certainly an ambivalence about sexuality, ranging from seeing it as always somehow evil all the way to considering it as purely recreational, without any moral significance at all. There is a notion, spoken or unspoken, of the body as somehow being our "possession." The body is treated as a tool, a means to an end, an instrument of pleasure or pain—while the real person remains somehow within and aloof from this all too material world.

There is certainly something of this in the way many view death. They cling to more than materialism and even believe in some sort of afterlife. But they are caught up in the notion that one finds salvation—at least from the pains of this life—in a liberation that sets us free from material limitations. The choice of setting ourselves free is up to us. It is not a matter of faith in a good God, in whose presence even suffering can have meaning, but a matter of taking it all into our own hands. Of course, I would not be so presumptuous as to imply that most of the modern practitioners of that position are truly guilty of thinking or that they have read the Scriptures well enough to know that they are in opposition to them. Sadly, many just "go with the flow."

In the end, Stoicism, Epicureanism and Gnosticism all come to the point at which the body and its life may be of no value. This can justify self-destruction. In practical attitudes to life and death, they seem hardly to differ. In our century we are faced, for example, with advocates for death who would do away with anyone who cannot keep up with the "quality of life" that *they* consider optimal. This results in a pragmatism that leads to abortion, suicide, assisted suicide and the willingness to encourage the helpless to die of starvation. In none of this is there any apparent awareness of the depth of God's love even in the midst of suffering. It is all so rational—and so far removed from the reality of our faith.

This idea of life and death is expressed in the writings of some whose morality reflects little consciousness of a bond with a living God. It is founded instead on the vaguest sort of altruism combined with norms which lack all objectivity and come down to no more than the rationalistic justification of what any individual happens to want to do. For example, when Joseph Fletcher looks at the person facing death, he sees no difference at all in moral terms between the acceptance of the dying process and the choice to kill oneself. He says:

Every person's fight with death is lost before it begins. What makes the struggle worthwhile, therefore, cannot lie in the outcome. It lies in the dignity with which the fight is waged and the way it finds an end.[14]

I would say that what makes the struggle worthwhile is *not* the dignity with which the fight is waged, but the relationship with God which causes us to place our lives and our welfare into His hands, even when the circumstances of that trust are the most painful and tempt us most deeply to take matters into our own hands. We seek neither autonomy nor oblivion nor simple liberation from the present condition. Instead, we seek the completion of a union already begun by God and to be brought to completion by Him.

157

4. Old Testament Visions:
Death, the Gateway to Gehenna

In the Old Testament the idea of an afterlife as a place of reward or punishment developed quite late. What idea there was in the earlier books was no comfort to believers. The underworld (Sheol שׁאול, Gehenna γέεννα) was not pictured as a place of happiness. In fact, the translations generally used in English for this realm of the dead are such words as "hell," "grave" and "pit." None of them conjure up an image of eternal bliss.

The Old Testament writings also face the problem of evil. It is at the heart of the creation account in *Genesis*, when God's good creation is marred by the sin of Adam and Eve—thus making it clear that the evil which we experience in this life was not put there by God. In fact, God had warned them that sin would result in death, but the tempter got them thinking along new lines:

> You would not die at all; for God knows that the very day you eat of it, your eyes will be opened, and you will be like gods who know good from evil.[15]

It sounds rather attractive, all that knowledge. We can be like children who are told not to do something because it will hurt, and that becomes a challenge. We just have to try it, to find out for sure. The experience is certain to be a real eye-opener.

The problem of evil may be explained in its origin by pointing to that original sin; but that does not give much comfort in the experience of that evil in our own lives. The Wisdom writers began to face that issue. How easy it would have been, if only they could have pointed to a comfortable life after this time of trial and tribulation. But they had no knowledge of such comfort.[16] The afterlife was still the murky existence of Sheol and there was precious little comfort in that. Yet those same Wisdom writers consistently held that we must focus our attention on God and obey His Law, and they held out the hope that the person who kept the Law would live long and prosper.

This is the best of advice, but it does have one catch: Experience tells us that the person who does truly live the Law does not always live long nor is he guaranteed to prosper. This brought the problem into the realm where it really hurts and there was scant consolation in simply looking back to its origin in the sin of Adam. Two books in particular face this head on: *Job* and *Ecclesiastes* (Qoheleth).

Job is a good man who is handed over to the power of Satan to have his goodness tested. When children, possessions and health are

158

all gone, and Job is seated on his dunghill, it is his loving wife who gives him the advice that seems to fit: "Do you still hold fast to your integrity? Curse God and die!"[17] Job answers: 'You speak as one of the foolish women might speak. Should we, indeed, receive good from God, and should we not receive evil?' Notwithstanding all this, Job did not sin with his lips."[18] This is the image of Job that most people have—the man of patience who simply accepts his lot. However, that is at the end of chapter 3. In chapters 4 through 41 he does little else but complain, and who can blame him? He has done everything he was supposed to do, he has not sinned, and here he is being treated like a sinner.

His friends come to comfort him, and a sad lot of comforters they are. They say: "Come on, Job, we're your friends. You can tell us what you really did. Why else would God be treating you this way?" In the end Job demands an interview with God and God grants his request. He appears in a whirlwind and Job is called to make his complaint. God answers it, but in a way that seems to be no answer at all. Part of the answer is this:

Behold, now, the hippopotamus which I made along with you;
He eats grass like the ox.
Behold, now, his strength in his loins,
And his might in the muscles of his body.
He stiffens his tail like a cedar;
The sinews of his thighs are knit together . . .
He is the chief of the ways of God;
Let him who made him bring near his sword! . . .
Can one seize him by his eyes?
Can one pierce his nose with traps? . . .

Can you draw up the crocodile with a fish-hook,
Or can you press down his tongue with a cord?
Can you put a rush-line through his nose,
Or pierce his jaw with a hook?
Will he make entreaties to you,
Or will he speak soft words to you? . . .
Can you play with him as with a bird,
And bind him for you maidens? . . .
Will you stick his hide full of darts,
Or his head full of harpoons?
Lay your hand upon him;
Think of the struggle; you will not do it again! . . .
Who then is he that can stand before me?

Who has ever come before me that I should repay him?
Whatever is under the whole heavens is mine.[19]

What seems to be no answer at all is a perfectly satisfactory answer for Job. It is simply this: He must trust God. God cannot be bribed by our good conduct or our protestations of innocence, even though they may be true! The hippopotami and crocodiles of this world that seem most powerful and most frightening to us are simply His playthings. How dare we challenge Him? The faith that Job expresses at the end of the book is the deepest sort of all. It is not faith in our ability to please God; it is not faith in our capacity to keep the Law of God; it is not faith in our own explanations of what God is or ought to be. It is simply faith in God *Himself,* in a living goodness as far beyond ourselves that we do not even have a proper explanation of his goodness. But we trust, and that is enough.

Qoheleth sets his tone in the first few words of the book: "Vanity of vanities! All is vanity! What does a man gain from all his toil at which he toils beneath the sun? One generation goes, and another comes, while the earth endures forever. The sun rises and the sun sets, and hastens to the place where he rose. The wind blows toward the south, and returns to the north. Turning, turning, the wind blows, and returns upon its circuit."[20]

Qoheleth sees no final reward for all that is done in the life of man. He sees only the end. Indeed, his words are much like the poem of Catullus that I quoted earlier:

Suns can set and rise once more,
While we, our brief light quenched forever,
Are forced to sleep for everlasting night.

But how different are the conclusions drawn by the two authors! The Roman fatalism of Catullus could as easily be expected from Qoheleth, yet when he comes to end of his book he writes:

The conclusion of the matter, all having been heard: Fear God and keep his commands; for this concerns all mankind, that God brings every work into judgement with regard to everything concealed, whether it be good or evil.[21]

In the Old Testament death is a mystery even more so than it is for us. God is good, yet death seems to lead nowhere but to Sheol, to Gehenna, to a kind of half-life. Yet even this is placed within a context of faith in God's goodness. Where the Stoics and Epicureans were led to

160

suicide and the Gnostics were led to find a way to save themselves, the People of God were led to a still deeper expression of faith in a God whose final goodness could not be doubted. His revelation was not a series of answers to their questions, but a presentation of Himself and a call to respond to Him beyond the limits of all doubt. Life was, therefore, a gift to be cherished and even its end, shrouded in mystery, was not to be within our control.

5. New Testament Visions: Death, the Gateway to Life

By the time of Jesus the Jews had come to an acceptance of the concept of an afterlife. This acceptance was not universal and that led to the conflict between the Pharisees and the Sadducees. From the beginning, however, Christianity accepted completely the notion that there was an afterlife and that it consisted in the most horrible punishment of the loss of God or in the most magnificent reward of eternal life in the arms of the Father.

The promise of eternal life is so clear in the New Testament, that it is not even necessary to say much about it here. All we need to is listen to the words with which we are all so familiar:

> Whoever believes in the Son possesses eternal life, but whoever disobeys the Son will not experience life, but will remain under the anger of God.[22]

> Anyone who drinks this water will be thirsty again, but anyone who drinks the water that I will give him will never be thirsty, but the water that I will give him will become a spring of water within him, bubbling up for eternal life.[23]

> This bread that comes down out of heaven is such that no one who eats it will ever die. I am this living bread that has come down out of heaven. Whoever eats this bread will live forever, and the bread that I will give for the world's life is my own flesh![24]

> But now that you have been freed from sin and have become slaves of God, the benefit you get is consecration, and the final result is eternal life. For the wages sin pays is death, but the gift God gives is eternal life through union with Christ Jesus our Lord.[25]

It is not possible to believe in Jesus without believing in his call to life—eternal life. The New Testament is incompatible with a philosophy of life that would see it as belonging only to this world. Yet the

161

promised life does not begin abruptly upon death. It is already present and operative in this world and it moves toward completion.

6. The Church and Death: A Gatekeeper Looking Both Ways

The Romans had a god of gateways, Janus, who had two faces and looked both ways. In a sense, the Church is like that. It looks at this life and calls us to the living of it with a sacred reverence for life itself. But it does so because it has a vision of where that life leads and how it is to be completed. It looks into the next life, and it sees a union between the two. Our traditional way of speaking of the Church Militant, the Church Suffering and the Church Triumphant is one way of expressing that continuity. Human life is a process which begins at the moment of conception and continues on past death.

Life is a gift to be cherished. For that reason the Church has been the protector of the unborn, the poor, the sick, the dying. It sees life with the vision of God Himself and so it sees it as a gift of which we are not the absolute owners but the fortunate stewards. It also sees the life of the whole person, body and soul, and realizes that salvation consists in the fulfillment of that whole person—and so it preaches the resurrection of the dead into a newness of life in which even the body shares in the final glory. "The body is sown in decay, it is raised free from decay. It is shown in humiliation, it is raised in splendor. It is sown in weakness, it is raised in strength. It is a physical body that is sown, it is a spiritual body that is raised. If there is a physical body, there is a spiritual body also."[26]

7. A Personal Experience with Death

No matter how clearly the Church presents its teaching on life or death or, for that matter, on anything else, I do not think that we can ever grasp it fully in an abstract sense. It must be lived, and it is the living of the experience that brings home to us the reality itself. So is also with the experience of death. For that reason, I would like to conclude my remarks with an experience of my own in that regard.

There were two deaths in particular that moved me most deeply and made me look at the reality as I had never done before. These were the deaths of my parents. Both of them were people of real faith and it is to them that I owe my own attitudes to both life and death. They lived with a real sense of God's love and care for them, and they were ready to do His will. Both of them died a death that was painful, but both of them did so with a sense of peace that was far more than mere resignation. Both were even able to see the humor of it at times. I can remember my mother, after she had suffered from diabetes, gall bladder disease, kidney stones and even a heart attack, being able to say, "Well, at least I've been spared the heartbreak of psoriasis."

It was my father's death that most changed my outlook. He was the first to die and the process of his dying was long and painful since he died of cancer. He went through a great deal of pain and yet one of the nurses in the hospital told me that when she had a patient who was really despondent, she would send him down to talk with my father for a while because he always seemed to be able to cheer them up. He used to say that if complaining could get rid of the pain, he would have complained a lot—but since it didn't, he didn't feel a need to do it.

He liked to pray the rosary. As the cancer progressed, and he had to take more pain killers, he would forget the words of the prayers. He asked my sister to write them out for him, which she did in print large enough to be easy to read. But there finally came a time when his eyes began to go, and he could not read them. On the day that he died, I was there in the morning to give him Communion. After he had received the Host, he said to me, "I feel bad that I can't think of the prayers I'd like to say. All I can think of is, 'Lord, I am not worthy.' Do you think that's a good prayer to say?" I could not have thought of a better one.

Both he, and my mother a few years later, died with a sense of real peace. Both of them said that they were ready to go to God and both of them did so with a sense of joy. Saint John of the Cross spoke of the death of holy people as being like the removing of three veils.[27] The first of those was the temporal veil which was composed of attachment to creatures. The second was the natural veil, composed of all those natural inclinations which have to be overcome in order to open us to the reality of God. The third was the sensitive veil which is composed simply of the union of body and soul in this life. Saint John says that he calls them veils because, although they separate us from the final union with God, they are still translucent enough to allow to us see that there is something beyond them. Gradually, and by mutual consent of God and the soul, the veils are lifted. John says:

> It should be known that the death of persons who have reached this state is far different in its cause and mode than the death of others, even though it is similar in natural circumstances. If the death of other people is caused by sickness or old age, the death of these persons is not so induced, in

spite of their being sick or old; their soul is not wrested from them unless by some impetus and encounter of love, far more sublime than the previous ones . . .

The death of such persons is very gentle and very sweet, sweeter and more gentle than was their whole spiritual life on earth . . . [28]

Death in itself is not something good. It is the result of sin and it is not something to which we usually look forward. But since we have been called to new life, and death is the gateway to that life, God has given it new meaning. Into His hands we must commend our spirits, and in His hands both life and death have meaning. It is one life, from beginning to end, and it is that whole life which has been transformed. Death will remove the last veil which will make fully visible that transformation of which we now have only glimpses.

NOTES

1. "It's Over, Debbie," *Journal of the American Medical Association*, Vol. 259, no. 2 (January 18, 1988), p. 272. The name of the author was withheld by request.

2. Cf. Franz Cumont, *After Life in Roman Paganism*, Lectures delivered at Yale University on the Silliman Foundation, Dover Publications, Inc, NY, 1959 [unaltered edition of 1922], pp. 1–43.

3. Callimachus, *Epigrammata*, 15, 3:   'ΩΧαριδα τι νρυ;—Πολυ σκοτοζ.
   Αιδ'ανοδοιτι;—Ψευδοζ.
   'ΟδΠλουτων;—Μυυοζ.
   'Απωλομυα.
   Quoted by Cumont, *op. cit.*, p. 17.

4. Catullus, V, 4:   Soles occidere et redire possunt;
   Nobis quum semel occidit brevis lux,
   Nox est perpetua una dormienda.

5. Cumont, *op. cit.*, p. 5: "Polybius, when speaking appreciatively of the religion of the Romans, praises them for having inculcated in the people a faith in numerous superstitious practices and tragic fictions. He considers this to be an excellent way of keeping them to their duty by the fear of infernal punishment. Hence we gather that if the historian thought it well for the people to believe in these inventions, then, in his opinion, enlightened persons, like his friends the Scipios, could see in them nothing but the stratagems of a prudent policy. But the scepticism of a narrow circle of aristocrats could not be confined to it for long when Greek ideas were more widely propagated."

6. Epicurus, quoted by Diogenes Laertius, *Lives of Eminent Philosophers*, bk. X, sec. 125.

7. "Non fui, fui, non sum, non curo." Quoted by Cumont, *op. cit.*, pp. 9–10.

8. "Evasi, effugi. Spes et Fortuna valete. Nil mihi vobiscum. Ludificate alios." Quoted by Cumont, *op. cit.*, p. 16, from Büchler, *Carmina epigrammatica*, 1498.

9. Theognis (fl. c. 545 BC), *Elegies*, I, 425.

10. "Ave, Caesar, morituri te salutamus." Taken from Suetonius (70-140 AD), *Life of Claudius*, 21.

11. For some brief treatments of the ideas of the Gnostics you might consult such standard texts as: Johannes Quasten, *Patrology,* Newman Press, Westminster, MD, 1962, Vol. I, pp. 254–277; F. Cayré, *Manual of Patrology and History of Theology,* Desclée & Co., Paris, 1935, Vol. I, pp. 97–107, 141–153. A more extended treatment is available in such books as: Kurt Rudolph, *Gnosis,* Harper & Row Publishers, San Francisco, 1977.

12. Romans 1, 19–20.

13. Cf. Cayré, *op. cit.,* p. 101.

14. Joseph Fletcher, "In Defense of Suicide," in *Suicide and Euthanasia: The Rights of Personhood,* edited by Samuel E. Wallace and Albin Eser, University of Tennessee Press, Knoxville, 1981, p. 48. The whole paragraph from which the sentence in the text was taken reads as follows: "How can it be right for a person to go over the cliff's edge helplessly blindfolded, while we stand by doing nothing to prevent it, but wrong if that person removes the blindfold and steps off with eyes open? It is naïve or obtuse to contend that if we choose to die slowly, forlornly, willy-nilly, by a natural disintegration from something like cancer or starvation, we have no complicity in our death and the death is not suicide; but if we deliberately our "quietus make with a bare bodkin," it is suicide. Every person's fight with death is lost before it begins. What makes the struggle worthwhile, therefore, cannot lie in the outcome. It lies in the dignity with which the fight is waged and the way it finds an end."

15. Genesis 3,5.

16. Some books that you might find useful in gaining insight into the attitudes of the Wisdom writers would be: J. Crenshaw, *Old Testament Wisdom, An Introduction,* Atlanta, 1981, and a number of relevant articles in R. Brown, J. Fitzmyer, R. Murphy, *The New Jerome Biblical Commentary,* Prentice Hall, 1990. Look especially at: R. Murphy, "Introduction to the Wisdom Literature," pp. 447–452; R.A.F. MacKenzie and R. Murphy, "Job," pp. 466–488; A.G. Wright, "Ecclesiastes (Qoheleth)," pp. 489–495; A.A. Di Lella, "Sirach," pp. 496–509.

17. Job 2, 9.

18. Job 2, 10.

19. Job 40,15–41,11.

20. Qoheleth 1, 2–6.

21. Qoheleth, 12, 13.

22. John 3, 36.

23. John 4, 14.

24. John 6, 50–51.

25. Rom 6, 22–23.

26. I Corinthians 15, 43–44.

27. Saint John of the Cross, *The Living Flame of Love,* Stanza 1, nn. 29–34.

28. Saint John of the Cross, *op. cit.,* n. 30. Translation from Kevin Kavanaugh, O.C.D., and Otilio Rodriguez, O.C.D., *The Collected Works of John of the Cross,* Doubleday and Company, 1964, pp. 591–592.

Chapter 12

COMMUNICATING THE CATHOLIC VISION: THE CULTURE OF LIFE

Richard M. Doerflinger

How do we communicate our concern about a moral issue to an audience that may not share our vision of human life?

The Church has always accepted the need for apologetics—we must always be ready to answer anyone who asks the reasons for the hope that is within us (1 Peter 3:15). St. Paul's famous speech to the Athenians in Acts 17 is a beautiful example of suiting a message to an audience, of taking people where they already are and guiding them to a new vision. And yet the Church is often suspicious of the arts of persuasion—especially in their modern forms of political advertising and "public relations."

The Church's wary attitude regarding rhetorical technique has an old philosophical pedigree. To Plato, rhetoric was a semblance of real politics, a form of flattery that tells the crowd what it wants to hear. He said that rhetoric is to justice as cookery is to medicine: it feeds people tasty food that appears good but is really bad for them.[1] The great rhetoricians thought "that probability deserves more respect than truth," and they "could make trifles seem important and important points trifles by the force of their language."[2] Thus the art of persuasion is an art of deception.

Aristotle took a more balanced view. Regarding the techniques of rhetoric he said: "A man can confer the greatest of benefits by a right use of these, and inflict the greatest of injuries by using them wrongly."[3] And the art of persuasion is generally more useful to those telling the truth, because things which are probable or easily believed are most often close to the truth. In any case, because some may use rhetoric to deceive those who know the truth, we must be prepared to marshal the facts effectively and refute such false claims. It would be absurd to say that men should be able to defend themselves with their limbs but not with their use of rational speech, when it is the latter that is more distinctive of human beings.

As Christians, of course, we should be prepared above all to use such skills to defend others, especially innocent human beings who cannot speak for themselves. Yet our Thomist tradition has inherited Plato's and Aristotle's ambivalence about rhetoric. And Church leaders rightly insist that their efforts to persuade cannot contradict the Church's primary obligation to teach divine *truth* in all its fullness and purity. To compound our dilemma, we live in an age that has drifted away from a Christian vision of life and death, that does not accept or understand the idea of redemptive suffering—so the gap between what is easily believed by our audience and what is really true may be wide indeed.

This problem is especially acute in the Church's efforts to persuade Americans not to legalize euthanasia and physician-assisted suicide. If anything our task here is more difficult than on the issue of abortion. Opinion polls indicate that most Americans think abortion is immoral, and most support restrictions on the practice; according to some polls, the general public thinks abortion should be illegal in all but the rarest of extreme circumstances. But opinion polls also show that Americans accept the idea of voluntary euthanasia and think it should be legal for dying patients. Here Americans' love affair with individual freedom can be given free rein: No helpless third party is harmed as in abortion, because the only victim is someone who (supposedly) has freely asked for death. In speaking up in defense of helpless lives at risk, we are told even by those who are living those lives to go mind our own business.

Yet legalized euthanasia has now been considered and rejected by two West coast states, Washington and California. These states were specially chosen by the Hemlock Society and other euthanasia advocates as ideal testing grounds, because they are politically "progressive" and have long supported legalized abortion. In a 1991 Roper poll commissioned by Hemlock, 68% of Washingtonians and 74% of Californians supported voluntary euthanasia. Yet Washington in 1991 and California in 1992 rejected Hemlock's proposal, 54 to 46 percent.

The Catholic Church was heavily involved in both campaigns. In both states it provided very fine educational materials to churchgoing Catholics communicating the Church's complete moral vision of life and death. But it did not distribute those same materials to the general public to try to persuade voters that euthanasia is morally wrong in principle—for it knew that message would fall on deaf ears. Instead, in both cases it helped form a much broader coalition of secular and religious groups, including state medical and hospice associations, and worked to convince the voters that this particular proposal was too dangerous, that it lacked the safeguards needed to prevent widespread abuse.

This decision was controversial both inside and outside the Church. Hemlock and its allies complained that the Church was hiding its *real* reasons for opposing the initiative. As one Hemlock official said to me during a radio debate, the real debate is a simple confrontation "between dogma and common sense." Of course he was confident that Hemlock would win if the debate were cast in those terms.

Some Catholics feared that this argument of "not enough safeguards" might seem to concede that there is such a thing as "safe" euthanasia. That message would contradict the Church's moral position on euthanasia, and could pave the way for a major defeat when our opponents devise a new proposal with the needed "safeguards" to ensure that euthanasia will be voluntary and kept within certain bounds.

In my view this need not be a problem, so long as we do not make the argument of "no real safeguards" our *only* or *final* argument. That argument is perfectly valid in its own sphere, but it lies on a spectrum. For there are many arguments against euthanasia, ranging from the most superficial and contingent to the most profound and timeless. An effective and lasting educational effort against euthanasia will guide people from the more superficial arguments to those which are more profound. Gradually we can wean people from their infatuation with "choice," to focus on *what is being chosen* and its implications for individuals and society.

I would like to outline five different types or levels of argument against euthanasia, and evaluate their effectiveness with the help of a poll of California voters which was commissioned immediately after the November 1992 election by the U.S. bishops' conference and other organizations.

First and most superficial, of course, is the argument which seems to have been decisive in Washington and California: the argument that a particular euthanasia proposal is too dangerous because it lacks safeguards against abuse. Most people who support euthanasia proposals claim to do so out of respect for individual freedom of choice; so the most damning charge against such a proposal is that it will kill people who did not really make a free and informed choice for death. This could include patients with treatable depression, with temporary setbacks, with unduly pessimistic or even completely mistaken diagnoses.

In all, 27% of those who voted against California's euthanasia proposal said they did so because of the lack of safeguards. And when they were asked which safeguards particularly concerned them, they pointed to factors directly related to the integrity of the patient's free and informed choice: The proposal had no requirement for family consultation, for psychological testing, for counseling on other alternatives, or for a waiting period to give the patient a chance to think over the decision.

In short, people could see the difference between making a free choice and being railroaded into that choice. There is nothing worse than a "pro-choice" law that prevents people from making real choices. A most effective spokesperson for this kind of argument is someone who has faced terminal illness and can explain how depressed and easily influenced people are upon first hearing a terminal prognosis. "If this proposal had been in effect when I was first diagnosed," they might say, "I would have just signed the form and had myself killed—and I would have been making a terrible and irreversible mistake."

While this argument was used very effectively in TV ads against specific proposals in both Washington and California, our poll suggested that most California voters do *not* presently believe that it is a valid charge against euthanasia proposals generally. Only 40% of the voters agreed with the following statement: "If doctors start taking the lives of people who want to die, soon it will spread to killing people who never asked to die." (I should note that some segments of the population did agree with the statement—for example, 51% of voters aged 65 or over agreed that voluntary euthanasia opens the door to involuntary euthanasia.) So this argument should be specific and concrete, pointing out those flaws in a *particular* proposal that *will* create that slippery slope toward involuntary killing.

At a second level we can invite people to widen their perspective and look at the way individual choices would be shaped by a new social

170

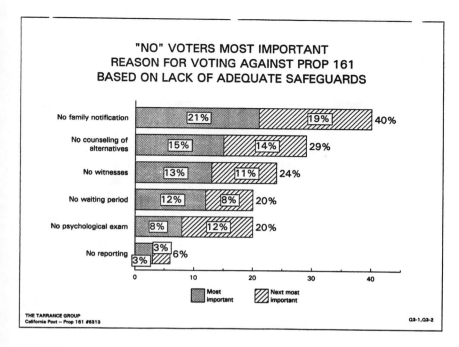

"NO" VOTERS MOST IMPORTANT
REASON FOR VOTING AGAINST PROP 161
BASED ON LACK OF ADEQUATE SAFEGUARDS

	Most important	Next most important	Total
No family notification	21%	19%	40%
No counseling of alternatives	15%	14%	29%
No witnesses	13%	11%	24%
No waiting period	12%	8%	20%
No psychological exam	8%	12%	20%
No reporting	3%	3%	6%

THE TARRANCE GROUP
California Post — Prop 161 #6313

Q3-1,Q3-2

TABLE 1

policy on euthanasia. Under that policy, choices may be superficially "free" but made under restrictions and pressures that actually bias the choice. Here also we can attack an allegedly "pro-choice" proposal in the very name of choice; but we appeal to a broader and richer notion of freedom. Society makes its own choice when it authorizes assisted suicide for certain classes of patients, while continuing to prohibit it for everyone else—it is saying that some people's lives are objectively without value, that their deaths are not as worth preventing as the deaths of others are.

The most informed and persuasive spokespersons for this argument are people with disabilities, who can speak from bitter experience about the ways a society and its prejudices can prevent people from making truly free choices. For a disabled person who is frustrated in every attempt at self-fulfillment and self-advancement, society's eagerness to allow a "quick and easy" death is a mockery of the ideal of individual freedom—it looks like the *only* choice society is really offering. A social bias in favor of death can also arise from prejudice based on age or race, or from the economic pressures of our financially strapped health care system. Surely the poor and the marginalized—

those with no real access to health care *supporting* life—would be the first to be persuaded to make a quick "final exit" under a regime of legalized euthanasia.

This line of argument depends on the existence of certain social and economic inequities—but those inequities are so enduring in most societies that its validity does not depend on the wording of any one proposal. It was with such arguments that the American Bar Association's Commission on Legal Problems of the Elderly persuaded the ABA to reject a euthanasia resolution a year ago, here in Dallas. The Commission said that "the proposed right to choose aid-in-dying freely and without undue influence is illusory and, indeed, dangerous for the thousands of Americans who have no or inadequate access to quality health and long-term care services." Or as Dr. Carlos Gomez has written in *Commonweal* magazine: "It would be the triumph of illusion over reality to suggest that we could safely incorporate physician-assisted suicide into the existing madness that passes for a system of health care in this country."

This line of argument does not presume that euthanasia is morally wrong in principle—but it does presume that it is wrong for society to push people toward such actions. It will appeal to people with a social conscience who are concerned about the poor and vulnerable of our society. It also has obvious links with Catholic teachings on social and economic justice.

At a third level we can try to persuade people that euthanasia is *unnecessary*—that is, there are better solutions to all the problems that have led people to want euthanasia. At the very least, we must make this case to respond to the rhetorical excesses of the pro-euthanasia movement, which continually brings forth horror stories about lingering, painful death to convince people that they need euthanasia. In fact people need not resort to such an extreme solution, because there are effective and life-affirming alternatives that do not entail the dangers of legalized euthanasia. This line of argument becomes more compelling with each passing day: Unwanted overtreatment is less common than it once was, pain control techniques have made enormous progress, and the medical profession is waking up to the need to be better trained in these techniques.

The natural spokespersons for this argument are hospice nurses and other professionals involved in compassionate care of the dying, as well as terminally ill patients themselves. Many hospices, of course, are under direct Catholic sponsorship; our institutional involvement in the health care system gives us an important role at this level of the debate. The hospice movement itself has a strong official position *against* euthanasia; we must encourage and cultivate this stand, es-

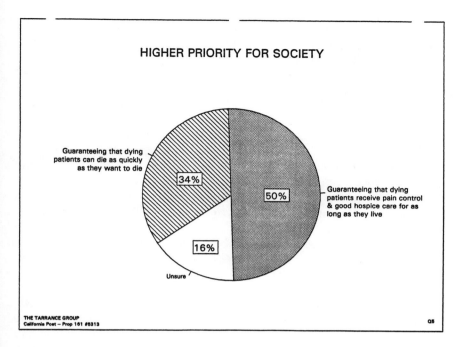

HIGHER PRIORITY FOR SOCIETY

Guaranteeing that dying
patients can die as quickly
as they want to die

34%

Guaranteeing that dying
patients receive pain control
& good hospice care for as
long as they live

50%

16%

Unsure

THE TARRANCE GROUP
California Post – Prop 161 #6313

Q5

TABLE 2

pecially since Hemlock and other groups are constantly working to reverse it.

This argument is more profound than the previous two because it does presume in our audience some moral misgivings about euthanasia, some awareness that it is a radical and questionable solution that should not be tried until all other avenues are exhausted. The first two levels of argument, outlining the dangers of the "slippery slope," are helpful in cultivating these misgivings.

In any case, our post-election poll showed a potential for broad support for this theme. California voters were asked which should be a higher priority for society—guaranteeing that dying patients can die as quickly as they want to die, or guaranteeing that dying patients receive pain control and good hospice care for as long as they live. Only 34% said ensuring a quick death is more important, while 50% said priority should be given to pain control and hospice care.

In response to this argument, euthanasia supporters will simply say this is not an either/or situation: We can have improved care of the dying, *as well as* euthanasia as a last resort for those not satisfied

173

with that care. We must be prepared to argue that you cannot have it both ways: If society has already decided that it has no special reason to prevent suicide for certain classes of patients, because their kind of life is no real use to themselves or anyone else, it will lose the incentive to work for *real* solutions to the problems of dying patients. This will be true on the individual as well as social level. One of the most serious problems terminally ill patients have is that medical personnel do not want to spend very much time with them, in part because (understandably) they do not want to become too attached to someone who they know will die soon. How much more distant will doctors become when they must see each dying patient as someone they might be asked to kill soon? And how much worse will dying patients feel as a result, so that they are more likely to choose euthanasia out of loneliness and despair?

This argument about choosing better solutions is also more profound than the previous two arguments in another way: It is not only an argument we can express verbally, but also an argument we must work to make more compelling in reality through our efforts to improve care of the dying. One of the most positive results in the 1991 vote on euthanasia in Washington state was that immediately after the vote, physicians who had helped defeat the Hemlock proposal worked with state medical and hospice associations to produce a new handbook on pain control and care of the dying, designed especially for the physician in general practice. Having argued that better care, not euthanasia, is the answer to modern problems in dying, they knew they had to ensure that this better care was really available. Our Catholic Health Association of the United States has launched a project of this kind on a national scale.

At a fourth level, people can be asked to reflect on the *meaning* of medicine as a healing profession, so they will understand why *doctors* in particular must not be allowed to kill. *Even if* a society may want to let some people kill themselves, we might argue, doctors are the last people in the world that we should involve in that kind of choice. In short, to choose medicine as a profession is to choose to use one's expertise only to heal, never to kill. This theme cuts across issues like abortion, euthanasia and capital punishment.

This kind of argument may take on a different tone depending on whether it is directed at doctors themselves or the general public. In speaking to doctors we must appeal to their ideals of what medicine should be: A noble profession that goes far beyond mere technique or scientific know-how, because it has its own internal ethic demanding that medical skills always be devoted to healing and not killing. In

174

speaking to the general public we might point out how much power doctors already have over life and death for the rest of us, and we might ask whether it is wise to give over to them the final power to take life.

It is easy to see how legalized euthanasia could break down the bond of instinctive trust that should define the physician-patient relationship. As Dr. Leon Kass has written in *Commonweal* magazine: "Imagine the scene: you are old, poor, in failing health, and alone in the world; you are brought to the city hospital with fractured ribs and pneumonia. The nurse or intern enters late at night with a syringe full of yellow stuff for your intravenous drip. How soundly will you sleep? It will not matter that your doctor has never yet put anyone to death; that he is legally entitled to do so will make a world of difference."

Whether we are appealing to doctors' high ideals, or to patients' concern that doctors may not all live up to those ideals, these arguments have a profound element in common: An understanding that we are able to give doctors such enormous authority and power over us precisely because they have their own internal code forbidding them to use that power to harm a patient. Undermine that code, and the doctor becomes the most dangerous person in society.

Our post-election poll showed that people do respond to this theme: 69% agreed with the statement, "Doctors should be healers, never killers." Fifty percent expressed strong agreement, while only 22% disagreed.

This argument does not necessarily conclude that all legalized euthanasia is wrong. For example, society could appoint an entirely separate profession, much like that of state executioner, to take care of such cases. These specialists need have only a minimum of medical training, for it does not take much medical knowledge to know the lethal dosages of various drugs. But in reality, without the involvement of doctors these proposals lose much of their appeal. It is by "medicalizing" suicide for the seriously ill that pro-euthanasia groups hope to make the act seem orderly and respectable, and distinguish it from ordinary suicide. We should make sure that doctors know this, that the euthanasia movement is trying to exploit the profession's status and prestige for its own ends.

Finally, of course, the question arises: If all safeguards were included, if social and economic inequities were addressed, if hospice care were readily available to all, and the integrity of the medical profession would not be destroyed, why would it still be wrong to allow euthanasia? Here we must move from an ethical argument about the medical profession to a moral argument about our obligations as human beings. We must bring forth our philosophical and theological arguments about why euthanasia is wrong in principle, regardless of the circumstances.

I will not repeat here what you have already heard about the Catholic moral stance on euthanasia. But I would like to give you an idea of how I try to present the moral argument against euthanasia to secular American audiences. I think this approach is well suited to the United States, because it directly confronts the theme of "freedom of choice" and highlights what a strange freedom the liberty to kill yourself is. I make my case as follows:

"We must continue to value all human life—even, or especially, in life's final and most vulnerable moments.

"Why should we do so? From a *religious* viewpoint the answer is clear enough: Life is our first and most precious gift from a loving God, over which we are called to exercise stewardship but not absolute dominion. Responsible stewardship—especially on the part of physicians—calls us to use our knowledge and skills in reverent humility, recognizing our own finitude and the incompleteness of our wisdom. It means we cannot claim an absolute mandate to prolong life, as though we could actually defeat death by our own puny mortal efforts; but it also means we must never arrogate to ourselves the authority to take life, as though we were its lords and masters. To do either of those things would be to "play God" in the pejorative sense.

"The vision of life as a gift of the Creator is shared by Catholics, Protestants, Jews and many others, and is reflected in the founding documents of our nation. But I understand that it is not shared by all. To those who find it unappealing I would say this: If life is not a divine gift, it is at least the most basic and fundamental of the human goods which societies like ours are established to protect. And it is precisely an ethical devotion to this good that makes the physician a member of a *profession,* rather than just another technician with a good-paying job. Life is *basic* because it is the pre-condition for every other human good and human right, even freedom. You cannot enhance someone's freedom by taking his life, because corpses have no freedom. Freely taking your life, like freely selling yourself into slavery, is the ultimate self-contradiction of freedom, not its ultimate triumph.

"In fact, if we devalue the *lives* of the seriously ill we will end up asking ourselves why the freedom of their request is so important. This is because life is not just another good—it is the bodily reality of an individual human *person.* And a human person of little value will surely have freedom that is of little value. Thus do the assumptions behind voluntary euthanasia pave the way for involuntary euthanasia.

176

The reason respondents voted against Prop 161 are summarized below.

Main Reason For Voting "NO"	%
Moral/religious beliefs	39%
Lack of safeguards	27%
Doctors shouldn't perform it	19%
Poor wording of prop	5%

TABLE 3

"Some have asked, 'Whose life is it anyway?' My own answer is: 'It is God's first of all, and it is mine in trust to respect and care for.' But if my answer is wrong, then the only *other* answer that makes sense is: 'It doesn't *belong* to anyone, not even to me. My life is *me,* not just another piece of property that I own. That is why I can't ethically sell myself into slavery or prostitution or a life of drug addiction—because my life is not just a possession, even to me. And to treat certain kinds of human life as disposable property will be to treat particular classes of *people* as disposable property.' "

How many of our citizens are moved by moral principles of this kind? In a post-election poll in Washington state a year ago, 41% of those who voted against the euthanasia initiative said they did so out of moral or religious conviction; another 17% said they were against *doctors* taking life, and 12% said the measure lacked safeguards. In our post-election poll in California, 39% cited moral or religious beliefs, 19% were worried about doctors taking life, and 27% cited lack of safeguards. While arguments about the lack of safeguards were paramount in the campaign, and clearly provided the winning margin, in both cases the largest single group opposing these measures was made up of people explicitly acting from moral conviction. Among regular churchgoers, of course, the percentage of those citing moral or religious arguments was far higher; the vast majority of regular churchgoing Catholics voted against the California proposal, and 61% of them cited moral or religious concerns as their most important reason.

We should not assume that everyone *else* voting against these proposals acted with absolute *indifference* to moral concerns. They had some moral qualms about killing as well—why else would they cry out so intensely for strong safeguards, if they did not think the practice is close to the edge of moral behavior in the first place? After all, we do

177

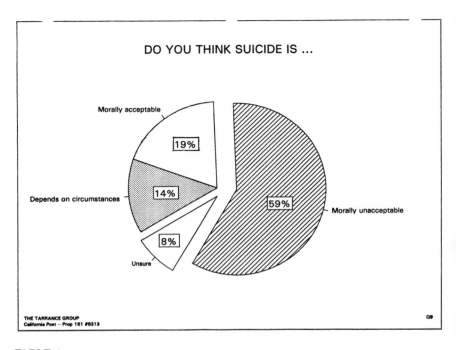

DO YOU THINK SUICIDE IS ...

Morally acceptable

19%

Depends on circumstances

14%

59%

Morally unacceptable

8%

Unsure

THE TARRANCE GROUP
California Post – Prop 161 #6313

Q9

TABLE 4

not call for firm witnessing requirements and family notification whenever people make perfectly legitimate medical decisions about themselves.

In fact, a clear majority of Californians in our poll did say that they think suicide is morally unacceptable, and only 19% said it is morally acceptable. To many people, the immoral character of suicide was not necessarily enough by itself to warrant keeping assisted suicide illegal for the terminally ill—but it did raise enough questions in people's minds to make arguments about slippery slopes and the need for safeguards more persuasive. And our position receives even more support if we *combine* it with the theme of life-affirming alternatives: 79% of voters agreed with the statement, "People who want to commit suicide should be helped with their problems, not helped to die." Only 13% expressed disagreement.

In short, we must see these five levels of argument as mutually supportive. People see the need for safeguards precisely because they know in their heart of hearts that there is something wrong about this practice; by providing their conscious minds with practical and concrete reasons for opposing particular proposals, we can also cultivate

178

and give firmer shape to those unformed moral qualms that they always really had deep down.

So we have come full circle back to Plato, who insisted that real education only reminds us of what we always knew. At the fifth level of argument, unvoiced moral qualms about killing can come into their own and be given fully explicit expression. How quickly and explicitly we should be bringing them into full expression in any given case will depend on how informed and morally mature our audience is.

If these levels of argument are really mutually supporting, then we should have no fundamental problem with an advertising campaign which has to appeal to the lowest common denominator of the public's attitudes, and therefore stresses the "lack of safeguards" argument. Such a campaign will not necessarily intensify people's demand for a *future* proposal that would include all the missing safeguards. In our post-election poll we asked California voters this question: "Let's say a measure legalizing physician-assisted suicide is said to have enough safeguards to ensure that doctors could kill only competent patients who voluntarily ask to be killed. Would you support or oppose such a law?" Remember, this is in a state which the previous year showed 74% support for such legislation. In the aftermath of the California campaign, only 47% said they would support a law *with* safeguards and 42% said they would oppose it. We asked this question a bit differently with half of our sample, using the much softer phrase "end life" instead of the blunt word "kill"; and even with this euphemism, support went up only to 55% (with 36% strongly supporting and 29% strongly opposing it). The voters' *principled* opposition to euthanasia proposals had increased, though moral principle was not the main theme of the campaign.

People's general misgivings about euthanasia proposals—*any* euthanasia proposal—were indeed cultivated by the debate over the dangers of the California initiative. The Church's next job in California would be to take the argument a level deeper with these voters and educate them about the slippery slope inherent in any and all legalized euthanasia.

My final point has to to do with the political advertising used in such campaigns. Because such advertising is broadcast to the general public, it is generally tailored to the "lowest common denominator" of moral maturity. The Church can and should support such advertising without creating any confusion as to its own principled moral stand. It can further minimize any chance of confusion by making sure that the ads are explicitly sponsored not by the Church as such but by a broad-based coalition of secular as well as religious groups. Forming such a coalition is also practically necessary because some of these other

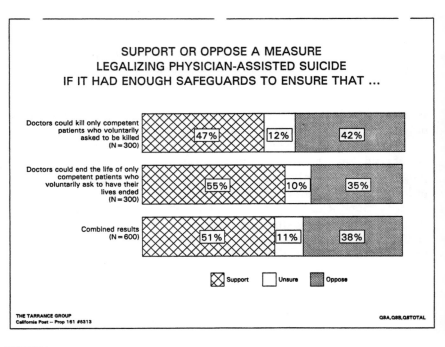

SUPPORT OR OPPOSE A MEASURE
LEGALIZING PHYSICIAN-ASSISTED SUICIDE
IF IT HAD ENOUGH SAFEGUARDS TO ENSURE THAT ...

Doctors could kill only competent patients who voluntarily asked to be killed (N = 300): 47% Support, 12% Unsure, 42% Oppose

Doctors could end the life of only competent patients who voluntarily ask to have their lives ended (N = 300): 55% Support, 10% Unsure, 35% Oppose

Combined results (N = 600): 51% Support, 11% Unsure, 38% Oppose

Legend: Support, Unsure, Oppose

THE TARRANCE GROUP
California Post -- Prop 161 #6313

Q8A,Q8B,Q8TOTAL

TABLE 5

groups—most notably medical and hospice associations—have far more credibility with many voters than the Church does.

Many factors will determine the content and tone of such advertising. To give one example: In Washington state, television air time is relatively inexpensive, and could be purchased over a period of eight to ten weeks to gradually build a case against the euthanasia initiative. In the much larger state of California, where sharing a commercial for one week can cost close to a million dollars, those opposing the euthanasia initiative could only afford to air a few ads in the last week or two before the vote; these ads had to grab people's attention and communicate in a very blunt way how radical the proposal really was. So the ads used in California communicated the same basic themes as those used in Washington—but they explicitly appealed to people's *fears* about being ushered out of life by someone else, and so had more of the character of "negative campaigning" about them. They were negative enough to prompt some misgivings and debates within Catholic groups that were part of the coalition against the euthanasia proposal. All I will say about these ads is (a) under the circumstances they seem to have worked, and (b) the best way to avoid having to use ads like

180

them in the future is to do fundraising and initial advertising early in the campaign, so a message can be built up gradually instead of scaring the daylights out of people in the last few days.

These and other dilemmas about tactics should be discussed more thoroughly within the Church in the months to come—we now have data from two successful campaigns to analyze, and the need for this kind of campaign is not going to go away any time soon. But whatever the exact structure or tactics of a given public education program, we should not be afraid to use any and all of the valid arguments against euthanasia legislation.

In the short term perhaps the best we can hope for is that people will say: "The reason that proposal is wrong is that it doesn't have effective safeguards." Our long-term challenge is to bring them to the point of saying: "The reason it's so hard to develop effective safeguards is that the whole idea is wrong."

NOTES

1. Gorgias, 463–465.
2. Phaedrus, 267.
3. Rhetoric, 1355b.

Chapter 13

PAIN MANAGMENT AND HOSPICE CARE

L. L. de Veber, M.D.

Introduction

First of all, I would like to say what a great privilege and honour it is to address your Excellencies and how I hope that by sharing my thoughts and experience with you that I can help you further understand the current status of palliative care, or hospice care, and pain control specifically, in cancer patients. My background in coming to the subject consists of 30 years of practice in pediatric oncology including some 500 cases where children have died of cancer. Happily, this is becoming a much more rare occurrence as our cure rates for this disease begin to reach 80% in general, but still leaves us with some difficult management problems. I also have had access to many discussions of adult palliative care and hospice care. Perhaps here I should mention that I feel hospice and palliative care are similar words and we will use them interchangeably. I belong to an International Work Group on Death, Dying and Bereavement which includes some of the outstanding leaders in this field, was vice chairman of the committee on Ethics, and am currently on a committee on Palliative Care in Children and was also on a committee on Spiritual Care with my wife, which I will refer to later. I have also been involved in directing the teaching of ethics and palliative care at the medical school at The University of Western Ontario since 1970, and I am also on a planning committee for the King's College Centre for Bereavement, as well as some other district bereavement committees.

Section I: Hospice or Palliative Care

This is a very old concept in one sense, but also very new in terms of the medical speciality. The hospice concept goes back at least to the Crusades where hospices were resting places for weary, sick, or dying Crusaders. From that time until the beginnings of the last century I am sure that the principles of hospice care were carried out in many parts of the world until the rapid advance of technology and the relative loss of religion in the health care systems began to produce an increasingly bad environment for the dying patient. The advanced centers for modern medicine concentrated on technology and curing patients and generally ignored the problems of the dying patient. Dr. Elizabeth Kubler-Ross was one of the first pioneers in the hospice movement when she listened to the dying patients in large numbers (over 200) and then wrote her famous books on death and dying outlining the stages of patients' and families' reaction to death. As well as outlining the stages, she found out many problems with these dying patients that were not being attended to by the medical and nursing profession and became internationally known for her crusade for this cause. The next major development was the creation of the hospice system in England led by Dame Cecily Saunders. She is a remarkable lady who trained as a social worker, a nurse, then a physician, and then spent two years studying the pharmacology of pain control before raising a large sum of money that was used to design and build St. Christopher's Hospice. This is a free standing building which was specifically designed for the care of dying patients and has some unusual features compared to the standard hospital. First of all, patients were in four bedroom units so that the death of a patient was clearly seen by the other patients. This was felt to be an unorthodox approach but Dr. Saunders felt that since death was almost always peaceful that it

184

was an important lesson for other patients to learn. The windows of these rooms go right to the ground so that the patients can see out to flower gardens and the outside. She then developed a team of doctors, nurses, and volunteers to give expert care to these dying patients, particularly with regard to pain control, and also her concept of total pain, recognizing that patients not only have physical pain but social, psychological, and spiritual pain. Where possible, patients were treated at home in cooperation with the district nurses, physicians, and volunteers, which became a closely related program of the hospice. Dr. Saunders, using her hospice as a teaching center, spread the hospice message throughout England where many other hospices developed and eventually this spread across the ocean to the United States, where I believe the Yale New Haven hospice was one of the first hospices. Of course, now there are many hundreds of hospices with a very powerful national hospice association. I should also mention that in England palliative care is now a recognized specialty by The Royal College of Physicians and Surgeons, so that physicians there can now train and be certified in palliative care in a similar manner to surgeons, obstetricians, pediatricians, etc.

Palliative care took a different form in Canada under the leadership of Dr. Balfour Mount at The Royal Victoria Hospital in Montreal. Dr. Mount is a urological surgeon who became concerned about the care of dying patients and spent six months with Dr. Saunders at St. Christopher's Hospice and then returned to his hospital. There he had a survey conducted which indicated some serious gaps in care of the dying, and eventually the hospital agreed to start a unit within the hospital for the care of dying patients. This, again, like Dr. Saunders, was a revolutionary concept since, as I mentioned before, dying patients are generally ignored in teaching hospitals. Dr. Mount's unit quickly became recognized as a center of excellent care for dying patients and palliative care units began to spread across Canada. As did Dr. Saunders, Dr. Mount of course published articles in journals and spoke at meetings to spread the message of palliative care.

The main difference in palliative care is that it is directed to the care of dying patients which explains why it was relatively new to develop in medicine and is still not accepted as a bonafide medical specialty in many areas. Certainly, when I went through medical school it was unheard of and, of course, like all physicians I was trained to cure, and to ignore dying patients since they were a symptom of a total failure of our medical knowledge and scientific system. Palliative care also differs from other medical specialties, except family medicine, in that it is really holistic or "whole person" medicine since it looks at not only the physical but also the psychological, social, and spiritual needs of the dying patients and their families. It is similar to other specialties in that multi-disciplinary teams are an important feature of the care of the patient. Palliative care also focuses on home care which, with proper supports, is almost always the most satisfactory place for the patient to die. There are also hospice organizations such as one in Windsor, Ontario, near where I live, which does not have an official building but runs programs out of an office with large numbers of well trained volunteers both for hospital and home care.

Another important part of palliative care is to bring the patient and family into the treatment place, to respect the patient's complaints and wishes and to try to make information available as required. This, of course, like many palliative care principles, should apply to any medical caregiver situation.

One of the most striking differences in palliative care professionals is that most have an obvious, strong faith system, in contrast to any other specialty groups I have known (Pediatrics, Haematology, Cancer Immunology, etc.) While working in an International Work Group committee on spiritual care (with my wife), we had to struggle with the differences between religion, which expresses spirituality through a formalized set of values and rituals in an institutional setting as different from spirituality, which is a more universal quest for ultimate issues and life principles and a search for meaning in a person's life-questions such as why me, why her/him, etc. It can be difficult for someone, eg., a chaplain from a specific religion, to render "spiritual care" to a patient or family with no such background. Yet, we concluded, just as there are "few atheists in foxholes", most dying patients and their families want "spiritual care", which should be provided by a sensitive health care worker. Our committee found little evidence of this subject in medical or nursing school curricula, unless of course they were affiliated with a religious institution.

It is unfortunate that some clergy, including our own, appear ill prepared to deal with this area, according to what some families have told me, and may miss a golden opportunity to restore a patient's and family's faith. I wonder how much of this subject is taught in our seminaries, which could be done conveniently as an adjunct to moral theology and ethics. Most centers where there are seminars would have a hospice system and some of the experts from this field might be a welcome addition to the teaching of the seminary students. Also, with regard to bereavement which is an important part of palliative care, the Association for Death Education and Counselling has centers in many parts of the United States and Canada and would be ideal for teaching in seminaries.

Pain Control

It is difficult to practice holistic palliative care and attend to all the needs of the patient and family if the patient is in agony from uncontrolled pain. First of all, I would like to point out the tremendous explosion of scientific knowledge with regard to pain mechanisms in the basic science of physiology, and it is critical that the TEAM, particularly the physician managing the patient, go to some effort as in any other patients, to make the proper diagnosis of the pain. For example, neuropathic pain due to nervous degeneration, does not respond to normal narcotic control but requires other medications including in some cases, anti-depressants. Similarly, musculoskeletal pain sometimes responds extremely well to simple anti-arthritic medications and aspirin, and increased intracranial pressure from brain tumours can respond dramatically to corticosteroids with very little response to narcotics. Along with the rapidly expanding scientific knowledge about pain mechanisms there has been development of newer narcotics and techniques for using narcotics. For instance, oral morphine can now be administered in a long acting form lasting up to 12 hours which has been a tremendous advance for patients on continual morphine where four hourly doses are often neglected even by the patients themselves. Similarly, morphine can now be administered through computerized, battery driven pumps into subcutaneous tissues, and this has been shown to be just as effective as intravenous infusions and, of course, can be used by patients and the care staff at home to avoid a hospital stay. This administration of morphine by the patient is controlled so that extra boluses may be delivered occasionally, and an overdose would be very difficult. On the other hand, many patients have been sent home with large amounts of oral morphine and attempted suicides are unknown as far as I know in this area. Intravenous doses give an immediate and high peak but disappear quickly whereas oral doses give a slower but more sustained peak and is much better for regular administration. Dilaudid, a very powerful narcotic, is very soluble and can be used in large amounts of small fluid for parenteral injections and has pretty well replaced Heroin in that regard. Again, as in many other areas of palliative care, proper knowledge and use of pain medications requires study and attention to detail, etc. I showed through a series of slides, briefly, the principles of pain control where it is critical in chronic incurable cancer pain so that the patient's level of pain control medication may be maintained and that gaps in this level must not be allowed to develop since the patient will then develop pain and the whole cycle can start over again. Doses should be at regular intervals (eg., every four hours) and not p.r.n. (as necessary) which means the patient has to ask (or sometimes beg) for medication. Also, one has to watch for side effects of chronic narcotic medication, particularly constipation, which can be extremely difficult to resolve if not prevented, some degree of nausea and vomiting which may require adjustment of medications and, of course, sedation and drowsiness which can be minimized if the correct dose of narcotic is used. Additional medications such as tranquilizers, antidepressants, occasional nerve blocks, and epidural anaesthetics in the spinal canal, can be extremely important in particular cases for pain control. In this regard most centres now have pain clinics or pain teams which include an anesthesiologist to assist in some of the more difficult technical areas of pain control.

In summary, there has been a tremendous advance in the knowledge and techniques for pain control which is widely available in many publications, books, and monographs and, in fact, in Canada there is now a curriculum for palliative care and pain control available through medical schools for the teaching of medical students and, of course, this would apply to nursing students and other paramedical areas.

In the next section I will discuss some of the reasons why we do not have good pain control in many areas of our countries.

Problems in Pain Control

1. For those of us, such as myself, involved in trying to promote proper palliative care for the last 30 years, who have seen the rapid advances in knowledge and techniques, it is very discouraging to continually hear stories of patients left in agony in their last days because of inadequate knowledge or fears or myths on the part of the medical staff. Part of the problems rest, of course, in the tremendous concern in the public, and in the health care professions, about drug addiction and the rampant social problems associated with this scourge on our society. Unfortunately, this, I think, has been one of the major obstacles to proper pain control in the terminal patients. In fact, in some countries, notably Italy and Spain, narcotics are not available for treatment of patients at home because of the very strict laws to attempt to curb improper use of drugs on the streets. This is not a problem in North America but I am continually amazed and discouraged by the inhibitions of medical and nursing staff to use proper pain control even though the knowledge and orders for the use are clearly outlined. One reason given for failing to provide pain control by doctors is

the fear of addiction. This, like most of the fears of the medical and nursing profession, is mostly a myth. There is no comparison between the very mild addiction that may develop in long term cancer patients on narcotics as compared to the psychological and genetically determined drug dependence of the street addicts. In fact, most cancer patients can be withdrawn from huge doses of narcotics with little or no effect in contrast to the true street addicts. Even if there was an addiction problem surely one would not leave a dying patient in agony because of fear of an addiction which would have little effect on his personal or social life.

2. The nursing staff usually are concerned about respiratory depression which is still being taught in many nursing schools as a common complication of narcotic therapy. This is not true in cancer patients since pain itself is a very powerful antidote to respiratory depression. Obviously, respiratory depression, like other side effects, can occur if enough medication is given, but the amounts required to control pain do not produce significant respiratory depression unless the patient has some additional lung or heart problems.

3. Fear of an overdose leading to death of the patient and a possible charge of mercy killing, etc. This, again, is a myth since doses that control pain obviously will not kill the patient. Since patients can become refractory to long term use of narcotics, the amount they are receiving when they die may appear to be an overdose, which is not true. Long before a patient dies of an overdose of a narcotic he is becoming very drowsy and finally comatose and this, of course, can be reversed by narcotic antidotes. However, I believe this is a rather hidden fear which is not always admitted by the medical and nursing staff which further inhibits their proper use of narcotic pain control.

4. Another problem is that despite the rapid advance of palliative care and hospice care to the point where this is now a recognized specialty in the United Kingdom, there is still, in many areas, scarcity of properly trained medical and nursing personnel to provide the guidance and knowledge for proper pain control. Most large medical institutions now do have some type of hospice or palliative care team or consultant team but these consultants are not often used to best advantage and their advice is often ignored. Doctors can be a major obstacle to proper palliative care due to a combination of factors including their very high death denial, their focus on cure, their fear of narcotics and their general resistance to change. Family doctors also may see palliative care experts as a threat to one area of practice which they feel they can do properly (even though they often don't). Finally, there is a wide lack of knowledge in the public about the advances of pain control in palliative care and what can be done for dying

patients and this is obvious in looking at the media presentation of these problems.

5. Another attitude which blocks good pain control is the concept that a certain amount of cancer pain is inevitable, cannot be controlled, and simply is part of the terminal illness. This should not be accepted where modern medical care is available. As one of your Excellencies (from Central America, I believe) pointed out, in underdeveloped countries where modern palliative care does not exist, patients have a much high pain tolerance. It does not apply to individuals who have a very deep religious and spiritual approach to this problem and in the Christian tradition are prepared to suffer as Christ did as a way to greater salvation. Obviously, if this is the patients' path that they have chosen, the medical team should not interfere in spite of their misunderstanding of the basis of this approach.

6. Economic factors. This should not be a problem in Canada, or wherever there is universally available medical care but I am sure is a problem in many parts of the United States and other countries where proper funding of hospice and palliative care teams is not available to help patients die at home which, of course, is economically vastly different than hospitalization without insurance.

7. When children have pain, which is my area of experience, their complaints may be ignored due to the mistaken belief that children do not feel pain as adults do. Due to advances in knowledge and education, this is less true today, particularly in children's centres.

In closing this section, I should mention that it has been estimated that at least 70% of cancer patients at some point develop some type of pain and that, in general, outside of palliative care units and hospices about 25% of patients die with varying degrees of uncontrollable cancer pain. The generally quoted statistic in palliative care units and hospices is that less than 5% of patients cannot have their pain controlled with maintenance of consciousness and relative enjoyment of their last days. This difference in statistics simply emphasizes the comments made above about the challenge facing medical and nursing and other paramedical personnel education in this area. It has been estimated that less than 10% of dying cancer patients are treated in recognized palliative care units or programs. This means that 90% of people with terminal cancer, then, depend on the general medical and nursing community whose level of knowledge about palliative care and pain control varies widely. A second problem is, of course, that most Canadians, and Americans presumably, really don't know or understand what palliative care is, and don't know enough about it to ask for it or look for it when it might be the answer for themselves or their terminally ill relative. This emphasizes the tre-

190

mendous need for public education about this area as well as specific education in the health care fields. Another problem is that standardization of palliative care is difficult as in any new field, but is progressing well.

REPORT OF THE HUMAN LIFE RESEARCH INSTITUTE STUDY ON PALLIATIVE CARE PERSONNEL ATTENDING THE INTERNATIONAL PAIN CONFERENCE IN MONTREAL

Introduction

The Human Life Research Institute of which I am President, is comprised of academics and professors from various disciplines such as medicine, history, law, economics, as well as various religions, who conduct scholarly research on bioethical subjects that one doesn't see in the general academic press, e.g., the effectiveness of sex education, post-abortion psychological problems, sexual abuse, education, and euthanasia. This Institute, by the way, is quite similar to the Faculty for Life, which your Excellencies have supported and our two groups have met now on two occasions, thanks to the generosity of your support. We obtained a grant from a private foundation through the initiative of my own Bishop, John Sherlock, and we were able to conduct the study that is reported below. The main purpose of the study, from my point of view, was to document in a proper scientific scholarly way, what I already knew from my contacts in the palliative care field with regard to pain control, withdrawing treatment and mercy killing. Fortunately, a member of our Board, Professor Frank Henry from McMaster University Sociology Department, is an expert in designing and interpreting these questionnaires.

The object of this study, then, was to document attitudes of Health Care Givers of Terminal Patients regarding pain control, foregoing medical procedures, euthanasia, and other similar topics. Anonymous, self-completed mailed questionnaires were sent to a random sample of 545 (½) of 1049 North American registrants at the 1988 International Conference on Terminal Care in Montreal. This conference featured a major debate on euthanasia, which may be one reason for the 68% (372) returns which included 98 M.D.'s, 168 R.N.'s and 105 Social Workers, Psychologists, Chaplains and Volunteers.

A computer analysis showed, for example, that 75% of respondents believed that less than 5% of their patients had uncontrollable pain, and 84% felt that less than 5% of their patients' lives were shortened by pain medications. M.D.'s in general gave higher scores in this question than nurses. 70% believed patients could die comfortably without artificial hydration and nutrition. (Dying patients do not want intravenous feeding, but only oral fluids to keep their mouth wet. Actually, recent studies show that I.V. fluids may hasten death in these patients with end–stage organ failure. It is important to realize that this is not indirect or passive euthanasia as some Pro–Life people think.) 74% saw a difference between passive and active mercy killing, and 69% believed it was not ethical to directly end the life of a patient with 13% undecided. Older M.D.'s and R.N.'s with formal religious attachment were more opposed to active mercy killing, and more M.D.'s agreed with stopping all eight medical procedures listed (65%) than R.N.'s (47%) and others (43%). 70% of M.D.'s and 66% of R.N.'s replied that ending terminal patients' lives at their request should not be legalized, compared with 42% of other respondents (social workers, psychologist, volunteers, etc.)

We feel these results are vital information to consider in the growing public debate about the ethics of Terminal Care, since the respondents reflect the attitudes of those at the bedside of the dying patients. The Academy of Hospice Physicians comprised of doctors dedicated to palliative care also reported a questionnaire of 450 members who were 92% against legalizing active mercy killing and, of course, this supports the stand of the National Hospice Association. Another reason Palliative Care workers oppose mercy killing is that they see wonderful reconciliations at the end of life - such as Victor Frankl wrote of in "Man's Search for Meaning". This would be denied patients and families with aggressive mercy killing.

Dr. John Scott, a Minister and Doctor, and one of Canada's leading experts in Palliative Care has written of the "lament" of the dying - fearing abandonment, overtreatment, or undertreatment (of pain) wondering when they will die. This "cry for death" could be taken as a request for mercy killing, but is reallly a cry to live properly until they die. Dr. Scott has heard only rare requests for mercy killing, as I have heard from other experienced Palliative Care Doctors with thousands of terminal patients under their care over many years. Dr. Scott is afraid the mercy killing proponents will abuse Palliative Care in this way to their advantage.

RELATION OF THIS TOPIC TO THE SITUATION IN HOLLAND

Holland has become notorious for its widespread practice of active euthanasia (mercy killing) in terminal cancer patients. It is difficult to get an accurate picture of what's going on in Holland, particularly in later years since the Dutch Government and the Dutch medical profession are trying desperately to neutralize their image as a country where mercy killing is out of control. However, careful analysis of the Remmelink report which was an official government study along with many other reports and statements by Dutch medical authorities certainly paints a picture that would make one worry about a similar occurrence in other countries should legalized mercy killing occur. In fact, in Holland, of course, no law had been passed legalizing mercy killing but what has happened is that it has been widely practised and not prosecuted. Originally, Dutch physicians were required to report their acts of mercy killing to the prosecutor, who then had the option of bringing a legal action against them. Of course, this has never happened after two celebrated court cases where the physicians were exonerated and now, apparently, very few physicians are reporting their actions to the prosecutor and in many cases have admitted incorrectly filling out death certificates. For instance, indirect mercy killing, that is withdrawing treatment in order to terminate a patient's life, is not considered euthanasia, officially, in Holland, so there are no statistics concerning this practice, which is apparently widespread. We now know that over 90% of doctors in Holland do not report cases of mercy killing so the many figures we hear are obviously a gross under estimation. As far as cancer patients are concerned it was obvious that the widespread use of active mercy killing developed because there was no widely developed palliative care hospice care or pain control movements in Holland and active mercy killing by injection became an acceptable method of dealing with terminal cancer patients. In some hospitals up to 30 to 40% of cancer patients are killed this way, presumably with their own consent and request. Of course, one could understand that if there are no options and no attempted other forms of pain control that this might appear to be the only way out. This raises the question of whether, in the most expert and best palliative care or hospice care situations in England or North America, there is a place for active mercy killing and I suppose there might be an occasional case where it might be the only answer although I haven't personally been convinced of one. This is a different situation than the widespread movement that is happening in Holland that would happen in any state or any country where a law is passed to legalize this. I know personally of physicians who attempted to start hospice and palliative care in Holland, and have had very little encouragement and who have found patients fearful when they were approached for pain control, or cancer treatment, assuming they were going to be put to death. I know this is covered in another seminar but, obviously, this has now spread to many types of suffering, including mental illness, and is certainly looking very similar to the mercy killing movement in Germany in the early '30's which, of course, preceded for quite a long time the arrival of the Nazi Government which escalated mercy killing to genocide in Germany. (*The Globe and Mail*, Canada's national newspaper, reported that now that voluntary mercy killing is legal in Holland the Government plans to extend the indications to psychiatric and deformed patients. At a recent International Work Group on Death, Dying and Bereavement meeting in Portugal, physicians working in Holland confirmed that some senior citizens are carrying cards in their wallet saying "Don't Kill Me", and I also know from the brother of a physician in my home town, who runs a hospital in Holland, that in some areas senior citizens have had meetings and decided which hospital is safe. I think it is critical that the story in Holland be accurately documented and made public since this would be a very powerful antidote to the mercy killing movement in North America. I was encouraged to see a headline article in the *New York Times*, (Sunday, February 14, 1993, on Page 1 of Section 4 on the Dutch Parliament's approval of legalizing mercy killing). The subtitle of this article was *"The Powerless are More Afraid"*. Professor Dyck has already expanded on this subject and I will say no more).

In summary, I hope I have convinced you that with the knowledge and techniques available there is really no excuse for cancer patients to suffer severe pain, except in very unusual cases. I hope you can see the urgent need for widespread education of both health care personnel and the public with regard to the knowledge and research and publications in this field. When one hears of cases of terrible pain that should be candidates for mercy killing one can almost always assume that these patients need more narcotics but not a lethal dose.

If we cannot educate and convince the public and the health care professions about the effectiveness of palliative care then they will see legalized mercy killing as the only alternative. Also, hospices should be supported wherever possible since they prove a very economic and effective alternative to hospital care. In terms of communicating the Catholic vision of life, which is the title of your conference, I have always felt that hospice or palliative care is an ideal field for exemplifying the basic principles of Christian or Catholic care.

Another point that the Bishops should be aware of is the *Care for the Caregivers* concept. The health care personnel and volunteers working in the palliative care hospice setup are in a very intensive, stressful environment, and should be regularly monitored for signs of burnout through group meetings and support. It has been well shown that some of the main stresses of these units are not the patient

194

stresses, but trying to deal with one's fellow workers. On the other hand, palliative care and hospice workers usually have an extraordinarily good record of long service and small turnover, suggesting that the right type of people are attracted to this field. The Bishops might also be asked what training seminarians get in the concepts of palliative care and hospice care. I would be surprised if there is any major center now in North America that doesn't have some type of death education program. On a positive note, The Association for Death Education and Counselling has become a small but effective organization for education at all levels regarding palliative care and bereavement. Bereavement for survivors of a deceased patient is often neglected, but is a relatively inexpensive way to prevent major psychosocial problems in families, including serious mental and physical disease (mortality rates in widowers is ten times other groups in some age groups).

Solutions to these problems:

1. A greater effort in the health care professions to teach medical doctors, nurses and other professionals in the field about the current state of the art in pain control and palliative care. The palliative care curriculum for Canadian medical schools is a good example of a step in the right direction.

2. Massive public education as we saw in the Washington and California state legislation on mercy killing. As Richard Doerflinger pointed out it was the combined forces that put on the public education campaign along with the support of the Bishops that turned the tide in these states.

3. A more drastic solution has been proposed by Dr. Margaret Sommerville, Director of the McGill Center for Law and Ethics, who from personal experience and also extensive research and publication and speaking in this field, has concluded that doctors who allow patients to suffer severe pain should be sued for negligence. Although I hesitate to add any further impetus to the medical liability climate, this may be one dramatic way of educating doctors who are extremely conscious of legal threats. I believe there has already been one case in the United States where a doctor was sued for improper pain control.

4. To publicize the dark side of involuntary mercy killing in Holland, as contrasted with the official picture of safeguards and carefully controlled voluntary mercy killing.

Chapter 14

EUTHANASIA AND THE LAW: THE CALIFORNIA REFERENDUM

Julie Sly

Proposition 161, the California ballot initiative defeated this past November which would have legalized physician-assisted suicide, has energized a growing national debate over the morality of euthanasia.

Those who favored voluntary euthanasia for the terminally ill claimed that Proposition 161 was an extension of individual rights—the right to choose a painless and peaceful death. "People ought to be able to be architects of their own death," said one proponent, who described the choice as "a new civil right."[1]

Those who opposed physician-assisted suicide feared that laws such as Proposition 161 could make it too easy to end a life without agonizing about the significance of the act. As one opponent noted, "If we abolish terminal misery from our experience, we will foolishly hide an essential measure of our humanity."[2]

In the past two years, major euthanasia propositions—in the generally liberal states of Washington and California—although initially favored to win, have both met defeat. Yet, just two days after the defeat of Proposition 161, the *New England Journal of Medicine* published two opinion pieces by respected doctors at prestigious medical schools advocating physician-assisted suicide. And since November, we have seen legislative efforts to legalize euthanasia in a number of states.

Indeed, the stakes in the euthanasia debate are very high, because if one state legalizes physician-assisted suicide, many believe we will see other states adopting similar laws in a relatively short period of time.

In light of the present debate over the morality of euthanasia, I would like to review the recent efforts of the California Catholic Conference of Bishops, in conjunction with a broad coalition of groups, in working to defeat Proposition 161. I believe our experience will shed some light on current legislative and initiative battles, and have long-term implications for the euthanasia debate.

Background

Californians Against Human Suffering (CAHS), the political arm of the Hemlock Society in California, after failing to qualify an assisted suicide initiative for the ballot in 1988, sponsored Proposition 161. Beginning in October 1991, CAHS mounted a major campaign with paid signature gatherers and succeeded in gathering better than 10 percent more than the 385,000 valid signatures required. The measure qualified for the ballot on April 9, 1992. CAHS also hired Jack Nicholl, an experienced political consultant who helped guide a tobacco tax initiative to victory in 1988. The signature drive and the subsequent campaign were also boosted by the support of the state chapter of the National Organization for Women and the Gray Panthers.

What prompted some people to endorse such an initiative? Father Gerald Coleman of St. Patrick's Seminary in Menlo Park, Calif., a prominent theologian on medical-moral issues, has pointed to four significant factors:[3]

First, greatly influenced by the abortion debate's emphasis on the "right to choose," many people feel that we have the right to choose how and when we will die. Some people put it this way, "We should seek death before it finds us."

Second, the fear of dying is powerful. Today, even more powerful, is the fear of not dying—of being forced to endure destructive pain, or to live out a life of unrelieved, pointless suffering.

Third, self-gratification, economic pressures and a fear of being a burden to family and society urge some persons to request death.

Fourth, the fear of "high tech" medicine is pervasive—a shudder which creates in many people a profound anxiety that machines will keep me alive far beyond my desires or any reasonable measuring.

In Father Coleman's view, those who favored Proposition 161 and those who endorse euthanasia in general, do so for two clear philosophical reasons:

—To end a patient's suffering through euthanasia is a humane and charitable enterprise and it fits well with a physician's traditional role as alleviator of pain.
—The principle of autonomy suggests that freely consenting individuals—physicians and patients—should be relatively free to end a consenting patient's suffering by killing the patient.

The conclusion is that if a patient so chooses to end his or her life, and if a physician is a willing participant, then euthanasia is permissible.

SPECIFICS OF PROPOSITION 161

The questions posed by Proposition 161, with the ballot title, "Physician-Assisted Death. Terminal Condition," were these: Should terminally ill patients have a right to decide when and how they want to die? Should they have the right to ask their doctor to help them? Should there be a law protecting doctors who do so?

Even those who did not object to euthanasia in principle were opposed to this initiative because of its lack of adequate safeguards, its ambiguous language, its potential for malpractice claims, and the near impossibility of getting it amended once passed.[4]

There were many flaws in Proposition 161. Chief among them was the lack of adequate safeguards:

—There was no requirement for a psychological evaluation or counseling of the patient.
—There was no requirement for a waiting period between requests for euthanasia.
—There was no mention of pain and suffering as a criteria for euthanasia.

—There was no requirement for an exploration of alternatives to euthanasia.

—There was no requirement for notification of family, friends or loved ones.

—Any physician with a license could have certified terminal illness and performed euthanasia.

—There was no requirement that the physician have a previous relationship with the patient.

—Witnessing procedures were required when the directive was written, but no witnesses or other safeguards were required when the patient actually requested euthanasia or when the patient was put to death.

—Reporting of individual cases was to be done only annually and anonymously, making it all but impossible to monitor the process and detect abuses.

Finally, Proposition 161 could not be amended except by a two-thirds majority vote of both houses of the state Legislature. Since this is a highly unlikely possibility, Californians would have been stuck with a very flawed piece of legislation, not to mention the devastating implications for public and social policy if legalized euthanasia had passed.

STATEWIDE COALITION TO DEFEAT PROPOSITION 161

The California Catholic Conference of Bishops and its staff in Sacramento began working against the euthanasia initiative in the fall of 1991. After attending a briefing in Seattle early in 1992 by the opponents of Washington's Initiative 119, our staff at the CCC began immediately to work with the California Association of Catholic Hospitals and other organizations. In May, the coalition, called Californians Against the Euthanasia Initiative (and later, "No on 161"), incorporated and received its first contributions toward which the 12 dioceses in California contributed a total of $50,000. The coalition initially included organizations such as the St. Joseph Health System, the California Medical Association, the California Nurses Association, the State Commission on Aging, the state Hospice Association and the California Association of Hospitals and Health Systems.

The coalition screened and hired a well-known political consultant, Chuck Cavalier and Associates, as the primary consultant. The

Catholic Conference was instrumental in securing agreement to hire Bill Bannon and Associates to direct field operations, as they had been involved in the successful 119 campaign and had a long history of work with dioceses and pro-life organizations.

During the summer and fall, the coalition grew considerably, eventually having more than 160 organizations by election day, including some of the state's most respected groups, including the American Cancer Society and the American Lung Association. Many of these organizations simply lent their names to the opposition but were unable to contribute time or funding. The steering committee of the campaign, besides including representatives of the organizations just mentioned, included the California Pro-Life Council and the Scholl Institute for Bioethics.

The development and maintenance of this large and unusual coalition was remarkable in itself, given the diversity of the players. The strategy carried out by the coalition and its consultants included massive educational efforts through the printed and electronic media and the use of a far-flung field operation working with thousands of volunteers throughout the state. The campaign's emphasis was on Proposition 161's lack of safeguards, rather than on debating the merits or the morality of physician-assisted suicide, since early polling done by the coalition showed that the short-term campaign would not be won by engaging in this debate. The coalition also drew its strategy in part from the successful 119 campaign in Washington.

Polling done in March 1992 showed 74 percent of Californians in favor of 161, 24 percent opposed, and 2 percent undecided. Catholics polled no differently than the general public in supporting euthanasia. Polling conducted by the coalition at the end of June 1992 indicated that while 72 percent favored Proposition 161 at first reading, with very little direct education in the form of pointed questions, the support dropped to 51 percent and the opposition increased from 24 to 49 percent.

The process of educating 14 million voters about something such as Proposition 161 was very expensive. The coalition raised some $3.3 million to defeat Proposition 161, a dramatic reduction from the $5 to $8 million originally projected that was needed. In contract, the "Yes on 161" campaign raised more than $1 million.

Of the $3 million, about 65 percent was spent on direct voter contact, including literature, direct mail, electronic media and field operations. About 35 percent was spent on administration and overhead. Unfortunately, because fundraising failed to meet projections, the coalition was forced to direct nearly every available dollar toward its paid advertising campaign. As a result, the coalition ended the campaign with a deficit of approximately $100,000. (The deficit now stands at about $75,000.)

A majority of the coalition's funds came from Catholic sources, including approximately $1.5 million from the parish in-pew appeal (described later), $250,000 from the Catholic Health Association of the United States, $200,000 from the Knights of Columbus (national), and substantial contributions from the California Association of Catholic Hospitals, the St. Joseph Health System, individual California dioceses and individual Catholic hospitals.

Some of the coalition's efforts to defeat Proposition 161 included:

—*Paid advertising.* The coalition produced four television commercials. Two of them stressed the initiative's lack of safeguards. Two featured patients who were diagnosed as terminal but who remain alive years later, arguing that they might have asked for a lethal injection had Proposition 161 been in place. These commercials aired for four days prior to the election in the five major media markets in the state (the San Francisco-Oakland Bay Area, Sacramento, Los Angeles, San Diego and Fresno).

The measure's proponents had only about $55,000 to spend on radio ads aired in the final few days in Los Angeles and San Diego. In the radio campaign, they labeled opponents as a "group of powerful religious zealots" willing to distort the truth to get their way.

—*Free media.* Free media coverage was received through more than 100 interviews during the course of the campaign, and countless newspaper editorials opposing Proposition 161. Every major newspaper in the state editorialized against the measure—a rare occurrence—in most cases using language that virtually echoed the coalition's ballot arguments, fact sheets and literature.

Many newspapers and some television stations and networks also focused on the large financial contributions of the Catholic Church to the "No on 161" coalition. This was fueled in part by the proponents of 161, who used this as a tactic to divert the media from discussion of the real issues voters were facing. Great effort was taken in responding to media persons to clarify that this was not just a "Catholic" campaign.

—*Internal education.* Many coalition members made substantial efforts to educate their members about Proposition 161. Typical activities included mailings, newsletter articles, informational forums, grassroots activities and participation in the campaign speakers bureau.

—*Field activities*. These included a literature drop by volunteers of more than one million pieces during the final two weeks of the campaign, among the largest literature distribution programs ever conducted by a California ballot initiative campaign.

During the campaign, 100,000 lawn signs were distributed by campaign staff and volunteers. Again, this was among the largest activity of its kind in the history of initiative politics.

Suggested letters to the editor were distributed to more than 200 volunteers during the final weeks of the campaign and dozens of letters were published throughout the state.

—*Speaker's bureau*. The coalition's speaker's bureau provided trained speakers for hundreds of community engagements and forums throughout the state.

INTERNAL CATHOLIC CHURCH ACTIONS

As mentioned, the California Catholic Conference for the first time approved an in-pew solicitation in the 1,070 parishes in the state. In each parish, the pastor and/or celebrant on a designated Sunday spoke on Proposition 161, and parishioners received detailed information from a Catholic perspective.

Significantly, the California bishops, in a letter read from the pulpit by pastors, noted that "We are not attempting to impose morality. This is not a diocesan or parish collection. We prefer that moral issues be settled in the hearts of men and women. However, the issues allowing doctors to actively take the lives of people has been pushed into the public policy arena by proponents of the initiative, and this must be addressed and debated. Legislation may be passed which not only contradicts traditional Catholic morality, but also attacks the principles underlying our system of government and threatens the lives of the poor and powerless in our state."[5]

The California bishops approved the in-pew appeal in June 1992. The overall effort of the appeal was effective, but the shortness of time in preparing for the first attempts in some Northern California dioceses on July 26 led to difficulties. Unfortunately, the campaign was in need of money early on in order to stay alive. As the summer passed, there was more time for preparation, so the appeal went more smoothly and the returns were higher in the Southern California dioceses. We estimate that more than 150,000 Catholics donated to the in-pew appeal, totaling contributions of some $1.5 million.

The Conference staff also put together educational packets for each parish in the state as well as diocesan leaders, with specific and background materials on euthanasia and Proposition 161. The packets included homily notes, parish bulletin inserts (in Spanish and English) and a euthanasia study guide (for adults, high school and junior high students) adapted from the 1991 pastoral letter, "Living and Dying Well," by the bishops of Washington and Oregon.

During the summer of 1992, the Conference also brought together a few hundred diocesan leaders in northern and southern California in the first meeting of the Children and Families Council. One of the short-term goals of the council was to mobilize the Catholic community for the defeat of Proposition 161. The long-term goal, building on the U.S. bishops' campaign for children and families, is to continue to motivate people at the parish level to become politically active on a wide variety of issues.

ANALYSIS OF ELECTION RESULTS

Proposition 161 was fairly decisively turned down by California voters on Nov. 3 by a margin of 54 to 46 percent, even though the measure was in doubt up until the last days of the campaign. A month before the election, more than two-thirds of voters said they favored Proposition 161. The margin narrowed as the election approached, but movement became significant and the balance tipped only when television ads opposing the proposition appeared in the final days before the election.

Statewide, the measure won a majority of the vote in only 13 of California's 58 counties. In the critical counties of Los Angeles, San Diego and Orange, Proposition 161 won only 44.9, 47.8 and 41.7 percent of the vote, respectively.[6]

A post-election analysis done by the "No on 161" coalition's principal consultants[7] cited three main factors contributing to the defeat of Proposition 161:

> —*A well-developed message.* Polling showed that the coalition could beat Proposition 161 if, rather than debate the merits of assisted suicide, the coalition dramatized the initiative's lack of strong safeguards and enormous potential for abuse. Given 161's many flaws, this was both an effective and immensely practical strategy.

204

—A broad-based coalition opposing 161. Time and again the opposition attempted to portray the "No on 161" coalition as a group of "religious zealots" trying to impose their morals on the California public. With more than 160 of the state's most respected organizations opposing Proposition 161, the coalition successfully negated their argument.

—Proponents overestimated their support. With an astonishingly high level of early voter support for 161, proponents naively thought they could sit back and win the campaign without an aggressive grassroots, free media, speakers and paid media program. Quite simply, the coalition overwhelmed and outworked the opposition, forcing them to respond to our agenda. Toward the end of the campaign, many of their speakers were beginning to doubt themselves—several even remarked to coalition spokespersons that 161 was really "poorly written" and that they were expecting to lose.

According to the coalition's primary consultant, Chuck Cavalier, no other initiative campaign in California has ever trailed 74 percent to 24 percent and won by eight points on election day.[8]

Exit polls showed that the race for president was by far the most important to California voters. But second was Proposition 161; voters even saw it as more important than a series of other controversial contests, including Proposition 165 on welfare reform, the race between Barbara Boxer and Bruce Herschensohn for U.S. Senate, and Proposition 166, sponsored by the California Medical Association, to establish affordable basic health care coverage.

A "lack of safeguards" was cited by 43 percent of those voting "no" on the proposition. Another 30 percent opposed the measure because of moral or religious beliefs. Support for the proposition was based mainly on "right to choose" issues: 65 percent of "yes" voters said people have a right to die, and 12 percent cited as their reason an end to pain and suffering.

Significantly, a post-election poll conducted by the Tarrance Group noted that voters age 65 and older opposed Proposition 161 by a 64 to 36 percent margin. And women opposed it 60 to 40 percent.

According to Gayle Ensign, chairperson of the "No on 161" coalition and president of the California Association of Catholic Hospitals, "It became clear during the campaign that most Californians don't know their rights in end-of-life decisions.[9] A number of voters saw this as a 'pulling the plug' issue—which it certainly was not."

"Others saw it as a 'pain and suffering' issue. Intractable pain has no medical or spiritual value, and we have to increase our efforts to improve its control. Pain can and should be eliminated in virtually all patients—and if we do that it cannot be relevant to any initiative campaign."

The greater danger posed by Proposition 161, Ensign added, "is that it reflects a changing societal attitude that values life less. If so, our task will be more difficult but the stakes higher—today's 'terminally ill' will expand to include tomorrow's 'chronically ill.' "

"The proponents of Proposition 161 are committed and sincere," Ensign concluded. "We can expect more attempts to legalize physician-assisted deaths. We can feel good about winning an important battle— but the war is not over."

OUTLOOK FOR THE FUTURE

With California voters' rejection of Proposition 161, some could easily conclude that the issue of legalized euthanasia is dead. But this would be a grievous error for a number of reasons. It is well known, for example, that the Hemlock Society is gearing up to introduce physician-assisted suicide measures in other states, including Oregon, New Hampshire and once again in Washington. Should they be successful, it is highly likely that a similar measure will qualify for some future California ballot, perhaps as early as 1994.

In fact, California Hemlock leaders have publicly vowed to try again, and have also said they will draft a stronger measure for the Legislature to consider. Proponents of Proposition 161 have also said that they do not believe revising their measure to add more safeguards is the key to winning next time. Instead, educating voters and calming fears raised—primarily through small group discussions—might be more effective.

Derek Humphry, in an article after the California vote,[10] said that undoubtedly Hemlock would try an initiative again on the West Coast. "I am ready to see the death with dignity issue put to a public vote again and as soon as possible," he wrote. "Our wish is that our efforts would spur the medical profession and patients' rights groups to sit down together and work out a mutually acceptable way in which the dying can die, decently and lawfully. Even better would be if President Clinton called a 'president's commission' to investigate the entire right-to-die disaster, which modern medicine has landed us in, and come up with considered proposals which politicians can embrace."

It is clear that the so-called right-to-die debate will continue to rage within the mainstream medical community, despite vows by

206

groups such as the California Medical Association to defuse the issue by helping doctors develop more compassionate care for the terminally ill.

It would be a mistake for those involved in the "No on 161" coalition in California and those opposed to euthanasia across the country to simply rest on their laurels and ignore these facts. Now more than ever, a widespread campaign to educate the public about their rights as patients and about the dangers of legalized euthanasia is absolutely necessary. Clearly, many Californians, although they voted no on 161, made the decision without adequate understanding or reflection on the clear moral distinction between active and passive voluntary euthanasia.

Indeed, as ethicist Corrine Bayley noted during the campaign,[11] "the cry for euthanasia is most often a cry for help that can and should be met in other ways. Continuing to draw a bright line between euthanasia and justifiable refusal of treatment, as the Catholic Church does, is extremely important. If we do not see the difference now, we will see it only when it is too late."

The pragmatic arguments used in defeating Proposition 161—such as those voiced by cancer survivors who testified that life is worth fighting for, by hospice professionals meeting the needs of the dying every day, and by medical experts who argued that pain can be controlled—may provide the best grounds on which to fight the ongoing legislative battles.

To most people, these arguments are the strongest and most convincing. And people on both sides of the right to die issue should be able to agree on addressing the basic issue that surrounds this dilemma—how we treat patients at the end of life. At the same time, we must remember that these pragmatic arguments will not be convincing unless the public begins to see, and more important, to experience compassionate care and health care environments that are more sympathetic to the needs of terminally ill patients and their families.

Finally, we must continue to stress that while sufficient safeguards can always be added to measures such as Proposition 161 to make them better law, these measures will never be good social policy, nor good morality.[12] We cannot introduce a radical social change on behalf of very few people that would erode trust between physicians and patients, and divert attention away from improving the care, comfort and compassion provided for and desired by the vast majority of the dying.

As 13 Jewish and Christian theologians, philosophers and legal scholars noted after the defeat of Initiative 119 in Washington state, "we must relearn the wisdom that teaches us always to care, never to kill. . . Once we cross the boundary between killing and allowing to die, there will be no turning back."[13]

NOTES

1. Statement by Margaret P. Battin, University of Utah philosophy professor, in "Initiative Ignites Debate Over Morality of Euthanasia," by Paul Jacobs, *The Los Angeles Times,* Oct. 31, 1992, page A20.

2. Statement by Albert R. Jonsen, University of Washington bioethicist, in *The Los Angeles Times,* Oct. 31, 1992.

3. "Physician-Assisted Suicide," column by Father Gerald D. Coleman, S.S., July 13, 1992.

4. "Why We Should Vote No on Proposition 161," paper prepared by Corrine Bayley, Center for Healthcare Ethics, St Joseph Health System, July 1992.

5. Joint letter to parishioners by the Catholic bishops of California, July 1992.

6. Confidential final report on "No on 161," prepared by Cavalier and Associates, Dec. 12, 1992.

7. Final report by Cavalier and Associates, page 4.

8. Final report by Cavalier and Associates, page 8.

9. Quote by Gayle Ensign in California Association of Catholic Hospitals newsletter, *Networking,* Fall 1992, page 1.

10. Derek Humphry, "Death with Dignity Effort May Be Tried Here Again," *The San Francisco Chronicle,* Nov. 13, 1992, p. 25.

11. "Catholic Teaching on Euthanasia," by Corrine Bayley, Center for Healthcare Ethics, St. Joseph Health System, August 1992.

12. "A Closer Look at Physician-Assisted Suicide," article by Father Gerald D. Coleman, S.S., August 1992.

13. "Always to Care, Never to Kill," statement by 13 Jewish and Christian theologians, philosophers and legal scholars, *The Wall Street Journal,* Nov. 17, 1991.

Chapter 15

EFFECTIVE WAYS OF COUNTERING ABORTION TODAY

Dolores Bernadette Grier

Good afternoon. Your Eminence, Your Excellencies, it is a privilege and an honor for this convert to the Roman Catholic faith to be invited to speak at this The Twelfth Workshop for Bishops of the Caribbean, Canada, Central America, the United States, Mexico and the Philippines meeting here in Dallas, Texas with the theme *Communicating the Catholic Vision of Life*.

I have been asked to address the topic of "Effective Ways of Countering Abortion" or, if you will, "Winning the War Against Abortion." May God be praised and the Shepherds pleased.

Since 1973, when the United States Supreme Court legalized abortion with the Roe vs Wade Decision, we have been at war in a battle to save unborn children in their mother's womb from death by abortion against the enemy (pro-abortionists) who defends the so called right of a woman to choose the life or death of her unborn child.

On the front page of the Washington Post on Friday, January 22, 1993, a caption read—"America's Longest War" followed by this report— "Twenty years ago the U.S. Supreme handed down the monumental ruling that made abortion legal nationwide and *incited a war* that has shut down legislatures, divided political parties and splintered families. Strife over the issue has been so bitter and sustained that the only comparison which comes close is the country's conflict on race." The news article, however, did not mention the hundreds of Catholics who have become confused on the issue and are at odds with the teachings of their Roman Catholic faith.

Our Holy Father, Pope John Paul II, when addressing Americans on October 7, 1979 in Washington, D.C. stated— "all human life from the moment of conception and through all subsequent stages is sacred because human life is created in the image and likeness of God. Nothing surpasses the greatness or dignity of a human person. If a person's right to life is violated at the moment in which he is first conceived in his mother's womb, an indirect blow is struck also at the whole moral order."

True Roman Catholics have adhered to the directives of Our Holy Father with regard and respect for God's fifth commandment—"Thou shall not kill". *Catholic hypocrites* (members of the Roman Catholic faith who remain in the family but are disobedient to the head) succumb to political expediency and personal greed labeling themselves *pro-choice,* the "comfort zone" position, to shun any alliance to the death act of abortion. *Abortion* is defined in Webster's Medical Dictionary as "the termination of a pregnancy resulting in the *death* of a developing human." Regrettably the deceptive rhetoric of the pro-abortion army has confused and manipulated too many Roman Catholics into this "pro-choice" position. To name a few—"Catholics For a Free Choice," Pamela Moraldo, R.N., President of Planned Parenthood, Catholic medical doctors who disregard part of the Hippocratic Oath . . . "I will not give to a woman an abortive remedy" to become dealers in death instead of restorers of health, Catholic legislators who hide behind "personally opposed" and "pro-choice" (. . . if a Catholic must renounce what he or she believes in conscience in order to be elected to public office, then we are back to the days of "no Catholic need apply"—John Cardinal O'Connor)

Yes, we are at war. Who is at war? There is, of course, the *Pro-Life Movement*—haphazardly established, functioning without leadership, without focus, without training and organization, without funds and lacking in unity. Concerned people living their faith by endeavoring to combat society's promotion of a death ethic. Although not prepared for the battle in defense of life, nonetheless they have proudly served

God, the Creator of life. These courageous and dedicated volunteers who joined the pro-life movement are youth, homemakers, high school and college students, mothers, grandmothers, grandfathers, retirees, Religious Sisters and Brothers, seminarians, clergy, pro-life groups, anti-abortion organizations and many others. The are out on the battlefield to save unborn children from death by abortion.

As stated by my Shepherd, His Eminence, John Cardinal O'Connor—"Thus it can happen through the creative power of God's own mysterious love for each one of us that every child, *born or unborn*, wanted or unwanted, with or without limbs, hearing or sight, nurtured lovingly or horrifyingly battered, becomes something beautiful for God and someone extraordinarily beautiful for everyone of us, their brothers and sisters in the Lord." These soldiers for life have been on the battlefield, at the abortion centers involved in sidewalk counseling and leading prayer vigils or blocking entrances to the abortion chambers; they have been coordinating workshops and conferences to inform and update us on the abortion issue from the legal, medical and social perspectives; they have been operating pregnancy crisis centers, residences for unwed mothers and post abortion syndrome programs. They have been distributing pro-life literature and lobbying legislators with letter writing campaigns. Some have operated thrift shops, coordinated bake sales or bazaars to raise funds to purchase layettes or to publish pro-life newsletters and others travel near and far to respond to speaking engagements. Millions of pro-life people have paraded in the annual March For Life on January 22nd in Washington, D.C. with babies and banners to bear witness to their defense of all human life from the womb to the tomb, but especially the innocent life of the unborn children responding with compassion to curses, criticism and confrontation of the pro-abortion army.

Although the pro-life movement has been defending the cause for LIFE for almost twenty years, there has been only a minimum of legislative success. For example, in twenty years we have not attained a national protection bill for minor girls seeking an abortion (Parent Consent/Parent Notification). Girls under eighteen years of age who are not permitted to purchase alcohol or cigarettes are allowed to buy an abortion *without parental involvement* which is an invasive surgical operation involving the administering of medication and anesthesia. Adults today obtain a second and third opinion before surgery, yet minor girls' immature bodies are subjected to the unnecessary (no pathology) invasive surgery of abortion to stop the heartbeat and dismember the body of the developing human living and growing in their womb. The rights and responsibility of parents are usurped, thus there is no medical history provided and the pregnancy terminator (doctor) is not accountable to anyone. Since there are no follow-up post surgery visits, what of post abortion complications such as damaged cervix or uterus, infection, incomplete abortion (parts of the baby's body left in the womb), transmission of AIDS or sterilization? What happens if the minor daughter dies? Who would be notified? Where would the body be sent? Will the pregnancy terminator or staff member blackmail the girl to keep her "secret" abortion secret? And why is this surgery not performed in a hospital where emergency equipment is immediately available? Parents are legally responsible for the overall health of their children including medical, surgical and dental. Teenage girls are completely dependent on their parents for every facet of their lives, there should be *no exception* in the circumstance of the invasive surgery of abortion.

Thus the pro-life cause is desperately in need of revolution with focus on the leadership and legislative action.

And then there is the enemy—*The Pro-Abortion Army.* The star professionals of the pro-abortion army are 1) *The Legislators,* 2) *The Doctors of Medicine* and 3) *The Media*—trained, focused, financed and organized to "keep abortion legal" and to promote and support an ethic of death from the womb (*abortion*) to the tomb (*euthanasia.*) The pro-abortion special interest groups such as NOW (National Organization of Women), NARAL (National Abortion Rights Action League) and the National Women's Political Caucus unite their forces and focus *only* on "keeping abortion legal." The political power of these special interest groups was seen on January 22, 1993 two days after his election to the presidency of the United States of America when President Clinton signed into law two pro-abortion bills (Fetal Research and the "GAG" rule). This political power of the Pro-Abortion Army is continually flaunted at the Pro-Life Movement.

Pro-Abortion Army

1. The Legislators

The *Legislators* are elected by voters, paid by voters' taxes—but not held accountable. These lawmakers have granted permission to the medical doctors to kill unborn human beings legally. His Eminence, Cardinal O'Connor, writes in his column *"From My Viewpoint"* in *Catholic New York,* a special edition on abortion—"Some people argue that changing laws will not eliminate abortions. What is forgotten, however, is that the law is the great teacher. Children grow up believing that if a practice is legal, it must be moral. Adults who live in a society in which what was illegal and believed to be immoral is suddenly declared legal, soon grow accustomed to the new law and take the "new morality" for granted. Many fear that if they do not support the new law and the "new morality" it has introduced, they will be considered un-democratic and un-American."

Thus the lawmakers, members of the U.S. Congress and the U.S. Supreme Court legislate human behavior and structure society by law. They are the key to changes in the law, for example—a Human Life Amendment to the U.S. Constitution which would halt the death act of abortion on demand in this nation. The late Rev. Martin Luther King, Jr. preached that "laws cannot make a man love me but it will keep him from lynching me." A Human Life Amendment would control the behavior of the so-called doctors of medicine who have stooped to destroying human life in the womb instead of delivering new life into the world. The doctors of medicine, like the dealers of drugs, are death merchants who receive astronomical amounts of money to destroy human life. However, although people are protected from dope peddlers, there is no protection for unborn children who are alive and growing in the mother's womb. Why? Because of their residence, the womb, and *the law.*

Until 1973 when the U.S. Supreme Court by a 7 to 2 ruling said "legal personhood does not exist prenatally" and that the unborn child is not entitled to legal protection of his or her life, the child in the womb was protected by law regardless of age and could inherit or qualify for social security benefits.

2. *The Medical Doctors*

Medical Doctor is described in Webster's dictionary as a "person skilled in the art of healing, a doctor of medicine." It describes "doctoring" as "to treat wounds or sickness of body, to practice medicine."

Webster's Medical dictionary defines *abortion* as "the termination of a pregnancy resulting in the death of a developing human."

When a doctor of medicine chooses for personal greed and monetary gain to kill human life by abortion, a Jekyll and Hyde personality is revealed: The transformation of a Jekyll doctor of medicine to a Hyde doctor–terminator of pregnancy.

According to the law, only a doctor of medicine may perform an abortion. Before the U.S. Supreme Court decision in 1973—Roe vs Wade—legalized abortion-on-demand, a doctor of medicine was fined and imprisoned for committing the crime of performing an abortion. Unlike other professionals, the doctor of medicine practices in the "privacy" of his office with more professional autonomy. The phrase "solo practice" is frequently used in describing the practice of medicine. Thus the killing of unborn children by the doctor terminator is executed in privacy without accountability. The physical damage to the woman's body is not known but we do know that with steel instruments the doctor-terminator invades the pregnant woman's body, crushes the head and dismembers the body of the child in the womb. This is the only invasive surgery where the doctor has not seen or examined the patient first and where there are no post surgery follow-up visits. A doctor usually does not subject a patient to the risk of complications and the possibility of death in surgery unless it is believed that the operation will heal the patient's pathological condition. Being pregnant is not a pathological condition and does not require surgery. When metal or plastic instruments are brought into contact with the tissues of the vagina, cervix and uterus, inadvertent injury to internal organs could happen during the invasive surgery of an abortion.

What drives a doctor of medicine to stoop to killing unborn human beings? Personal greed, money and materialism—thirty pieces of silver? In the case of Dawn Ravenell, a fifteen year old pregnant girl from Brooklyn who died from complications of an abortion, it was noted in the media that her boyfriend paid $450 for the thirty minute surgical operation. At $900 an hour for a seven hour day the pregnancy terminator receives over $6,000 a day and over $30,000 for a five day week. A doctor of medicine turns to being a dealer in death for thirty pieces of silver, truly a JUDAS.

More than 25 million abortions have been performed by doctors of medicine in the United States of America since the 1973 U.S. Supreme Court Decision legalizing death by abortion. This is more than twenty times the combined number of Americans who died in the Civil War, World War I, World War II and the Vietnam War.

And when does LIFE begin. . . . Science has determined that at conception a new individual comes into being, possessing a unique genetic code that has already determined the individual's sex, fingerprints, hair, eye color and facial features (*Rites of Life: The Scientific Evidence for Life Before Birth*, Zondervan, 1983).

For 125 years the American Medical Association took a firm anti-abortion position declaring in 1859 that abortion is the "un-warranted destruction of human life." In 1871, the AMA denounced doctors of medicine who would perform abortion as "false to their professions, false to principle, false to honor, false to humanity, false to God."

214

(S. Krason, *Abortion:Politics, Morality and the Constitution*, Maryland University Press of America, 1984, pg. 80). However in 1989, the American Medical Association changed and called an abortion a "fundamental right" to be decided free of state interference in the absence of compelling justification (American Brief, American Medical Association-Webster vs Reproductive Health Services, U. S. Supreme Court).

The World Medical Association in 1948 adopted a new physician's code, the Declaration of Geneva, which states: "I will maintain the utmost respect for human life, from the time of conception." This declaration was reaffirmed in the 1970 Declaration of Oslo (World Health Association Bulletin, Vol. 1—1949). Six weeks after its first beginning, the embryo has a well formed body. It is very much alive and can even execute some movements with its arms. It has a heart that has been beating for two weeks. It has a brain and nervous system sending out impulses. It has the outlines of a complete though still soft skeleton and all the vital organs, some of them practicing their functions. On close examination, it is already possible to know whether this embryo is a boy or a girl. The forty day old embryo has fulfilled one sixth (40% of the 266 days) of the normal stay in the womb (Geraldine Lux Flanagan, "First Nine Months of Life" Simon and Shuster, New York 1962).

"Increasingly, as medical technology makes the fetus more and more accessible to pediatric surgeons, perceptions of the fetus may well change", states Rev. Richard McCormick of the Kennedy Institute of Ethics at Georgetown University. Already I hear the doctors involved in this refer to the fetus as their *patient*. The fetus now begins to make serious claim for a right to protection, to nutrition. How can tolerance of abortion be morally reconciled with those claims?" (*The Unborn Child as a Patient*, Jeanne Dalton, *N.Y. Times*—1982)

Dr. John Fletcher, a bioethicist at the National Institute of Health, applauds the dawn of fetal surgery and recognizes that "improvements in fetal therapy will establish a stronger ground *to protect the affected fetus' right to life and will collide with abortion practices (The Unborn Child as a Patient*, Jeanne Dalton, *N.Y. Times* 1982).

Advances in science have opened the womb, once hidden, and now we may observe through the technology of ultra-sound movements the growth of the child in the womb. Surgeons are performing corrective surgery and administering medication, electrocardiograms and blood transfusions to the unborn child.

Pro-abortionists deceive themselves and others by describing the child as a "FETUS." This medical term may be found in Webster's

Medical Dictionary with the definition, "a developing human." In other medical dictionaries the definitions are: "a child in the uterus," "a developing individual," "an unborn child." Medical terms are used by physicians, nurses and medical personnel, but in 1973 when the killing in the womb was legalized, the medical term FETUS was introduced to the general public to demean the humanness of the unborn child and his right to life.

Fetal experimentation and fetal implantation are not as offensive as child experimentation and child implantation.

3) The Media

The media, electronic and printed, promotes the pro-abortion army's propaganda with media manipulation and verbal engineering while ignoring the pro-life movement.

Propaganda is related to an attempt on the part of somebody to manipulate somebody else. By manipulate we mean to control, not only to control the attitudes of others but also their actions. Somebody (or some group) is predisposed to cause others to think a certain way. Propaganda then is the effort by which an initiating communicator intends to manage the attitudes and actions of others through playing on their pre-existing biases with messages designed to appeal to their emotions. The propagandist does not want his audience to analyze or to think seriously about his messages. Nor does he want to be questioned or forced to deal in specifics.

In the media, opinion is frequently disguised as fact and misleading headlines can be used to propagandize effectively because "by and large people come away from a story with the substance of the headline, not the story, in their minds" (J. C. Merrill and R. C. Lowenstein, *Media Messages and Men*, McKay & Co. 1971, pg. 214). When the pro-life movement through its educational and informational programs and publications enlightened the public to what an abortion is and that the so-called "blob of flesh" is after all a developing human with a heartbeat and brain waves, alive and growing in the mother's womb, the pro-abortion army responded with a woman's right to choose whether or not to kill her unborn child by abortion. The word pro-choice was introduced and the pro-abortion media promoted it.

Regrettably, a majority of people in America use the television as a primary source for information and news. Robin Day, in his article "Troubled Reflection of a Television Journalist," writes "the fact is that

216

television's dependence on pictures makes it not only a powerful means of communication but a crude one which tends to strike at the emotions rather than the intellect. Television means concentration on action rather than thought, on happenings rather than issues, on shock rather than explanation, on personalities rather than ideas" (*Encounter*, May 1970).

"In America, one could say that the press has as it main social function (its concept) basically to *inform*, to *interpret*, to *lead*, and to *entertain*. Another function traditionally held by the American press is that of community and national leadership which exerts influence and affects people's opinions and actions" (J. Merrill, *Media Messages and Men*, 1971).

The media has shown by its unjust and biased journalism, regarding the Roman Catholic Church's strong defense of LIFE that it is no longer objective in reporting the issue of abortion to the people.

Verbal engineering—half-truths and misinformation have contributed to the confusion, coercion and control of too many soldiers of LIFE who now seek the "comfort zone" position of pro-choice.

Thus the pro-life movement has not been successful in their battles for anti-abortion legislation, specifically a Human Life Amendment which would bring a complete halt to abortion-on-demand. The pro-life movement has focused on overturning the 1973 Roe vs Wade Supreme Court Decision and on legislation with compromises (Parent Consent-Notification) and *exceptions* (rape, incest). This has only confused the people in the parish pews because the sacredness of human life created in the image and to the likeness of God is being reduced to circumstances. What is desperately needed now is leadership, effective, vigorous pastoral leadership by the Shepherds of the church: Strategic planning, organizing the parishioners in the pews as a unified force for the Respect Life Cause, Parish Prayer Crusades for a Human Life Amendment, basic education on the unborn child and abortion, the teachings of the church on this issue. Persuasive preaching is essential in reaching the parishioner in the pews every Sunday. They must hear frequently and firmly the words of our Holy Father, Pope John Paul II: "all human life is sacred, a precious gift from God. And so we will stand up every time that human life is threatened. When the sacredness of life is attacked, we will stand up and proclaim that no one has the authority to destroy unborn life" (Pope John Paul II speaking in Capital Mall in Washington, D.C.).

The Roman Catholics in the parish pews must be informed and prepared and then led into battle by their Shepherd. The flock in the pews have not been invited to join the Respect Life Cause, the time is now, Shepherds of the Church—the time is now!

Suggested action—**POWER!**

Prayer Power—the basics, weekly novena, monthly holy hour, and parish rosary crusade for the *Respect Life Cause.*

Parish Political Power.

Voter Registration—every member of parish 18 years of age and over should be a registered voter. *Voter Education*—know your local, state and Congressional representatives. *Parish Lobbying Committee Members*—visit legislatures bringing a list of registered voters in the parish and discuss pro-life legislation. Support members of parishes who choose to run for public office and are pro-life.

Voter Power—as a citizen of the United States we have the privilege of voting for those you would like to run the government, as a Christian we have the responsibility to do so. At a time in this nation's history when the economy is in crisis, thousands and millions of dollars are being expended by political candidates to procure votes. What power is in the hands of the VOTERS.

The voter elects and re-elects legislators who will be the administrators of the government and once in charge, control how the government is run.

The participation of the voter in politics must not be shunned or dismissed but the powerful influence of the vote emphasized. In selecting legislators—and judges—voters must review thoroughly the candidate's performance in government and his/her position on issues that concern the family, the unemployed, the elderly, the youth, the homeless, the criminals and the victims of crime, and the unborn. To become informed, the voter should read the newspapers, listen carefully to the radio, watch and listen carefully to television announcements, interviews and debates, attend open meetings where the candidates will speak and ask questions of them.

As a registered voter, the citizen makes his/her voice heard through the power of the vote for the legislators; and through the power of the pen when writing to the legislators.

Pulpit Power—the Shepherds could hold clergy days for Pastors and associate Pastors to urge them to preach on the Respect Life Cause informing, enlightening and directing the parishioners thoroughly and firmly. "Thou shall not kill" is not a suggestion, it is a commandment of God. The killing of unborn children is a sin against God and not debatable. *Media action,* letters to editors, OP-ED articles, call–in radio programs, pro-life articles for organization newsletters and other publications are effective action.

I close with the words of our Holy Father, Pope John Paul II: "America, your deepest identity and truest character as a nation is revealed in the position you take toward the human person. The ultimate test of your greatness is the way you treat every human being but especially the weak and most defenseless ones" (*The Human Person God's Greatest Blessing: Pope John Paul In America—1987*).

I am grateful for your attention. May God be praised and the Shepherds pleased. Amen.

APPENDIX

CHANCERY OFFICE

VICE CHANCELLOR FOR COMMUNITY RELATIONS

Archdiocese of New York

1011 First Avenue • New York, NY 10022 • (212) 371-1000

March 5, 1993

Mrs. Annie B. Martin
President
N.Y.Branch - NAACP
144 West 125 Street
New York, NY 10027

Dear Mrs. Martin:

Congratulations on your appointment to the National Board of the NAACP. As you stated in our telephone conversation, you make history by becoming the first woman from the New York City Branch to be so honored.

I write to thank you for considering me to receive the New York City Branch of the NAACP's Women History Month Award for 1993. However, I am unable to accept this prestigious award since the National Board of the NAACP supports a pro-abortion/pro-choice position. As president of the Association of Black Catholics Against Abortion and Board Member of the African American Society Against Abortion, I believe abortion to be a racist weapon of genocide against Black people. Black women never demanded nor demonstrated for the so-called right to have their unborn children, living and growing in the womb, killed by abortion. It has been thrust upon Black women as the solution to their economic crises, confusion and concern. The white women's movement, **NOW, NARAL,** etc., are dictating to Black people what is best for us - death instead of life.

It is to be noted that the persuasive preaching of the Rev. Jesse Jackson brought me into the pro-life movement in 1979. At that time, Rev. Jackson stated "Human beings cannot give or create life by themselves, it is really a gift from God. Therefore, one does not have the right to take away through abortion that which he does not have the ability to give."

The late Rev. Martin Luther King, Jr. said, "....there comes a time when one must take a position that is neither safe, nor politic, nor popular but because conscious tells one it is right." I regrettably decline your 1993 Women's History Award because conscience tells me it is right.

With prayerful best wishes, I am

Sincerely in God, Our Father,

Dolores Bernadette Grier
Vice Chancellor for Community Relations

219

PART THREE

POPULATION QUESTIONS

Chapter 16

POPULATION QUESTIONS: FACTUAL STUDIES AND CONTEMPORARY DEBATES

Jacqueline Kasun, Ph.D.

When students enter my classes at Humboldt State University these days there are some things they are sure they already know. One thing they are all sure they know is that the consensus of so-called scientific opinion is that a crisis of overpopulation and environmental degradation is threatening the very survival of planet earth. In fact, there is no such scientific consensus. No reasonable person would deny

---

*The content of this essay is based on that of a pamphlet Prof. Kasun wrote, *Population and Environment: Debunking the Myths* (Population Research Institute; P.O. Box 2024; Baltimore, MD 21298-9559. Tel. 301-670-1864).

that we have problems of pollution, but this is a far different thing from the ecological catastrophe that so many of my students have been taught to fear.

One reason why it has been so easy for interested parties to persuade my students—and many other people throughout the world—that we face a crisis of overpopulation and environmental destruction is that we all know we are crowded. With 3000 persons per square mile, the city of Dallas is half again as crowded as Bangladesh. To quote a famous authority: "the world is . . . full, and the population is too large for the soil."[1] Another famous thinker has decried "our teeming population. Our numbers are burdensome to the world, which can hardly support us. . ."[2] These men, however, were not speaking about Dallas or San Francisco or New York in our time but about Carthage and Rome almost two thousand years ago. Neither of these men could soar over their cities, as I just have, and see that outside of their immediate view there were vast empty spaces with almost no people at all. Human beings crowd together, now as in ages past, not because of lack of space on the planet but because we need to work together, to buy and sell, to give and receive services from one another. Our cities and towns have always thronged with people and traffic—horses, donkeys, and camels in ages past, motor vehicles today.

If all of the people in the world moved into the state of Texas, each person could be given the space available in the typical American home and all the rest of the world would be empty[3]. The population density of this giant city would amount to about 20,000 persons per square mile; San Francisco has about 16,000 persons per square mile, inner London has about 20,000, and Brooklyn has more than 30,000[4]. Most of the earth is still empty, as we can see when we fly over it. It is estimated that the area occupied by human beings amounts to no more than 1 percent of the earth's land surface.[5]

My students are very surprised when I show them how rapidly the rate of world population growth is declining. In Europe and the United States fertility has been below replacement for almost two decades and population is declining in several countries. The birth rate in the United States fell 3 percent between 1990 and 1991 and the number of births fell by 2 percent. Relative to their numbers, women of childbearing age are having little more than half as many babies as they did in the late 1950s.[6]

If present declining trends continue, the less developed regions of the world will reach zero population growth well before the end of the next century. The crude birth rate in Mexico fell from 45 in 1965 to 29 in 1987, or by 36 percent, and is still declining. The annual rate of population growth in Asia fell from an estimated 2.3 percent in 1970 to 1.9

in 1990; in Latin America it fell from 2.9 in 1970 to 2.1 in 1990; though the rate of natural increase in Africa is estimated to have risen by three-tenths of a percentage point, the estimates for that continent have proved to be highly unreliable. In 1991, for example, the most careful census ever carried out in Nigeria found fewer than 90 million people, compared with the more than 122 million previously estimated by the Population Reference Bureau.[7] Several countries in Asia, including Singapore, Malaysia, and Japan, have become concerned about their low levels of fertility and the resulting aging of their populations, and are developing policies to deal with these trends.[8] The World Bank's projection of the ultimate population of the world is about 10 billion, about twice its present size. At that level of population, human beings may occupy 2 percent of the earth's land surface, and we might use a fifth of the land area for our crops; at present farmers use less than half of the available arable land.[9]

Not only do farmers use only a fraction of the world's arable land, they also use the available agricultural resources at only a fraction of their productive capability. Roger Revelle, former director of the Harvard Center for Population Studies, has estimated that the less-developed continents, those whose present food supplies are most precarious, are capable of feeding 18 billion people, or six times their present population.[10] War and socialism, not overpopulation, are the reasons for the mass starvation found in so many countries. Bandits stole the food raised by Somalian families. In Ethiopia, soldiers seized not only the food but the draft animals as well. In China, India, and Mexico, as well as the former Soviet Union, the government appointed itself as the only buyer of food crops, paying farmers less than the cost of their inputs. The result was tragically low food output. In all cases, when the government raised the price, farm output greatly increased. Nevertheless, in spite of war and socialism, world food output *per person* has increased about 25 percent in the past quarter century.[11] There truly is no economic reason for anyone on earth to go hungry.

There are other matters which are of even greater concern to my students. One of these is "deforestation." Not long ago, a speaker came to campus to tell them "Since 1950 we've lost half of the earth's forests." Several weeks earlier an exhibit in the library had carried the same message. In fact, the most recent United Nations data—these are the most authoritative figures we have—show that the world forested area of 4 billion hectares, or more than 30 percent of the world land area, in 1988 was the same as the 4 billion hectares in 1950. Lester Brown of Worldwatch, an organization dedicated to spreading environmental alarm, reports that "in 76 tropical countries. . . . 11 million hectares of forests are being cleared each year." What he does not report is that there are some two to three *billion* hectares of forest in these areas, depending on how one defines "closed" and "open" forests and "other formations."[12] His numbers, if true, amount to only six-tenths of one percent of the total, at most. The U.S. Agency for International Development in the Department of State has climbed onto the "global deforestation" bandwagon. The Agency urgently needs support for its unpopular program of requiring countries receiving U.S. foreign aid to reduce their birthrates;[13] it may be courting the environmental movement for that reason. It claims that only 1 billion hectares of tropical forests are left (compared with the 2 billion estimated by the Food and Agriculture Organization) and has published the threat that at present rates of cut, they could be "gone entirely by the end of the next century."[14] This calamity would require, however, not only that trees be cut twice as fast as even Lester Brown estimates but that *no trees grow* over the next century.

About 30 percent of the land area of the United States is covered with forests and woodlands. This area has not changed significantly since 1920, but the annual volume of timber growth has more than tripled over this period and significantly exceeds the rate of timber cut. Far from denuding our forests we are actually building up our inventories of standing timber.[15]

I live in the giant redwood country of northern California. Last year the television and newspapers were reporting that the redwoods are disappearing as the lumber companies cut the last of them down. In fact, however, there are about 2 million acres of redwoods in California.[16] More than 200,000 acres are in public parks and forests where they will never be cut.[17] This includes 90,000 acres of so-called "old growth"—that is, areas containing the oldest trees, those that are over 175 years old (with some being thousands of years old).[18] These figures are rounded estimates only. We have so many giant redwoods that we are unable to count them or even to measure the areas on which they stand. In addition to the trees in parks there are many thousands of acres in privately owned groves that will never be cut.

A main reason why we don't know how many redwoods we have is that they grow very rapidly. After a redwood is cut down, it will grow out of its own stump. In 30 years it will be 80 feet high and 16 inches in diameter. Timber companies maximize their profits not by cutting everything in sight as fast as possible but by keeping in mind the fact that each year's growth adds to the value of the tree. It is profitable for them to replant in places where they cut, and they do so.

California has many other kinds of splendid trees as well as redwoods. Forty percent of the land area of the state is in forest.[19] About half of this produces marketable timber.[20] The volume of annual timber growth in our forests is 27 percent greater than the volume cut.[21] It is significant that the largest volumes of growth per acre have been found on land belonging to the private forest industry, where the profit incentive impels the owners to take care of their resources and to cut trees before they begin to rot on the stump, which is the way old trees depart from this life.[22]

California has 5 million acres of forest in parks, wildlife refuges, and wilderness areas where logging is not allowed[23]; that is an area the size of the state of Massachusetts. Nevertheless, in spite of having these vast areas closed to logging, the state is now reducing still further the timber cut in northern California's national forests to a level which is less than half what it was last year, in response to pressure from environmentalists.[24]

There are many frightening stories about deforestation in Brazil. Population control groups say that this is an ecological catastrophe and that overpopulation is the cause. In fact, Brazil covers an area that is more than 12 times the size of Texas and has fewer [less than ¾ as many] people per square mile than Texas. Two-thirds of Brazil—an area eight times the size of Texas—is covered with forest.[25]

It may be true, as the London *Economist* claimed, that an area the size of Switzerland was logged in Brazil in 1989. But Switzerland would fit into the forested area of Brazil 138 times; that is, Brazil cut a fraction of 1 percent of its forested area in 1989. This was probably less than the volume of timber growth that was occurring. Moreover, during the 1970s Brazil planted over 250,000 hectares of forest per year.[26]

It is true, however, in my opinion, that mankind is cutting too many trees and not planting enough. This is happening, not in the forested regions, but in the towns and cities where people live, where every so-called landscape designer feels called upon to chop down all the trees on the campus or park before he can carry through with his grand designs, and the city chops down the trees that are in the way of the wider road. The result is that the places where we live are bare and ugly, our air is laden with filth that would be removed by trees, and we suffer from heat that would be cooled by the leaves of trees, as you know if you have ever sat under a shade tree with its thousands of little leafy fans on a hot day.

Those special interest groups who have always wanted to control other people's reproductive lives have hitched their wagons to the environmental star. It was Hugh Moore, chairman of the Population Reference Bureau, who saw in the first Earth Day in 1970 the opportunity he'd been waiting for. (Incidentally, the Population Reference Bureau receives federal grants for supplying much of the so-called "population education" materials which the schools use.) Moore had been campaigning for population control in the United States for years with moderate success, but on that first Earth Day he distributed by the hundreds of thousands his pamphlet titled *The Population Bomb,* which claimed that pollution was caused by "overpopulation." He later gave a Stanford University insect biologist, Paul Ehrlich, the right to use the title for the book which became a best seller[27]. Paul Ehrlich teaches that world population should be reduced to one-fifth its present size.[28]

Moore's efforts were successful. By 1981 the major environmental organizations in the United States—the Audubon Society, the Sierra Club, the National Wildlife Federation, the Natural Resources Defense Council, Environmental Action, the National Parks and Conservation Association, and others—had joined with the principal population control groups—the Population Crisis Committee, the Population Reference Bureau, Zero Population Growth, the Population Action Council, regional Planned Parenthood groups—to call upon Congress for a national plan to stop the growth of population.[29]

According to Werner Fornos who is head of the Population Institute and who has devoted his life since coming here from Germany after World War II to promoting world population control, "runaway population growth" is the reason "earth's forests are disappearing, its top-soils eroding, deserts expanding, its species vanishing, and its ozone layer thinning."[30] Richard Eliot Benedick, who wears two extremely important hats—one in the very powerful U.S. Agency for International Development in the Department of State and the other in the World Wildlife Fund, voices similar threats. He warns of "climate change, depletion of the ozone layer, pollution of oceans and fresh waters, loss of tropical forests, massive extinction of species, acid rain, toxic chemicals and hazardous waste."[31] He insists that population growth causes these problems and that the United States must sternly enforce the requirement that countries receiving U.S. aid reduce their population growth.[32] Benedick negotiated the 1987 Montreal treaty limits on chlorofluorocarbons.

Climate change is the most terrifying ecological threat. The known facts about climate, however, are less than illuminating. Experts agree and measurements clearly indicate that the carbon dioxide content of the air has increased since the last century from 280 parts per million by volume to 335 parts per million by volume,[33] perhaps as high as 350 ppmV[34]. (Our air consists mostly of oxygen and nitrogen; carbon dioxide makes up a tiny fraction of the total volume; "335 parts per million" means, of course, 335 parts of carbon dioxide in a million parts of air, which is a very small amount, but the change may matter, although we can't be sure.) Some scientists predict that this increase in carbon dioxide will cause global warming because of the reduction in the outgoing radiation from earth to space. On the other hand, it is also generally acknowledged that the radiation from the carbon dioxide will cool the stratosphere.[35] There are many unknown factors in the carbon-cycle, not the least of which are the effects of the oceans which cover more than 70 percent of the surface of the earth.

In this "cascade of uncertainty", as it has been called by two scientists,[36] it is possible to arrive at almost any conclusion, depending on the assumptions one programs into the computer model. The U.S. Environmental Protection Agency resolutely plunged through this sea of unknowns in a recent report to Congress; it simply *assumed* that the earth's temperature will increase by 5 to 9 degrees F,[37] which is significantly higher than the 2.7– 8.1 degree range of estimates by most other groups.[38] The lesson of this story is that if you want to forecast a catastrophe, just go ahead and do it and forget about reasoning or evidence.

Is there any evidence of global warming in the actual measurements of earth's temperature? James Hansen of the U.S. National Aeronautics and Space Administration says that the globe has warmed by one-half of a degree to seven-tenths of a degree centigrade over the past century.[39] However, a group of scientists at the National Oceanic and Atmospheric Administration studied temperature and rainfall records at 6000 stations in the United States for the past century. They found a great deal of year-to-year variability but no trend upward or downward.[40] Scientists at Massachusetts Institute of Technology have studied records of ocean temperatures which have been collected since the mid-19th century. They report finding "no appreciable difference between 1856 and 1986."[41]

Whom then should we believe and what should we do? In view of the uncertainties and disagreements, probably the best counsel is that of Professor H. E. Landsberg, former president of the American Geophysical Union, who, along with other scientists, recommends that we continue measurements and observations until we know more about the situation, and, in the meantime, plant more trees.[42] If this were done intensively in urban areas, it would counteract the buildup of carbon dioxide from the burning of fossil fuels because trees transform carbon dioxide into oxygen.

The alleged depletion of ozone is also fraught with uncertainty. The phenomenon of declining ozone in the stratosphere over Antartica begins in August or September and disappears by November, apparently in relation to the intensity of the sun's rays reaching the area at that season. It has been monitored only during the past decade. The models which have been created to try to explain the occurrence do not account for half the ozone occurring in the stratosphere.[43] This means that we are very far from being able to explain the phenomenon. We don't know whether man-made chlorofluorocarbons or natural sources of chlorine, such as volcanoes in the region, are the cause. We don't know whether the reductions in the use of chlorofluorocarbons (CFC's) agreed upon in 1987 will reduce the so-called "hole"—so-called because it is believed to be confined to Antartica. CFC's are used in refrigeration equipment; a ban on them will be especially burdensome to the developing countries which are beginning to use refrigeration.

It has been suggested that one reason the ozone hole has become such a popular cause is that the existing patents on chlorofluorocarbons are expiring and their manufacturers now hope to establish new patent monopolies on the substitutes which they are creating. They could do this more easily if the old CFC's were banned.[44]

The danger in the loss of ozone is that greater amounts of solar ultraviolet radiation could reach the earth, causing somewhat higher rates of skin cancer among fair-skinned people, who could however avert this danger by wearing sunhats. Moreover, measurements in the United States between 1974 and 1985 show an actual *decrease* in ultraviolet radiation, the exact opposite of what should be expected if ozone is being depleted.[45]

This decrease may be related to the production of *excess* ozone which is a genuine problem in urban areas such as Los Angeles.[46]

Air pollution and traffic congestion are serious problems in most American cities. But this is not global climate change. And it is not the result of population growth.

For decades the federal and state governments have dedicated massive efforts to providing unlimited, "free" access for automobiles. An estimated two-thirds of the land space in the central business district of Los Angeles is used for roads.[47] In the course of this development urban areas have been built not only to accommodate but to require private automobile use on a one-person, one-car basis; buses, trolleys, and trains have been rendered impracticable, and many cities now suffer daily "gridlock"—that is, masses of vehicles unable to move, totally blocking the roads for hours at a time, creating dense clouds of air pollution.

The cause of this problem is not human "overpopulation" but mistaken transportation policy on the part of government. The human population of California grew by about 7 million persons between 1970 and 1988. But the motor vehicle population grew by 9 million during that same period.[48] The situation could be significantly improved by

230

charging for the use of congested roadways. Already, in some cities, devices on cars activate signals on the streets which compute a metered charge which the motorist then pays on a periodic basis just as he does for his home electricity. In Germany, metered charges for water pollution returned the heavily polluted Ruhr River, in one of the most heavily industrialized areas of the world, to recreational quality.[49]

Extremists have similarly exaggerated the other environmental threats and have wrongly attributed them to population growth. There are no data to support the wild charges about the disappearance of thousands of species. But there is no doubt that the African elephant and some other wonderful animals are declining in numbers. The reason for this is that the elephants are not private property like the horses and cows and they have no human owners with an interest in keeping them alive.

If agencies such as the World Bank were really interested in protecting elephants they could devote some of the resources they are using on population control in Africa to establish and police game refuges.

Similarly there is no evidence of resource exhaustion or massive soil erosion or desertification or exhaustion of water supplies[50]. In the opinion of competent investigators, the acid rain problem has been exaggerated.[51] Above all, there is no evidence that any of our environmental problems is the result of "overpopulation" or would be improved by limiting population growth. Barry Commoner demonstrated in 1971 that increases in pollution were not proportional to population growth but to changes in technology.[52] To reduce pollution we would need to attack the polluting technologies directly. Correcting our behavior is far more important than reducing our numbers.

The contrast between the centrally planned economies and the West is instructive on this point. The International Monetary Fund has reported that levels of industrial pollution in the Soviet Union are 10 to 100 times greater than in the West.[53] But the Soviet Union has one of the lowest birth rates and one of the smallest populations relative to its land area in the world. The terrible nuclear accident at Chernobyl was clearly the result of careless behavior. It could not have been prevented by distributing condoms or birth control pills to the people of Chernobyl. East Germany is far less densely populated but far more polluted than West Germany. Pollution in the industrial areas of Poland is legendary, but Poland is less than half as densely populated as West Germany.

Economists believe that prices are very important in improving the environment. When people are allowed to use the air and rivers, lakes, and oceans as "free" dumping grounds for every kind of waste, as has happened in many countries, these resources become polluted. Free access, or subsidized access, to any good, whether it is a highway or a fishing ground or a herd of buffalo or elephants or a forest, invites overuse and abuse.

Aristotle noticed that people take the best care of their own land and homes and animals because they reap the benefits of their own good work and pay the costs of their own mistakes. Our Lord taught us that the Good Shepherd is not the hireling or the government but the one who owns the sheep. Government planners, on the other hand, pass the costs of their mistakes to the public. It is therefore not at all surprising that modern governmental planning for progress is the source of so many environmental as well as economic disasters. The planners have a handy alibi for their failures in alleged "overpopulation." But "overpopulation" is in no way responsible. The problem is misuse of resources and this is the fault of government policy. When government ignores the full costs of its own projects or allows private citizens to ignore the full costs of their activities, those costs do not disappear but in fact become much larger than they otherwise would be. When no one owns the trees, as in some parts of Africa, no one plants trees but everyone who can find one pulls it up for firewood.

Modern governments, eager to manage everything, are now responding to the perceived environmental threat by spending massive amounts of the taxpayers' money on it. The government money serves as an incentive to invent environmental crises and do all the wrong things about them.

People do respond to economic incentives. This is why we need not fear "overpopulation." It has become increasingly costly to raise children and therefore the birth rate has fallen to a lower level than may be optimal in some countries.

But some very special interest groups see in the alleged environmental crisis an opportunity to press their agenda of population control. Herman Daly, who works for the World Bank, is a longtime advocate of birth licenses which would be issued in limited numbers by the government and would be required of any person who gave birth. He claims that the alleged environmental crisis justifies his scheme. He calls for the abolition of private land ownership,[54] a conversion of "half or more" of the land area of the United States to unsettled wilderness inhabited by wild animals;[55] government controls to reduce output and trade;[56] and the resettlement of large numbers of the population in rural areas.[57] Daly has many sympathizers in the host of organizations that promote world population control with their millions of dollars in U.S. government grants.

232

Far from promoting the security of the United States these organizations are creating enemies in places where we need friends. One example of this is Iran. Under intense pressure from tax-funded population organizations in the United States, the late Shah and his sister became enthusiastic proponents of family planning, urging other less developed countries to follow their lead. In the teeth of strict traditional religious teachings to the contrary, all methods of reducing births were legalized, including abortion and sterilization. On a per capita basis, these American-financed public expenditures on birth control were among the highest in the developing world. The Ministries of Health and Education redesigned the school curriculum, rewrote the textbooks, and retrained thousands of teachers to emphasize "population education" and sex education.[58]

It was a massive program, and it enkindled a massive rage which, in the revolution, threw out the Shah, threw out the family planning apparatus, threw out the law allowing abortion and sterilization, and, in short order, threw out the United States.[59] Some part of the responsibility for the Iranian debacle lies at the feet of International Planned Parenthood, the Pathfinder Fund, the Population Council, and the Association for Voluntary Sterilization (now calling itself the "Association for Voluntary Surgical Contraception"), who were making free-wheeling private foreign policy for the United States at the expense of the American taxpayers. Similar scenarios have occurred elsewhere, including the Philippines and Nicaragua.[60]

My point is that these groups have their own agenda, which departs significantly from Christian teaching, and they are now parading under the environmental banner, threatening us with ecological catastrophe unless we give them our money and our obedience.

We do need strict implementation of wise policies to reduce pollution. We do need wise economic policies to alleviate unemployment, poverty, and hunger. At the same time we must be extremely wary of those who would use the environment or the existence of poverty and hunger as excuses to establish their dictatorship.

REFERENCES

1. Jerome, *The Principal Works,* cited in Jacob Viner, *Relgious Thought and Economic Society* (Durham: Duke University Press, 1978), pp. 33–34.

2. Tertullian, *De Anima: A Treatise on the Soul,* cited in Viner, *op. cit.,* p. 34.

3. 5.3 billion world population divided by 262,000 square miles of land in Texas = 20,000 persons per square mile or 1400 square feet per person.

4. Based on city sizes and populations given in *Encyclopedia Britannica.*

5. Peter M. Vitousek, Paul R. Ehrlich, Anned H. Ehrlich, and Pamela A. Matson, "Human Appropriation of the Products of Photosynthesis," *BioScience,* Vol. 36, No. 6, June 1986, p. 369. See also C. A. Doxiadis and G. Papaioannou, *Ecumenopolis, the Inevitable City of the Future* (New York: W. W. Norton & Co., 1974), p. 179 and Jacqueline R. Kasun, *The War Against Population: The Economics and Ideology of World Population Control* (San Francisco: Ignatius, 1988), p. 37.

6. Based on figures published by the World Bank, the U.S. Bureau of the Census, and the National Center for Health Statistics.

7. Population Reference Bureau, *Population Today,* May 1992, p. 10.

8. Linda G. Martin, "Population Aging Policies in East Asia and the United States, *Science,* Vol. 251, 1 February 1991, pp. 527–531.

9. Food and Agriculture Organization of the United Nations, *Production Yearbook,* 1988; Roger Revelle, "The World Supply of Agricultural Land" in Julian L. Simon and Herman Kahn, eds., *The Resourceful Earth: A Response to Global 2000* (Oxford, England: Basil Blackwell Inc., 1984); Roger Revelle, "The Resources Available for Agriculture," *Scientific American,* Vol. 235, No. 3, September 1976, pp. 165–178.

10. Roger Revelle, "The World Supply. . .", *op. cit.,* p. 186.

11. See Julian Simon, *Population Matters,* New Brunswick: Transaction Publishers, 1990, 42–43. Also see FAO *Production Yearbooks.*

12. FAO, *Production Yearbooks;* Roger A. Sedjo and Marion Clawson, "Global Forests," in Julian L. Simon and Herman Kahn, *The Resourceful Earth,* (Oxford: Basil Blackwell, 1984), pp. 147–159.

13. Section 104(d) International Development and Food Assistance Act of 1978 (22 U.S. Code, sec. 2151-1, sec. 2151a). 22 U.S.C. sec. 2151-1(b) (4) provides: "Development assistance . . . shall be concentrated in countries which . . . make the most effective use of such assistance . . . the President shall assess the commitment and progress of countries . . . by utilizing criteria, including . . . the following: . . . control of population growth . ." Sec. 2151b provides that "the President is authorized to furnish assistance . . . for voluntary population planning . . . . population planning programs shall emphasize motivation for small families . ." and "All . . activities proposed for financing . . . shall be designed to build motivation for smaller families . . ."

14. *U.S. AID Highlights,* Vol. 6, No. 1, Winter 1989, p. 1.

15. FAO, Production Yearbooks; Sedjo and Clawson, op. cit., p. 142.

16. California Department of Forestry and Fire Protection, *California's Forests and Rangelands: Growing Conflict Over Changing Uses,* 1988, p. 313.

17. *Ibid.,* Table 7–10, p. 322.

18. *Ibid.,* p. 313.

19. U.S. Bureau of the Census, *Statistical Abstract of the United States,* 1989, Tables 331, 1144.

20. *Ibid.*

21. California Department of Forestry and Fire Protection, *op. cit.,* p. 116.

22. California Department of Forestry, *California's Forest Resources,* 1979, p. 244.

23. California Department of Forestry and Fire Protection, *op. cit.,* Table 7–9, p. 320.

24. Gary Gundlach, "Current Forestry Research Hopeful," in brochure prepared for Redwood Region Logging Conference, March 14–16, 1991.

25. *FAO Production Yearbook, 1988.*

26. Sedjo and Clawson, *op. cit.,* p. 153.

27. See Jacqueline R. Kasun, *The War Against Population: The Economics and Ideology of World Population Control,* (San Francisco: Ignatius Press, 1988), pp. 162–3.

28. Paul R. Ehrlich, "Our Earth is Past the Point of No Return," *Newsday,* February 6, 1989; Paul R. Ehrlich, *How to Be a Survivor: A Plan to Save Spaceship Earth,* (New York: Ballantine, 1971), pp. 26–27.

29. Kasun, *op. cit.,* p. 196.

30. Population Institute, mailer for World Population Awareness Week, April, 1988.

31. Richard Elliot Benedick, "Ecological Diplomacy: An Agenda for 1990, *Scientific American,* January 1990, p. 154.

32. Kasun, *op. cit.,* p. 87.

33. H. E. Landsberg, "Global Climatic Trends," in Simon and Kahn, *op. cit.,* p. 290.

34. Warren T. Brookes, "The Global Warming Panic," *Forbes,* December 25, 1989, pp. 96–102.

35. Landsberg, *op. cit.*

36. *Ibid.,* pp. 290–291.

37. U.S. Environmental Protection Agency, "The Potential Effects of Global Climate Change on the United States," Draft Report to Congress, October, 1988.

38. Landsberg, *op. cit.,* pp. 292–293.

39. J. Hansen and S. Lebedeff, "Global Trends of Measured Surface Air Temperature," *Journal of Geophysics Research* Vol. 92, No. 13, 1987, pp. 345–413.

40. Kirby Hanson, George A. Maul, and Thomas R. Karl, "Are Atmospheric 'Greenhouse' Effects Apparent in the Climatic Record of the Contiguous U.S. (1895–1987) ?" manuscript, copyright 1988 by the American Geophysical Union; see also Richard S. Lindzen, "Some Coolness Concerning Global Warming," *Bulletin American Meteorological Society,* Vol. 71, no. 3, March 1990, pp. 288–299.

41. Reginald E. Newell, Jane Hsiung, Wu Zhongxiang *et al, Global Ocean Surface Temperature Atlas,* forthcoming Massachusetts Institute of Technology Press, reported in *Technology Review,* November/December 1989.

42. Landsberg, *op. cit.*

43. T. G. Slanger et al, "A New Laboratory Source of Ozone and Its Potential Atmospheric Implications," *Science,* Vol 241, No. 4868, August, 1988, p. 945.

44. George Melloan, "Is Science, or Private Gain, Driving Ozone Policy?" *The Wall Street Journal,* October 24, 1989, p. A19.

45. Joseph Scotto et al, "Biologically Effective Ultraviolet Radiation: Surface Measurements in the United States, 1974 to 1985," *Science,* Vol. 239, February 1988, pp. 762–764.

46. Robert Pease, professor emeritus of physical climatology, University of California, Riverside, personal correspondence with J. Kasun, 1990.

47. Christian G. Kling, *Urban Transportation,* (New York: Vantage Press, 1976), p. 26.

48. U.S. Bureau of the Census; *Motor Vehicle Facts and Figures,* 1990, pp. 22–23.

49. Allen V. Kneese, "Water Quality Management by Regional Authorities in the Ruhr Area", in Marshall I. Goldman (ed.), *Controlling Pollution: The Economics of a Cleaner America* (Englewood Cliffs: Prentice Hall, 1967), pp. 109–129.

50. See Julian L. Simon, *Population Matters* (New Brunswick: Transaction, 1990.)

51. John Christy, of NASA Marshall Space Flight Institute and the University of Alabama, quoted in *Human Events,* March 2, 1991, p. 11.

52. Barry Commoner, "The Environmental Costs of Economic Growth", in Robert Dorfman and Nancy S. Dorfman, eds., *Ecnonomics of the Environment: Selected Readings* (New York: W. W. Norton & Co., 1972), pp. 261–283.

53. International Monetary Fund, The World Bank *et al, The Economy of the USSR: Summary and Recommendations,* 1990, p. 37.

54. Herman E. Daly and John B. Cobb, Jr., *For the Common Good: Redirecting the Economy Towards Community, the Environment and a Sustainable Future* (London: Green Print of The Merlin Press, 1990), (pp. 256–259).

55. *Ibid.*, p. 255.

56. *Ibid.*, pp. 143, 229–235, 269–272.

57. *Ibid.*, pp. 264, 311.

58. Kasun, *op. cit.*, pp. 88–89.

59. *Ibid.*

60. *Ibid.*, pp. 89–91.

Chapter 17

CATHOLIC CONCERNS ABOUT POPULATION QUESTIONS

The Reverend Monsignor Diarmuid Martin, S.T.D.

It might be useful to begin our reflection on the theme of *Catholic Concerns on Population* by thinking aloud for a few moments on the title of my talk.

In the first place, I think it is useful to clarify the notion *Catholic concerns*. There is no need to recall that the Catholic Church has a teaching on population questions which is special and is not shared by other Christian Churches. In the same way, the Holy See, in the area of inter-governmental organizations, presents a position concerning population policy which is not shared—or at least not shared in full—by other governments.

There is thus no doubt that the Catholic Church has specific concerns on population issues. But one must be careful in labelling these concerns simply 'Catholic concerns'. If these concerns were exclusively based on the teaching of revelation, if they were explicitly drawn from the religious understanding of one Christian Church, then one would have to be very reserved in presenting these concerns as concerns for public policy within our own countries, which pride themselves on being secular and pluralist, and within the international community. We would have only a very limited right to propose as desirable as a norm of public social policy what would be an exclusively religious position, and that of one specific Church. Governments and international organizations would be justifiably reticent in inserting our concerns within their programmes and guidelines.

The concern of the Catholic Church on population issues belongs rather to that area of reflection which considers, certainly in the light of the teaching and the accumulated wisdom of the Church, the nature of the human person and the common good of society. And like many other aspects of the Church's social teaching, it is accessible to and is concretely shared by many others, of different religious convictions or none. In this important sense we are not dealing with exclusively 'Catholic concerns'.

In presenting the concerns of the Church on population issues we are not trying to impose a specifically religious or Catholic position on society. The contribution of the Church in the area of population is drawn from the common heritage of reflection on the human person in dialogue with the contribution of scientific reflection, especially the reflection of the human sciences.

We have heard in the first talk this morning some reflections on the demographic situation in the world today. The Catholic Church respects the results of the science of demography. There are no specifically Catholic statistics. There is no specific Catholic demography. If the Catholic Church takes task with the findings of certain demographers or schools of demography, it must do so within the terms of *demographic* and not theological discussion. Theology cannot substitute for demography.

This does not mean, however, that the Church cannot in any way challenge, from the point of view of its heritage and understanding of the human person, certain demographic conclusions. Demography, in fact, is not simply the science of collecting data. It is not simple census taking. Demographers go on to interpret facts, they go on to forecast tendencies and inevitably express preferences concerning policy choices. The subject matter of demography is not simply numbers. It concerns the behaviour of human persons in their free choices concerning one of the key dimensions of their humanity.

Population study—which incorporates the findings of economics and sociology as well as demography—interprets and forecasts reali-

238

ties which are not simply mathematical, but which are influenced by—and, in fact, influence—free human behaviour. Thus population study, perhaps even more than many other human and social sciences, can be influenced by underlying philosophical presumptions, about who the human person is, and about the future and the destiny of society and humanity. Conclusions concerning policy options in the population field are inevitably influenced by *anthropological* options (in the philosophical sense). It is here above all that the Church can challenge certain demographic conclusions. It is from her understanding of the nature of human persons, of society and of human destiny that the Church establishes her concerns on population issues.

Continuing this 'thinking aloud', it is good also to clarify what we mean by population. In day-to-day language we hear about *'the* population problem' or *'the* demographic question', understood almost exclusively as the problem or question of 'over-population' on a world level, or at least in the developing countries. The mass-media, popular writers, reports of international organizations and even theological commentators speak of the 'population explosion' or the 'population time-bomb' or of a threat to the earth's resources and even to the survival of the universe.

Here we must turn to scientists to clarify the questions under consideration and to avoid naive simplifications of what is a quite complex terrain. All too often 'population' has become an umbrella term which is used, unscientifically, in the analysis of very diversified situations. There is not *one* population problem in today's world. The dynamics of population growth and distribution cannot be reduced to a simplistic and unequivocal notion of 'over-population'. The inter-relationship between the health, nutritional, agricultural, educational, economic and political dimensions of world development is not respected when one factor, population growth, is singled out as the sole obstacle to development.

The health component of development policy will only be resolved when it is approached as a health component; the problems of agricultural development and provision of food will only be resolved when they are explicitly addressed for what they are. Attributing them to 'the population problem' will only prolong their eventual solution.

As I have said, there is not *one* population problem. On the question, for example, of fertility rates, there is great diversity around the world. There are questions concerning high fertility rates in some countries or regions: what is *high* fertility? Is moderate population growth always negative? There are problems concerning *low* fertility rates, often below replacement level, in others. Demography and population policy touch also on other questions: population density, pop-

239

ulation structure especially according to age, population distribution (for example the problem of urbanization), population movement (perhaps one of the most important questions facing many societies today is the question of migration, refugees and asylum seekers), the general health of the population. The Church has concerns about all of these questions and wishes to make its contribution to the debates that are taking place about them throughout the world.

Finally it is important to remember that the debate about population issues today, goes to the heart of the debate on the *meaning of human sexuality*. It is often said, especially within the Church, that the point of divergence between the Catholic Church and the general international reflection on population issues is that concerning which methods of family planning are to be considered morally licit. Put very simply, the difference between the Catholic Church and others concerns the question of the use and distribution of contraceptive methods, as opposed to the natural methods for the regulation of fertility. This is too simplistic and in many ways misleading.

In recent years, in fact, the fundamental inspiration for the majority of population control policies has distanced itself more and more substantially from the basic understanding of marriage and the family proposed by the Church. Since the 1974 U.N. International Population conference (held at Bucharest) the agreed international language in population policy has tended to refer to a "human right" of all *"individuals* and couples" to family planning. That is, to decision-making concerning sexual intimacy and the transmission of life, and to access to relevant information and services.

The assertion of a "human right of all individuals" to determine choices concerning sexual intimacy and the transmission of life constitutes a direct challenge to the Church's position, which reserves such a right to married couples.

Many of those who in 1974 supported the introduction of the term "individuals" did so because they felt that it was necessary to recognize, or at least not to close one's eyes to, the fact that many persons— including adolescents—are sexually active outside marriage and that society must take account of this fact. Such a position implies, however, that society as a whole can renounce establishing any common accepted set of norms concerning sexuality. The only norm that remains is that of the right of all to be sexually active, possibly coupled with the responsibility to take measures to avoid sexually transmitted diseases. "Safe sex" becomes the only 'moral' norm which society feels it may foster.

But with the passage of time, the recognition in population policy of the fact that many young people were sexually active has moved to

240

the acceptance of a right to such activity and thus to a weakening of the institution of the family within society. The very notion of *family* planning is falsified, however, when it is used and applied not just to married couples, but also to unmarried individuals and adolescents. An analysis of the fundamental inspiration of recent family planning literature shows that it is inspired by a noticeable individualism, which can quickly become the driving force accepting, and in fact fostering, sexual permissiveness on a wide scale.

The Holy See has consistently, over the past years, drawn attention to the consequences of this trend and has asked public authorities to reflect on the long-term effects of any weakening of the family institution, especially when this becomes an integral, if not always evident, component of development policy. For the moment, however, our process of thinking aloud can conclude with the constatation of the fact that the fundamental ethos of current family planning and population policy reflection is much more distanced from the position of the Church than many imagine.

Let us now look more closely at the Church's position.

The Church's reflection on population issues has always placed the *affirmation of the family as the basic social unit,* as one of its constituent elements. The theme of the family is also the point of contact between the two central areas of reflection which go to make up the Church's concern regarding population questions: one area which concerns conjugal morality, the other which is situated within the social teaching of the Church concerning human dignity and the development of society.

Sometimes it is said that the Church has concentrated its reflection on population too much within the area of its teaching on marriage and the family, on conjugal morality, and that the theme has not been adequately treated within the social teaching of the Church. It has been said that the social teaching of the Church has somehow avoided seriously facing the 'population question' and that the very credibility of the social teaching is put in question by this fact.

It might be useful therefore to draw attention briefly to the development of the two strands of the Church's reflection on population issues to examine their content and *their fundamental unity.*

The Church's teaching on population is something recent. It emerges from the application of various general principles to certain new situations which have developed, especially within this century. The moral questions which have to be faced are linked to two developments. One is specifically demographic. The key factor is probably that of increase in life expectancy, due to improved overall levels in health care. This has resulted in a decrease in mortality, including infant mortality. As a result more children survive and people also live longer. The adjustments in fertility rates which emerge when people are confident that their existing children will survive requires time before it takes effect. This led, especially in the late 1960's, to a very high rate of population growth and to anxiety about the consequences of uncontrolled population growth. The 1960's thus saw a revival of Malthusian theories which had already been current in the last century and to the emergence of dramatic predictions about world food supplies, natural resources and even about human survival.

The second factor, which also emerged during the 1960's, following on developments in the earlier decades of this century, concerned the development of contraceptive technology, and especially the contraceptive pill.

Especially in the 1960's these two strands became intertwined in reflection and controversy within the Church, which reached its climax at the time of the publication of Pope Paul VI's Encyclical *Humanae vitae.*

The basic response of the Church to the emerging situation had however already been set out by Pope John XXIII in his Encyclical of 1961 *Mater et magistra,* which was part of the remarkable chain of Church documents which have been published to commemorate the anniversaries of *Rerum novarum* and which have greatly influenced the destiny of the 20th century Church.

Mater et magistra (n. 185) first of all sets out the basic question as it was posed at the time: "How can economic development and the supply of food keep pace with the growth in population?", the Pope asks. He then looks at the question both as a world question and as to how it affects the less developed countries.

The basic tone of the answer that John XXIII gives is quite different from the doomsday forecasts which were common at the time. He expresses confidence in the God-given intelligence of the human person to discover ways of exploiting the earth's resources responsibly. But he immediately warns that "the real solution of the problem is not to be found in expedients which offend against the divinely established moral order or which attack human life at its very source" (*MM* n. 189).

It is also interesting today to note that Pope John, when speaking of the exploitation of resources and of the double command to our first parents to transmit human life and to place nature at the service of human person, affirms that this does not involve "destroying nature" (*MM* n. 197), thus anticipating the current concern for the environment.

Pope John, however, recognizes the gravity of the problem for developing countries of a disproportion between population growth and an inadequate availability of resources (cf. *MM* n. 198), at least in the concrete situation in which those countries found themselves. It is important to remember that the social teaching of the Church has never refused to address and recognize the problems connected with population growth, while at the same time never allowing itself to be overcome by pessimism or by apocalyptic visions, which already in 1961 the Pope recognized were "based on such unreliable and controversial data that they can only be of very uncertain validity" (*MM* n. 188).

"The only solution to this question", Pope John notes, "is one which envisages the social and economic progress of both individuals and of the whole of human society, and which respects and promotes true human values" (*MM* n. 192). He also draws attention to the "deficient economic and social organization" in developing countries and to "the lack of effective solidarity" among the peoples of those countries (cf. *MM* n. 190).

Pope John then takes up the theme of the family, based on marriage, to which the mission of the transmission of human life is entrusted. He speaks of the responsibility which must be exercised by parents in the procreation and education of their children.

The notion of the responsible planning of family size emerges more clearly in the Pastoral Constitution *Gaudium et spes* which, in the first place, recognizes that "in certain modern conditions" couples "find themselves in circumstances where at least temporarily the size of their family should not be increased" (*GS* n. 51). Later in the same document, addressing specifically the population issue, the Council notes that the decision concerning the number of children parents will have "depends on the correct judgement of the parents and it cannot be left to the judgement of public authority" (*GS* n. 87). *Gaudium et spes* notes however that "the judgement of the parents presupposes a rightly formed conscience" adding that it is of the utmost importance that the way be open to "develop a correct and genuinely human responsibility which respects the divine law and takes into consideration the circumstances of the place and the time" *(ibid)*.

The respective rights of parents and of public authorities with regard to responsible parenthood and population policy are further developed in Pope Paul VI's Encyclical *Populorum progressio*. Pope Paul stresses the need to respect "the rightful freedom of married couples" (*PP* n. 37) and he clearly stresses the factors which parents must take into account regarding the responsible planning of family size and the number of children: "It is for parents to take a thorough look at the matter and decide on the number of their children. This is an obligation they take upon themselves, before their children already born and before the community to which they belong following the dictates of their own consciences informed by God's law authentically interpreted, and bolstered by their trust in him" *(ibid)*.[1]

The Pope also indicates the areas in which "public authorities can intervene in this matter". As in *Gaudium et spes* for *Populorum progressio* government competence is specifically indicated in the area of providing information on the situation and needs of the nation. Governments are also especially requested to provide programmes which support the institution of the family (also in such areas as housing etc.).

As the years passed, the overall thrust of governmental and intergovernmental population policy developed and not always in the sense desired by the Church. In his Apostolic Exhortation *Octagesimo adveniens* of 1971 Pope Paul VI referred to his disquiet at "a kind of fatalism which is gaining a hold even on people in positions of responsibility. This feeling sometimes leads to Malthusian solutions inculcated by active propaganda for contraception and abortion" (n. 18).

This statement however just touches the tip of the iceberg of a new and very difficult situation which was to develop during the 1970's and the early 1980's. A series of concomitant factors, both positive and negative, both within and outside the Church, were to emerge which greatly influenced the effectiveness of the Church in presenting her message. This is a period concerning which it is still difficult to present a serene reflection. It will be the task of social historians to draw the final conclusions concerning the effects both on individuals and on society in general of the period. However, already it is possible to draw some tentative judgements.

On the one hand, following on the general social revolution associated, in Europe at least, with 1968, models of authority, institution and traditional family arrangements were challenged. Maternity and childbearing began to be looked upon often as burdens which should not be placed in the way of the full development of women and their participation in political, economic and social leadership roles in society. The institutional role of marriage began to be questioned and to be substituted by a more personalistic understanding in which the fulfilment and happiness of each of the spouses became determinate. Children tended to be seen as a factor which could further enhance the fulfilment and happiness of the spouses, only at the moment when they, the spouses, considered that this was a worthwhile and desired aim. The care and education of children began to be assigned to a greater extent to other agencies, under the auspices of public authorities—perhaps there are differences here between the United States and Europe or perhaps Canada—who could free the parents, and especially women, for other social commitments.

244

Rapid transformations also took place within developing countries, especially through urbanization and a movement into large cities. People were removed from the cultural and traditional roots which had provided a basic moral framework for them. This led at times also to a breakdown in traditional behaviour and norms and brought about a spread of new forms of promiscuity. It was in this general cultural context that the vast campaign of population control began to spread in the various sectors of the world.

Just as a 'sexual revolution' was taking place in various parts of the world, the Catholic Church was undergoing radical changes and at times widespread dissent from its teaching precisely in the area of marriage and the family. Rather than being a focal point of security and certainty, there was the danger that the Church might come a catalyst in provoking an even greater ferment.

This created an uncertainty among clergy and Church leaders who did not seem to possess sufficient confidence to be able to present the Church's teaching in the face of population campaigns.

The first strong reaction to these tendencies came interestingly from the episcopates of the developing countries, who were to see the negative effects of population control programmes within their nations. It must also be noted that even the organizations involved in such international campaigns began early to see that their lack of concern with the cultural values of the people in developing countries rendered their programmes less effective.

In addition to their various interventions, common pastoral letters and declarations, the Bishops of the developing countries drew attention at the 1980 Synod of Bishops to the many abuses they noticed in the application of family planning and population programmes in developing countries.[2] These concerns are fully reflected in *Familiaris consortio* (cf. *FC* n. 30) and in the *Charter of the Rights of the Family.*

In particular the bishops objected to the imposition of specific demographic targets and to the conditioning of economic aid on the acceptance of family planning or population programmes. In various subsequent interventions of the Holy See (especially at the time of the 1984 Population Conference [Mexico City]) there have been calls for complete transparency concerning the terms in which multilateral and bilateral international programmes of economic aid are elaborated concerning their population component.

One of the major Catholic concerns in recent years is the extent to which programmes of population control have recourse to sterilization, particularly female sterilization, especially in developing countries, in which extremely high proportions of women have been sterilized. Sterilization is in fact the family planning means most open to abuse on human rights grounds. Because of its irreversibility, sterilization leaves no room for change in childbearing plans. These are serious worries as to whether these effects are fully disclosed to poor or illiterate women. At times their acceptance of sterilization is influenced by incentives or very modest payments.

In addition to demanding that couples should be free from any form of coercion or undue pressure from governments, the Church has also expressed concern about the possible health hazards of certain family planning methods, which have not received medical approval in the producer nations but which are used in developing countries where legal controls are less demanding.

Finally the Holy See has been especially attentive to the attempts of international organizations to introduce abortion as a means of family planning. At the 1984 World Population Conference held in Mexico City, it was possible for the Holy See to create a consensus among the delegates on a recommendation which urged States not to promote abortion as a means of family planning.[3]

In the complex cultural situation of the 1960's to the mid 1980's especially, much of the effort of the Church was dedicated to the task of reacting to abuses in international population programmes. This activity has been of great importance and has contributed to limiting the advance of a population control movement which lacked total respect for the rights and dignity of all individuals. In recent times more and more, some family planning organizations and governments have themselves recognized abuses in this regard: something which would not have happened some years ago.

But still many will ask: what is the Church's *answer* to the 'population question'? Does it simply criticize the approach of others? What positive answer does it offer to humanity today and to those who bear responsibility for the destiny of society? Does the Church simply deny the existence of a population problem?

The first principle which the Catholic Church has constantly stressed is the link between population and development. Pope Paul VI summed this up most vividly in his well known address to the United Nations in New York in 1960 when he recalled that it is not a question of "limiting the number of those who have access to the banquet of life, but rather to ensure that there is sufficient bread for all at the table of humanity."

The years that have passed have shown in fact that it is more often poverty which is the cause of rapid population growth, than that population growth is a cause of poverty. Only when reflection on population and development are intertwined will one come to solutions worthy of mankind. It is interesting to note that the very title of the 1994 Population conference, planned for Cairo, is International Conference on Population and Development.

Development of course means not just economic development but above all social development. One of the major factors which influences population growth and fertility rates is the educational level of the community, especially of women. When women realize that their already existing children can survive, they will consider the question of the spacing of the children and limiting the size of their families. The survival of children is of course closely linked with the basic level of health education within a community and of primary health care services aimed at mothers and children. This is an area in which the Catholic Church makes a very important contribution.[4]

A policy which aims at the human and social development of women and of the community—and which involves also education of men to a greater sense of responsibility—may seem a more complex, difficult process to that of many of the population control programmes which stress rather the massive distribution of means of birth regulation. But in the long term it is only through education and responsibilization that any programme of behavioural change will work. Programmes which lead people to human development and maturity are also in the long term those which respond to the dignity of the person.

The Catholic concern about population thus advocates recourse to the natural methods for the regulation of fertility, not only for ethical reasons, but because these methods respect the health of women and men. Both unity and equality among spouses are strengthened through the use of these methods, which by their very nature enlist the full involvement and commitment of the man to understand and respect his spouse. In the allocation of public funds (and, indeed, Church funds) these methods should receive appropriate support.

I have said on various occasions in these reflections that there is not one population problem in today's world. The problem of a *decline in fertility,* for example, is a serious one for many developed countries. It is one of the concerns of the Church to draw attention to the consequences of this factor, from the social, cultural, economic and ethical point of view. The questions must be posed: How can one ensure the rejuvenation of a society which has seemed to have lost its desire to transmit its identity and values through a flourishing new generation? To what extent is the ageing of Western society and a certain resistance to encouraging childbearing a sign of a malaise and of a certain pessimistic view of life?

The Catholic concern about population must also direct its attention to the problem of *population movement*. Today's world is marked in a special way by the millions of those who are forced to leave their homes involuntarily, either for political motives, or because of wars and conflicts or because of intolerable economic situations. The presence in any region of a large number of persons who are excluded from social, economic and political participation constitutes an overall threat to democracy and peaceful coexistence in the entire region. No country can close its eyes to the plight of people in other parts of the same region.

The Church must take a lead and encourage society, either through programmes of development or through controlled migration, to realize in practice the principle of the "universal destination of the goods of creation", one of the great principles of the Church's social teaching. When God created the goods of the earth, he intended them to be accessible to all.

For the most unfortunate, our societies must correctly and generously apply the recognized norms of humanitarian protection, where necessary adjusting the existing juridical instruments and international structures.

This is a challenge which the nations of the region represented here must face in a particular way, both out of a concern for the good of the most vulnerable and also for the safeguarding and fostering of stable democracy in the entire region. There are important social, legislative and political choices involved.

Another aspect of the Church's concern, of pastoral importance, is that of the *aging of the population*. Our societies have witnessed an increase in life expectancy and a concurrent drop in fertility. This has resulted in an imbalance in the population structures with an increasingly large number of aging persons and a smaller group of children and youth. This puts pressure on pension and health-care services, at a period in which the overall economic climate is already producing cut-backs. In the future, responsibility for the care of the aged and the chronically ill will be assigned more and more to the family and the community. Moral aspects of end-of-life issues also require close attention by the Church—on a policy and a pastoral level.

But past experience shows that the community must be helped and educated to assume its role in such a situation through programmes of sensibilization and training for community based, often voluntary, workers. The Church can again here give a lead in this regard.

The Church's concern for the population question is not the result, as is claimed by some, of the desire to propose its own particular viewpoint or ideology, but comes out of its concern for *people* and especially the poorest or most vulnerable.

At a time in which one might be tempted to suspect that population programmes target the poorest precisely because they are poor, the Church must give a counter witness. This counter witness will involve a number of levels of Church policy, especially in and towards developing nations:

—The first is *concern*. The vast network of the Church's caring institutions, from the huge funding agencies to the local based projects of voluntary workers, must be a witness of the care of Christ for all persons, especially for the weakest.

—Then there is *education*. The eradiction of poverty depends on the level of basic education that the people receive, especially regarding literacy, health care and training in basic skill. The first contribution to the work of justice and peace is that of education of people to effectively be in a position to make moral decisions concerning their own lives and destinies.

—Then there is the task of *challenging current models* which are not based on a philosophy which fully respects the dignity and the rights of persons, as well as their cultural and religious traditions. This will also involve proposing new models of legislation, of economic cooperation, of local and regional development, of openness in trade relations, of breaking down barriers which divide the world into richer and poorer blocks.

But fundamentally, the Church must dedicate itself to the work of *conversion* of the minds and hearts of persons, to overcome the selfishness that is in individuals and in the structures of our societies. This selfishness is also accompanied by a fear of the other, of anything that might challenge our comfortable life style. The comfortable life style of the richer nations, and of the rich in the poorer nations, is one of the population problems about which we all speak too little.

The principal Catholic concern in the area of population is the evangelization of the members of the Church, and their conversion to fidelity to the Church's teaching on marriage and the family and on solidarity with all of humankind, sons and daughters of the same God, the creator of the universe, which is given to all as our common charge.

NOTES

1. The Encyclical *Humanae vitae* n. 10 notes, in very similar terms: "In relation to physical, economic, psychological and social conditions, responsible parenthood is exercised, either by the deliberate and generous decision to raise a numerous family or by the decision, made for grave motives and with due respect for the moral law, to avoid for the time being, or even for an indefinite period, a new birth".

2. The *Message* of the 1980 Synod to the Christian Families of the World (24 October 1980) contains a very strong criticism of certain population control programmes.

3. Report of the UN International Population Conference on Population 1984, Recommendation 18, pp. 21,22. United Nations, New York 1984.

4. Cf. for example Vice President Al Gore, *Earth in the Balance* (revised edition, New York 1993) p. 316, on the Catholic Church as "one of the most forceful and effective advocates for literacy and education programs and for measures to dramatically reduce infant mortality". One would have however to challenge some other affirmations in the same paragraph.

Chapter 18

COMMUNICATING THE CATHOLIC VISION OF POPULATION QUESTIONS

The Reverend Monsignor Frank J. Dewane, J.C.L.

The demographic picture in today's world and the teachings of the Church on the issue of population growth have already been presented. The task now focuses on how to effectively communicate to the world at large and more specifically, to the followers of Jesus Christ in dioceses, the "Catholic Vision" on the Population issue and Population questions.

The communication referred to is human communication. This is not a topic where the means or the objective of communication is other than the human being. Those who do argue from the point of departure of "overpopulation" work from computer-supported decisions to computer models often losing sight of human factors. In approaching the topic of population, the full dignity and freedom of whoever might be affected must be respected.

The approach taken and method used to examine the population issue is in light of my experience as a member of the staff of the Permanent Observer Mission of the Holy See to the United Nations. Prior to entering the seminary I worked for NBC television, and thus have had professional experience in the field of communications. The remarks I make today are primarily from this background and are an attempt to suggest a broad understanding for and pastoral application of the communication of the Catholic Vision on the Population Issue. There are no quick fixes or foolproof formulas offered in this presentation.

Introduction

The Population issue has clearly emerged as a major media subject in the 1990's and the opportunity must be seized to effectively communicate the position of the Catholic Church. This Catholic Vision on the issue of population, in certain respects, mirrors that of other interested parties but does have the unique component drawn from the moral and ethical principles which constitute a two thousand year tradition. Thus, the central question is how can we most effectively communicate, and thus teach, the position of the Church in societies which receive one-sided coverage in the popular press emphasizing the strong adverse consequences of population growth and the questions which surround this topic.

"Sensitive" is an attribute often applied to the population question and is sometimes even given as the excuse for skirting communication on the issue. Sensitivity in this case includes, but is not limited to, the nature of belief and not only a religious belief. However, this claim of the sensitivity of the topic, while certainly valid, does not provide a reason to ignore or shut the door on a subject that is center stage in the domestic and global policy forums. Yet sensitivity is not the only attribute present. Complexity and confusion have equalled, and in some cases surpassed, that of sensitivity in the population field.

In attempting to set out this road map, or what may seem to some more like a maze, for communicating the position of the Church on the issue of population, three central aspects will be examined.

First, to effectively communicate, on any issue, one must understand the language of the discipline—that is to say the theory and the vocabulary for communicating the issue at hand. Highlighting the importance of the language of population, how it is used, misused and confused, will facilitate communicating the teaching of the Church.

This very exercise of examining vocabulary and language will set the stage that challenges many of the assumptions which have been allowed to exist in the discussion of population. Thus, issues such as population theories, the world food supply, the HIV/AIDS pandemic, urbanization, poverty and economic development will be noted and an attempt to demonstrate how the population issue is defined and communicated in the context of each will follow.

Secondly, an agenda regarding the population issue is being put forth by numerous diverse groups: environmentalists, feminists, industrialists, bankers, governments, international organizations, health organizations, and many more. According to the position held by these interest groups on population, information is being communicated which is often unbalanced, sometimes even incorrect, allowing for manipulation and/or deception to shape the population issue and questions of population growth and force it in various directions. Is it the questions put forth by these interest groups or the responses given that frame the issue of population? Have we been asking the questions or merely giving the responses? Or neither because of an unfamiliarity with the whole issue?

Thirdly, for the teachings of the Church on the issue of population to be put forth, a pastoral approach must be developed which addresses population from a faith perspective and demonstrates the concern that the Church has for all the components which make up the population growth issue. Ethically and morally acceptable means in accord with the teaching of the Church are available in addressing population issues. This moral vision of the Church needs to be communicated within a positive, action orientated framework at the personal, diocesan, regional and international level.

"You Are the Message"

One basic premise which underlies this entire presentation is that, "You Are the Message." In this particular case it is not only you who present the Catholic vision on the issue of population growth but, "YOU ARE THE MESSAGE."

This point of departure for communication of the Catholic Vision is important and will be implicated in the styles and manners of communication advocated here relating to population. This is not a model. Rather it is a context that frames the process of communication. It is about you!

All public communication, regardless of the issue, is simple, strategic and thus must be explicitly chosen. At the same time, communication is automatic and is implicitly activated. Therefore, communication on population questions needs to be goal-directed, to those moral and ethical goals set forth by the Church, and constantly responsive to the general population debate. You, the message and the messenger, must adjust communication for these goals and the constraints which may be encountered. This constant process of adjustment makes the communication of the vision inherently strategic.

In the area of communication the world has changed drastically in a brief period of time. Major innovations have changed all the rules of communications. Thus, a few very practical points essential in all communicating, regardless of the topic and certainly not limited to the topic of population, follow and serve as a reminder.

—The media will selectively edit anything you say.

—You do not have to answer all questions.

—Choose your words, rephrase the question.

—Responses need to be rehearsed.

—Work out the rules in advance for the editing process.

Remember, in any media situation where a message is to be communicated, there exists a natural adversarial relationship. The reporter is a professional and must be responded to in like manner. You are not only the messenger, "YOU ARE THE MESSAGE!"

The Language of Population

The study of communication of any topic necessitates a familiarization with the jargon, the language and vocabulary, of the discipline. The population issue is no exception. The language needs to be familiar in order to respond effectively, accurately and to communicate the Catholic vision. Just how important are the words being used in the communicating of population issues?

To illustrate a number of key concepts and jargon in the population field brief examples will be noted which highlight the importance of the language used in addressing population issues and communicating the Church's position in the world.

Initial contact from the Pope John Center identified the general topic of "Communicating the Catholic Concern about Overpopulation Issues" as the segment to be addressed in this portion of the program. Aware of the reputation of the Center, the choice of the word "overpopulation" seemed peculiar. By its very use, the issue had already been defined and if "overpopulation" was the presupposition, the discussion was finished and there was no need for the presentation. This myth of overpopulation is one of the most pervasive myths in Western society.

There are valid concerns for the growth of the world population but this in itself does not constitute overpopulation. World population has indeed increased over the past decades. Yet, world commodities, from food to metals to other raw materials, have increased over that same period of time. The world is not overpopulated. Say it loudly and clearly!!

Terms often used by supporters of population control are "rapid population growth" and "population explosion." "Rapid population growth" has a specific demographic meaning but is often misused to refer to almost any area that has a population growth. The use of the term "explosion" puts population in the category of a destructive force. In reality, there are but a few Less Developed Countries which have rapid population growth and any use of the term "explosion" is hardly indicative of the true picture and certainly misleading. This jargon is a trap and must be recognized as such when communicating the Catholic Vision. People are born not only with mouths to be fed, but also with hands that can produce and minds that can create and innovate.

Poverty and economic development are two topics emphasized in the international discussion of population. The poor are blamed for the so-called "overpopulation" problem and attempts to communicate this point have been very effective. Less Developed Countries of the world, with higher fertility rates, are identified as proof. Continually, the Holy See is the voice for the poor at international meetings precisely on this issue. Yet the key to lower fertility rates—if that is what one wants—is precisely higher economic-growth rates by ensuring employment, education and primary health care for mothers and children as well as overcoming child mortality. Noble prize winner Simon Kuznets, among many others, has found that population growth does not retard economic development.

Food supply, or food security as it is called, has been the issue that the scaremongers have most often and most effectively used in trumpeting the cause of population control. In 1968 ecologist Paul Ehrlich warned, "The battle to feed all humanity is over. In the 1970s the world will undergo famines—hundred of millions of people will starve to death." Such tactics continue to be used and continually underestimate human ingenuity. However, the issue of food security, which is central to arguments supporting population control, is not really a component of the population question but one of agriculture. Still for purposes of examining communication on the topic, let us allow the point to remain.

In October of 1992, the United Nations Food and Agricultural Organization issued a report noting that the "world now makes enough food to nourish everyone." Globally, there is enough food for all. Responding to scaremongers who identify famines, malnutrition and world hunger with overpopulation, it must be communicated that, "The food supply and the farmers have actually kept up with growth and exceeded it." Thus, the world presently produces enough food to feed all people with fewer malnourished people than two decades ago. The supporters of population control fail to communicate that there is enough food to feed everyone if in fact it could get to the people who need it. The use of such misconception and misinformation in the population discussion must be communicated and countered.

Another non-issue that is central in the discussion of population is urbanization. The fact is, however, that urbanization is not the result of high population growth. It derives from the pull of large cities, especially capital cities. This attraction results from the limitations of rural life as well as higher incomes and other benefits available or associated with life in cities. Crowding in large cities is neither strictly nor primarily a function of the growth of the national population but an economic phenomenon in the majority of cases.

The most recent insertion into the population issue is that of HIV/AIDS. The best weapon against the spread of AIDS is knowledge—and here is where the leap is made—so that since population control programs are vital carriers of information and they are also major suppliers of condoms, HIV/AIDS is a population issue. The promotion of the use of condoms comes to the core of why supporters of population control wish to add HIV/AIDS as a component of the population question. In reality, this is another non-issue in the population question since HIV/AIDS is at its core a health issue.

These have been but a few examples of the pitfalls in communication within the context of the jargon and language used in addressing the issue of population.

The Agenda

The vocabulary and jargon used to communicate the population issue evolves from the various groups which attempt to set the agenda in the population field and mark out their turf. Seeing that this process is in most cases policy-driven, and not always related to a single area of public policy concern, the entire issue is forced in countless directions. Often there is overlap by interest groups resulting in added confusion in the field. The biased agendas of these interest groups need to be considered and understood to clearly identify what is being communicated by them and what needs to be communicated to them.

What is meant by the use of the term "agenda"? An agenda is a plan, public or hidden, for any organization; it is a set of themes or topics requiring action in a designated time period; an agenda guides the organization. In communicating the Catholic Vision on population the agenda, moral and ethical in nature and substance, has been set and it is from this that the communications on the issue is derived. Yet, it is precisely when agendas of different parties collide, that either serious dialogue or conflict may result. The agenda of most organizations will both shape that of others and be shaped by others. Thus, it is not enough to say that adversaries have agendas against each other or against the Catholic Vision. Agendas competing with the Catholic Vision on population must be studied and that which is meaningful and valid must be acknowledged. No single agenda will be found identical to the Catholic vision; however, there are common concerns which form the basis for dialogue.

Independent of any single interest group agenda, a discipline or topic can over time develop its own agenda. In its totality this agenda may be supported by few but enjoy, in principle, broad general support. That is exactly what has occurred in the population field.

In studying various agendas on population, causality problems are often at the core of communicating population topics. Because of the global scale of the issue in a complex social system, evidence can be, and is, construed to back up almost everyone's claims. Even the "so-called" experts do not and cannot agree as to the causes and consequences of population growth itself and many of the associated issues. It is very important to communicate this and to realize that the claims made by diverse interest groups which invoke "experts" are not always based on "experts" in the population field.

The question of causality has another facet, that being the tendency of interest groups supporting population control to dismiss any causal explanation which does not support their agenda or general premise on the population issue.

Having highlighted the confusion regarding causality and the invoking of so-called "experts," the possibility for deception in communicating the population issue is very high. Deception is defined as doing something which tricks or is morally wrong. However, in analyzing journalistic deception, the consent of the person being deceived almost always provides adequate moral justification for the deception on the part of the journalist. This concept of deception can be seen to be operative in a number of agendas set forth on the population issue.

Who are the groups which are setting the agenda in the population field today and how are they communicating their agendas? Several governmental, intergovernmental and non-governmental groups will be examined as to their agenda on the population issue. The understanding of differing agendas is central to communicating the Catholic Vision on Population since these are the actors shaping the population issue, its agenda and evolution. As the Catholic Church asks the questions and responds to others put forward, the dialogue with these groups and others is essential and inherently strategic.

One of the principle actors in setting the population agenda are governments. Unfortunately, most writers on population make no distinction between concepts that "The correct thing should be done by the government" and "The government should decide what is correct and do it." The reality of government population control programs is a series of stories that need to be communicated. Some of these are: factories and offices that hang up blackboards listing each female worker's contraceptive measure; required insertion of an IUD after the first child is born with severe penalties if it is removed; abortion squads that search the countryside rounding up women, checking for expectant mothers and delivering them to clinics; sterilization campaigns connected to "pay-offs". This is all within the population control "myth" of "voluntary decision", incentives", "negotiated annual population targets" and "remarkable progress". These and many more abuses need to be communicated, and in a very personalized manner, so the listener can envision this violation in his/her own life. The possibility that any government, our governments, might make the wrong decision on population and act in the wrong direction is rarely discussed and needs to be clearly communicated.

In bilateral relations, foreign aid is a mechanism or tool used by some countries to suggest or encourage population goals or targets. Receiving the often needed funds is conditional to accepting and achieving the targets. Often conditionality is targeted to particular racial or ethnic groups with a country.

While the government of your respective country may not be engaged in an active population control policy or on either side of the conditionality of foreign aid, that same country may be a member of international organizations which do actively support population controls. Intergovernmental organizations today seek to assert and to play an active role in the formulation of population policies and control. It is precisely at this level that one finds the agenda of the discipline being shaped and thrust upon the world.

One such organization is the United Nations Population Fund (UNFPA). The documents from the 1974 and 1984 UN Conferences on World Population might be described as a vision of the omnipresent and omnipotent state guided by the all powerful international organization with the "expertise" in the population field. In the area of population matters most governments, in response to the encouragement of global intergovernmental organizations, can be accurately described as "overextended". This needs to be communicated. 1994 will witness yet another World Conference on Population and Development and the tone is not expected to change. The World Health Organization has also been active in supporting population controls under the cover of health concerns, particularly regarding reproduction health.

International financial organizations are also active and possibly more influential than most people realize. For example, in many countries the World Bank urges countries to place populations control on a par with basic health care. Countries are pressured to relax prescription guidelines for contraceptives and aggressively push those methods considered most "effective" despite the absence of adequate screening and treatment for side effects. Thus, it is the less developed countries, that is to say the poor, who become the experimental laboratories for new drugs to control population growth. This story must be told.

Feminists constitute an interest group active in the population field. A situation exists in this relationship where the Catholic Vision finds agreement in some points on the feminists' agenda and strong opposition on others. Issues regarding experimentation, since the majority of fertility control drugs are for women, non-voluntary procedures and programs as well as marriage at a later age are areas where agreement is found. However, regarding the issues of total availability of all methods for population control and the free choice of a woman to do as she wishes (not even accepting language referring to "couples") are well known points of diversion. Some groups have accused the feminists of making the population question solely an agenda of women's health issues, focusing almost exclusively on reproductive health.

Environmentalists have proposed that population growth, especially in densely populated areas, destroys the environment. But, this is simply not true. Some of the most densely populated countries are the most environmentally advanced—Switzerland being one example. It can also be noted that countries with as little as 5% of the world population are responsible for more than one quarter of the principal greenhouse gas, while countries with up to a quarter of the world population contribute as little as 5% of the same green house gas. Population control is an over simplistic response to a very complex and interrelational problem.

This has been a general overview of some of the competing agendas of groups interested in shaping the population issue, often by manipulation and deception. The agenda of the Catholic Vision on population cannot merely be responsive to the others but must begin questioning and thus shaping the agenda of the population issue.

Pastoral Application

The final part of this analysis is to briefly examine what could be the central elements for a pastoral approach to "Communicating the Catholic Vision" on the issue of population, recognizing that media conditions and the opportunities presented to the Church in the field of social communications differ from nation to nation and even from diocese to diocese within the same country and need to be tailored to the local situation. Every Conference of Bishops and diocese should develop an integrated pastoral plan for communicating the agenda of the Catholic Vision on Population. The general framework for such a pastoral plan will now be presented in a summary fashion to highlight the more central components.

The Catholic agenda will be the core in communicating on the population questions and in establishing guidelines for a pastoral plan. The guidelines for this pastoral plan should include an assessment of the general media environment including audiences, public and commercial media, delivery systems, and the Catholic media organizations and resources available, including religious communities. The structure of the guidelines of the plan should support evangelization, catechesis and education, social services and ecumenical cooperation where possible. The question of finance should be dealt with at this stage in the process.

With guidelines, the process for creating the pastoral plan continues in two phases: research and design. The elements of the research phase are needs assessment, information gathering, an analysis of the internal communications environment and an examination of how the issue of population can be incorporated in that process. Areas of ministry requiring particular attention and involvement are to be identified.

The beginning of the design phase is not initiated and the following issues should be addressed as relates to the issue of the Catholic Vision on Population.

1. *Education* is key in the design of a pastoral plan on the issue of population. Education programs should be developed for seminarians, priests, religious and lay leaders which teach the Catholic agenda on population. Catholic schools and universities should offer programs and courses related to the communication of the Catholic vision on population. Courses, workshops and seminars that address ethics and

policy issues, as well as broad education programs, should include the issue of population. Media education, focusing on the Catholic vision of the population questions, needs to be designed in dialogue with media professionals in the area, with special emphasis on the relationship of media and values.

2. *Spiritual formation and pastoral care* of lay Catholic professionals, particularly those in the areas of media and communications, should include the topic of population. The Catholic vision on population can serve as the theme or portion thereof for days of recollection, retreats, seminars and meetings of professional groups.

3. *Cooperation* among all interested parties must be encouraged and fostered in the design of the pastoral plan, especially in regard to common concerns on religious, moral, ethical, cultural, educational and social aspects of the population issue.

4. Last but certainly not least is *public relations*. Public relations by the Church means active communication with the community through both secular and religious media. Readiness to communicate values expressed in the Catholic vision on population and to make possible, and maintain, effective communication between the Church and the community as a whole is essential.

In summary, any pastoral approach to communicating the Catholic vision on the population issue must focus on (1) communication, (2) education and (3) total development of peoples. In this way, more responsible and widespread representation can be fostered in the articulation of the ethical and moral components of the population issue. It is preciously in this way that the prophetic role, of speaking out in timely fashion from a Gospel perspective concerning the moral dimensions of this significant public issue, will be realized.

Conclusion

In the introduction, and by implication throughout this presentation, the issue of population and the formulation of the agenda has been identified as policy driven. The Church is not a pressure group or interest group which solely seeks to form policy. The agenda of the Catholic Church on population has however been set, and stands not on political measures but moral and ethic values. Pastoral education and the formation of laity, priests and religious in the area of the population issue must be from a faith perspective and demonstrate, as well as clearly state, the concern that the Church has for all the components which make up the issue of population growth. The Church, in communicating the Catholic vision on the population issue, whether directly or even indirectly intervening in the political process, can make a major contribution to the political order by shaping the ideas of the faithful, the persons who constitute the society, enabling them to be morally and spiritually capable of responsible self-government. To do this, however, population must become a pastoral issue for education in every diocese in every country. "You are the Message" and the messenger; despite the sensitivity of the population question strategic communication is needed to shape the future agenda.

PART FOUR

COMMEMORATION OF THE TWENTY-FIFTH ANNIVERSARY OF HUMANAE VITAE

THEOLOGICAL DEVELOPMENT OF CATHOLIC TEACHING ON CONTRACEPTION AND FAMILY PLANNING

The Reverend Kevin T. McMahon, S.T.D.

Introduction

As we celebrate the twenty-fifth anniversary of *Humanae vitae* a fundamental proposition of the encyclical continues to be overlooked: Its restatement of the Church's teaching on marriage and the family, and on the responsible generation of life, is not simply a reflection of the position of the Magisterium, but is derived from the eternal plan of God. This oversight is due largely to an interpretation of the phrase "the Church teaches," as meaning "those who have power to impose." This misunderstanding betrays a legalism which views moral norms as arbitrary rules that can be enacted on one day and repealed on the next, rather than as truths that guide human persons to their true fulfillment.

Legalism is evident, for example, in the way the media report on official Church documents. Whatever the topic, however long and comprehensive the treatment, however positive its message, the statement is invariably reduced to: the Vatican continues its ban on . . . on contraception, on abortion, on pre-marital intercourse, on homosexual acts, and so forth. Opinion polls among Catholics are produced to support the conclusion that the Magisterium is hopelessly out of step with the Church's membership, and that its laws are no longer an expression of a commonly accepted standard.

What the secular media do not realize, and to some degree cannot be expected to understand, is that the teaching originates not with the persons of the pope and the bishops, but in the wisdom and love of God.[1] As Pope Paul said regarding the transmission of life, the couple "must conform their activity to the creative intention of God expressed in the very nature of marriage and its acts" (HV 10). This may be the real challenge: to demonstrate that according to the plan of God who created and redeemed us, our fulfillment as sexual human beings is tied to the intrinsic meanings and purposes of human sexuality. And, specifically with regard to contraception, that these meanings and purposes are protected by the "inseparable connection, willed by God and unable to be broken by man on his own initiative, between the two meanings of the conjugal act: the unitive meaning and the procreative meaning" (HV 12).[2]

The reasons supporting this conclusion will be highlighted as we examine some of the arguments presented against the Church's teaching on contraception, particularly as it was presented in *Humanae vitae.*

The Arguments

However legalistic their view, the fact remains that theological dissent from the teaching of *Humanae vitae,* both private and public, was immediate and widespread. Fr. Dulles will discuss the reasons for dissent, and its effects on the Church over these past twenty-five years. Our task here is more narrowly focused; it is to present and respond to some of the major arguments of dissenting theologians against the teaching of *Humanae vitae.*

The three general categories of objections are: 1) ecclesiological, 2) socio/economic, and 3) philosophical/theological. In the time allotted, I will provide only a synthesis of the ecclesiological and socio/economic arguments, in order to concentrate more fully on the philosophical/ theological ones. In responding to these arguments, I will draw heavily upon *Gaudium et spes*, *Humanae vitae*, and *Familiaris consortio*.

An Ecclesiological Argument

The principle argument based on ecclesiological concerns faulted Paul VI for failing to listen to three major voices in the debate: first, the witness of Christian couples who were using contraceptives and considered the practice beneficial; second, the opinions of theologians who had decided that contraceptive acts were not intrinsically evil and that the teaching should be changed; third, the recommendations of the majority of his own papal commission which, after broad consultation and study, had reached the conclusion that the teaching should be changed. By "listen," it seems, the proponents of this argument meant "accept," inasmuch as they considered these "majorities" either to represent the *sensus fidelium* going in a new direction, or, at the very least, to prove that there was no *sensus fidelium* in favor of the teaching. But, these objections prove neither point.

Even accepting that the dissenting voices represented the majority, there is no reason to suppose that they, rather than their counterparts who embraced the teaching, represented the true *sensus fidelium*. Moreover, considering the uninterrupted teaching and practice of the Church, there is every reason to believe that the *sensus fidelium* was with those who accepted the teaching. Beyond this, as Pope John Paul II reminds us: "The 'supernatural sense of faith' . . . does not consist solely or necessarily in the consensus of the faithful. Following Christ, the Church seeks the truth, which is not always the same as the majority opinion. She listens to conscience and not to power . . ." (FC 5).

Regarding Pope Paul's rejection of the papal commission's recommendation for change three things should be noted: first, that the commission was established by the Pope as an advisory body, and did not, indeed could not, exercise deliberative power; second, that every teaching of the Church must be measured against divine revelation as it is known through sacred Scripture and tradition; and third, that the Church can teach natural law morality in an authoritative manner (*Dei verbum* 6; HV 4). In stating that the commission had proposed criteria for solutions that "departed from the moral teaching on marriage proposed with constant firmness by the teaching authority of the Church" (HV 5), Pope Paul made it clear that his objection to its recommendation for change was made in fidelity to the eternal law as it is known through "the natural law illuminated and enriched by divine revelation" (HV 4). In the end this ecclesiological argument proves empty.

Three Socio/Economic Arguments

The three socio/economic objections deal with the issues of population, the changing role of women, and financial strains placed upon the modern family. The line of argumentation with respect to all three is the same: The generation of more human lives can tax human resources so that the children and others are made to suffer. Therefore, contraception is morally permissible, and in some cases necessary.

The general response of the tradition to this concern is found in its insistence that children themselves should never be viewed as a burden, but always as a blessing from God. As *Gaudium et spes* states: "Children are really the supreme gift of marriage and contribute very substantially to the welfare of their parents"; therefore, the couple should "be ready with stout hearts to cooperate with the love of the Creator and the Savior, who through them will enlarge and enrich His own family day by day" (GS 50).

Such statements, repeated in *Humanae vitae,* are not invitations to an attitude of reckless abandon, but rather they are admonitions not to see the solution to human problems in the prevention or destruction of human life (GS 51). Nevertheless, recognizing that there are couples who "find themselves in circumstances where at least temporarily the size of their family should not be increased," the Council Fathers restate the Catholic teaching on *Responsible Parenthood*.[3] On the same topic Paul VI notes: "In relation to physical, economic, psychological and social conditions, responsible parenthood is exercised, either by the deliberate and generous decision to raise a numerous family, or by the decision, made for grave motives and with due respect for the moral law, to avoid for the time being, or even for an indeterminate period, a new birth" (HV 10). However, in saying this *Gaudium et spes, Humanae vitae* and *Familiaris consortio* also identify the proper criteria for a true judgment of conscience on the matter.

> In the task of transmitting life, . . . the couple are not free to proceed completely at will, as if they could determine in a wholly autonomous way the honest path to follow; but they must conform their activity to the creative intention of God,

268

expressed in the very nature of marriage and of its acts, and manifested by the constant teaching of the Church (HV 10).

Although time does not permit a full discussion of how to apply these criteria to the specific questions of population, the changing role of women, and economic strains on the modern family, a summary of the Church's response to these arguments can be given.

Population

The question of overpopulation is addressed by the Church's Social Teaching as well as by its teaching on the responsible generation of human life. As the Church views it, the remedy for problems found among populations whose needs exceed their resources is achieved primarily by increasing resources and productivity—agricultural or manufacturing—and only secondarily by limiting population growth through moral means. It is not to be accomplished by government programs that dehumanize couples by removing free choice and personal responsibility through mandating contraception (FC 30).

Changing role of women

The Church's consideration of the argument that contraceptive control of reproductivity is necessary for modern women who want to pursue new opportunities for education, employment, and professional careers, or who want to be free from what some consider subjugation by men through pregnancy and motherhood has been twofold: first, to insist on the obligation to promote all that pertains to the human dignity of woman including her noble roles of wife and mother; and second, to warn against the dangers to women, the family, and society that accompany a "false liberty," and the use of contraception.

Economic strains on the modern family

The Church's response to the argument that the cost of providing for children is so high that it is virtually impossible to raise a large family is straightforward and simple, even if following it is not. It is first to remind couples of their vocation to be pro-creators, and to warn against any personal or societal goals that devalue the importance of children and family life such as an exaggerated sense of personal autonomy, or materialism and consumerism. Second, to call upon society to fulfill "its fundamental task of respecting and fostering the family" (FC 45). And finally, to acknowledge that when conditions prevail that prevent the couple from responsibly transmitting new life, they may use the methods of natural family planning to limit the size of their family (HV 10).

Section summary

These three socio/economic arguments have been answered by the Church, at least in part, in its teaching on responsible parenthood. Many will argue that if legitimate reasons exist for spouses to use natural family planning methods, these same reasons should justify contraception as well. In other words, they see no moral difference between contraception and natural family in such situations. This difficulty will be addressed in the next section.

Four Philosophical/Theological Arguments

The four major arguments against the teaching of *Humanae vitae* which challenge some of its philosophical and theological reasoning have two different goals. The first two arguments appeal to moral principles that have a firm rooting in the tradition to *justify* the practice of contraception in some circumstances. These are: the principle of totality and the principle of double effect. The second two arguments aim at showing that the *teaching is wrong* because of its reliance on *biologism* which identifies the natural law with the laws of biological nature; and, *physicalism* which sees the moral evaluation of human acts solely in terms of their *physical* structure. The latter of these, the critics claim, leads the tradition to accept natural family planning, but to condemn contraception. Since these arguments are among those most often repeated today, it will be helpful to examine each one carefully, beginning with the principle of totality.

Appeal to the principle of totality

Accepting the value of procreation as a true purpose of marriage, the first of these arguments takes exception to the teaching's condemnation of *"every action* which . . . proposes to render procreation impossible" (HV 13, emphasis added). This objection looks at couples who

270

already have children and may be open to more, but who sometimes use contraception. They conclude that considered in their totality, the conjugal acts of the couple are open to the transmission of life even if some are contraceptive, and that this practice is justified by the principle of totality. They add that for the total good of their conjugal life, the couple may sometimes have recourse to contraception.

The first response is that their application of the principle of totality goes beyond its use in the tradition. The principle, which has come to be used exclusively with regard to questions of medical ethics such as amputation and organ donation, has not been used in the tradition to determine the morality of individual human acts by referring to the person's overall behavior. Their appeal, in fact, is not to the tradition at all, but to some contemporary theories of *fundamental option* that deny the moral significance of individual actions and define moral character in terms of the overall thrust of a person's life.

The attraction of such fundamental option theories for some is that they provide a clever rationalization for occasionally performing acts traditionally viewed as gravely immoral. This denies the traditional teaching that some actions, irrespective of motive and circumstance, are intrinsically and gravely evil, and ought never to be chosen. Thus, an occasional affair outside of marriage, an occasional pocketing of the day's receipts, an occasional taking of a human life, may not be seriously evil. And this is the case because overall the husband is faithful to his marriage vows; the cashier honest in business; and the doctor dedicated to saving life. By such an account, one is morally good if overall, or in the long run, he does more good things than bad.[4]

Appeal to the principle of double effect

The reinterpretation of the principle of totality is closely linked to the justification of contraception by identifying it as a choice of a *lesser evil*. The argument starts by noting that a marriage can be seriously strained when the couple has to abstain from sexual intercourse in order to avoid conception, and that this strain, which can jeopardize the marriage, is itself an evil.[5] Thus, by their account, choosing to contracept and continue to have sexual intercourse for the sake of unity in marriage is a choice of the *lesser evil*. Such a choice, they contend, is justified by the tradition. But, where exactly in the tradition?

The words *lesser evil* are used in the tradition with respect to two moral principles: the counseling of the *lesser evil (minus malum),* and the principle of double effect with respect to the toleration of an evil that is less serious than the good to be achieved by the same action. To which of these are the proponents of this argument appealing? Considering that counseling the *lesser evil* applies to a situation in which a person is planning to do something that involves extensive or serious evil consequences from which he cannot be dissuaded, but in substitution for which he may be willing to do something that would have fewer or less serious evil consequences, it is difficult to see how this principle is what they have in mind. If it were, they would have to be saying something like this: That the couple is planning to choose against the unitive good and the procreative good, and so should be counseled to go against only the procreative. This is not, however, what the proponents of this argument are saying. Rather, they are looking at contraception as one act from which two effects flow: one, the preservation of the marriage, and two, the loss of conception. In this they are seeking justification by an appeal to the principle of double effect. But, are they correct?

The principle of double effect does allow for the *toleration* of an evil for the attainment of a greater good; however, it has never permitted the *doing* of a moral evil for any reason (see HV 14). Therefore, justifying actions by claiming that in conflict situations the tradition supported the choice of the lesser evil, requires a reinterpretation of the principle itself. It was just such an effort that led to the creation of the moral methodology known as *proportionalism*.[6]

In proportionalism, no specific kind of behavior can be absolutely forbidden. Rather, in a given situation one must consider the possible consequences of a particular course of action, and calculate whether it will result in the attainment of the greater good or the avoidance of a greater evil. The person must then choose that option which promises to do either. By this account using contraception to save a marriage is considered a choice of a *lesser evil*.

Without offering a full critique of proportionalism here, it is sufficient to note that its novelty is in its justification of doing evil to achieve good.[7] Whatever else can be said, it must be said that the tradition has never allowed the intentional doing of evil to achieve good—no good end can justify an evil means. They try to get around this by redefining evil. Contraception becomes *not a moral* evil, *but a pre-moral* evil that can be rightly chosen provided one has a proportionate reason.

Far from proving that the traditional principle of the double effect justifies contraception in some cases, this argument, through a reinterpretation of that principle, seeks to show that contraception is not intrinsically evil. If this were true, there would be no reason to bother with the argument at all: there would be no need to justify contraception.[8]

Biologism

Perhaps the most often repeated argument against the teaching on contraception is that it rests on an understanding of the natural law that identifies it with the laws of physical or biological nature.[9] Those who hold this position maintain that this error "easily leads to a morality based on the finality of a faculty independent of any considerations of the total human person or the total human community."[10] This is to say, a morality that ignores the importance of human reason, a morality that somehow makes man a slave to his biology.

The argument's proponents ask: If it is morally right for man to use his reason to develop the technology to replace forests with cities, redirect the course of rivers, and defy gravity through aviation, then why can he not take control of the forces of nature within his own body? Why can he not use the technology he has to prevent ovulation, or to destroy sperm? Why can he not intervene to prevent conception?

The basis for the charge of biologism lies in the interpretation of various statements in the Church's teaching on the meanings of the generative faculties. Consider, for example this statement from *Humanae vitae*:

> ... to make use of the gift of conjugal love while respecting the laws of the generative process means to acknowledge oneself not to be the arbiter of the sources of human life, but rather the minister of the design established by the Creator. In fact, just as a man does not have unlimited dominion over his body in general, so also, with particular reason, he has no such dominion over his generative faculties as such, because of their intrinsic ordination towards raising up life, of which God is the principle (HV 13).

To interpret this passage as locating the immorality of contraception in its perversion of the generative faculties ignores the teaching's insistence that God's design has purpose, and that knowing and following this purpose is a function of human reason. As Paul VI put it: "In relation to the biological processes, responsible parenthood means the knowledge and respect of their functions; human intellect discovers in the power of giving life biological laws which are part of the human person" (HV 10).

Man is no more a slave to his biology than he is to the material world; nevertheless, he still needs to understand, respect, and cooperate with the purposes of both. Stewardship of our physical health requires that we carefully consider the adverse side-effects of all drugs and medical procedures. Others have been making the same point with respect to the environment, warning that if man uses his reason and technology with no thought to the laws of nature, he will end up destroying the environment.

To say that the Church's teaching is based on biologism is far too simplistic. To say that human biology has nothing to do with the meanings and purposes of human sexuality is to deny that the body is a constitutive element of the human person. While theologians continue to argue about the exact significance human biology has on the morality of contraception,[11] we can easily reject the accusation of biologism. The Church's teaching affirms the truth that the bodily dimension of the human person—the fact that God created them male and female—discloses something of God's purpose. As Pope Paul states: "The Church is the first to praise and recommend the intervention of intelligence in a function which so closely associates the rational creature with his Creator; but she affirms that this must be done with respect for the order established by God" (HV 16).

Reflection on this order allows us to discover the intrinsic meanings and purposes of human sexuality, to see "the inseparable connection, willed by God and unable to be broken by man on his own initiative, between the two meanings of the conjugal act: the unitive meaning and the procreative meaning" (HV 12). Therefore, the teaching is not founded upon biological processes, but on the power of reason to discern in those processes God's design for the procreation of new life.

Physicalism

The fourth of the philosophical/theological arguments is so closely related to biologism that they are often treated as one. But, this argument, because it applies to the broader spectrum of moral questions, should be treated separately. The argument accuses the Church's teaching of looking only at the physical structure of the act; that is, at the object of the act. In doing so, the tradition has paid insufficient attention to the motives and circumstances that are part of the contraceptive design.

274

These people point to the Church's teaching on responsible parenthood. They correctly note that this teaching allows a couple for serious reasons to limit the size of their family through natural family planning methods. They correctly note that as long as this serious reason exists, the couple may continue to practice natural family planning. They correctly note that the moral difference between contraception and natural family planning is not in the fact that one is artificial and the other natural.[12] They conclude that if two couples with the same good motives and in identical circumstances have reason to limit the size of their families, then the difference in the methods used can only be found at the level of the physical structure of the act. That is, in *what* the couples are doing. And this, they say, denies the truly personal aspects of human action.

Even a superficial polling of Catholics will demonstrate how widespread is the opinion that there is no moral difference between natural family planning methods and contraception. It must be admitted that the difference is not immediately apparent, primarily because it requires one to look beyond consequences to see *how* those consequences come about. Perhaps an example will be helpful here.

Let us consider two couples who in identical circumstances wish for serious reasons to limit the size of their families. Both couples wish to express the two-in-one reality of their conjugal covenant in the two-in-one flesh union of sexual intercourse, but neither couple wants to conceive. Couple "A" uses a method of natural family planning; couple "B" uses a contraceptive device. Prescinding from any question about the abortive effects of some contraceptives, let us say that couple "B" uses a condom. Both couples, using their respective methods, engage in the conjugal act and no conception takes place.

As described, couple "A" would be justified in their actions according to the teaching on responsible parenthood; however, couple "B" would be engaging in an immoral practice. Clearly the difference between the two acts is not in motive, circumstance, or even in the immediate consequences. The difference is in the choices by which these consequences came about.

As Germain Grisez and others have pointed out: there is a real moral difference between not pursuing a good when one has no obligation to do so, and choosing against it.[13] With regard to sexual intercourse two goods may be pursued: the unitive which is always available, and the procreative which is only sometimes available. The teaching of the Church is not that couples may have sexual intercourse only during the fertile period as if the conjugal act during a time of natural infertility would be evil. No, what the Church condemns are only those actions which intend to render procreation impossible (HV

275

14). *What* the agent is doing—the object of the act—is an integral part of human act and discloses a level of human intention. The agent intends that towards which the act is directed.

Contraception, by reason of the end towards which it is directed, always represents a choice against life at its transmission.[14] Whereas natural family planning methods represent a choice not to pursue the procreative good. These methods do not require an intention that is against the transmission of life, although they, too, are immoral when at the level of motive there is a contraceptive will.

To choose against either the unitive or procreative dimension of human sexuality—to separate the intrinsic God-given connection between them—is where the immorality is to be found. This is the case with contraception which violates the procreative dimension just as it is true of those acts which violate the unitive dimension. As *Humanae vitae* puts it: "a conjugal act imposed upon one's partner without regard for his or her condition and lawful desires is not a true act of love, and therefore denies an exigency of right moral order in the relationships between husband and wife" (HV 13).

While the choice against the procreative good is what distinguishes contraception from periodic abstinence and makes the former immoral, there is another reason implicitly given in *Humanae vitae*, but made explicit in *Familiaris consortio;* namely, that through contraception the couple

> "manipulate" and degrade human sexuality—and with it themselves and their married partner—by altering its value of "total self-giving". This leads not only to a positive refusal to be open to life but also to a falsification of the inner truth of conjugal love, which is called upon to give itself in personal totality.
>
> When, instead, by means of recourse to periods of infertility, the couple respect the inseparable connection between the unitive and procreative meanings of human sexuality, they are acting as "ministers" of God's plan and they "benefit from" their sexuality according to the original dynamism of "total" self-giving, without manipulation or alteration (FC 32).

The Church teaches that marriage is a covenant between persons that is human, total, faithful and exclusive, and fruitful (HV 9). It is *human* inasmuch as it is a communion of *persons* established by a free and informed act of mutual self-donation. It is *total* inasmuch as no part of the self is held in reserve, assuring that the two-in-one reality of their conjugal covenant is not counterfeit; this totality argues for *exclusivity* and *fidelity*. Finally, their relationship is *fruitful* inasmuch as the covenant itself is *uniquely* ordained to the procreation and education of children. This teaching insists that any action which violates these God-given meanings is immoral. As others have noted: "The arguments brought against the teaching of the Church concerning the marital act have not demonstrated it to be fallacious nor provided an alternative consistent with the theological data."[15]

CONCLUSION

As John T. Noonan has remarked: "The time for debate over doctrine itself is past. The teaching of *Humanae vitae* is a given of Catholic doctrine. The time now is to understand the encyclical and to answer questions within its framework."[16] Dealing with the teaching is a matter of pastoral practice. And so I will conclude our examination by presenting the pastoral approach to the question of contraception envisioned by the teaching itself.

Pope Paul VI was well aware of how widespread the practice of contraception had become among Catholics prior to 1968. He was aware that reaffirming the teaching would be viewed by many as foolish and would perhaps be a serious stumbling block to their practice of the faith. As he put it:

the Church is not surprised to be made, like her divine Founder, a "sign of contradiction," yet she does not because of this cease to proclaim with humble firmness the entire moral law both natural and evangelical. Of such laws the Church was not the author; nor can she . . . declare to be licit that which is not so by reason of its intimate and unchangeable opposition to the true good of man (HV 18).

To demonstrate that contraception is destructive of the true good of man, the Pope invites all to reflect upon human experience and the consequences of contraception. "Let them consider, first of all, how wide and easy a road would thus be opened up towards conjugal infidelity and the general lowering of morality" (HV 17).

The warnings against the dangers of contraception were well founded. This is clear in societal changes regarding the morality of sexual activity. Although there are certainly other factors at work, one cannot deny that promiscuity in sexual behavior is due largely to the repudiation of the procreative meaning of human sexuality through contraception. Such repudiation places the value of genital sexual activity in its ability to promote interpersonal harmony. By this account, there is little reason to deny the practice of genital sexual expression to the single person who wants to grow in a relationship with someone of the opposite or, for that matter, of the same sex; little reason to deny the legitimacy of extramarital affairs when they are directed toward promoting human growth and development.

Accentuating the unitive dimension by separating it from the procreative has led to a *further dualism* in an understanding of the human person; that is, the separation of personal subjectivity from its bodily dimension. Genital sexual expression becomes a means for personal subjectivities to interact. They are able to *use* their male or female modes of being—their bodies—in order to promote what they think is creative growth toward integration.[17] The separation between the two meanings has also led to an acceptance of technological procedures that violate the unitive dimension and turn human *procreation* into an act of human *reproduction*. It is logically consistent, therefore, that those who reject the Church's teaching on contraception should also reject its teaching on these other matters.

Pope Paul's warnings were prophetic. Any pastor might well ask the question: Are we any better off now than we were twenty-five years ago, or it is time for a wake-up call that is attentive to the plan of God known through natural law illuminated by divine revelation and taught by the Church?

As Pope John Paul II notes: "The teaching of the Church in our day is placed in a social and cultural context which renders it more difficult to understand and yet more urgent and irreplaceable for promoting the true good of men and women" (FC 30). But, he insists, in fidelity to its founder, the Church must be willing to be that "sign of contradiction." It can never shrink from preaching the message in season and out; the gospel must form culture and not the other way around.

The Pope goes on to describe this task by referring to the Church as Teacher and Mother. These roles provide the framework for the Church's pastoral approach on the matter: first, to teach that contraception is intrinsically and gravely evil,[18] and that is it injurious to human goodness and fulfillment; second, to call all to live according to this truth, while recognizing that conversion and upright moral behavior require prolonged and determined effort. The couple cannot, however,

> look on the law as merely an ideal to be achieved in the future: they must consider it as a command of Christ the Lord

to overcome difficulties with constancy. . . . In God's plan, all husbands and wives should first of all recognize clearly the teaching of *Humanae vitae* as indicating the norm for the exercise of their sexuality, and that they should endeavor to establish the conditions necessary for observing that norm" (FC 34).

The Church's teaching on the immorality of contraception is not an imposition of a regulatory law that bans a particular behavior. Rather, it is an instance of the Church's proclamation of the gospel (FC 10ff). The good news for every married couple is this: a married life which respects the God-given meanings and purposes of marriage and human sexuality is a true blessing; and more, that living according to these meanings and purposes as they are expressed in the teaching of the Church is possible by the grace of God.

NOTES

1. That the teaching of the Church on marriage and sexual morality is based on natural law illuminated by divine revelation is a recurrent theme in the modern Magisterial teachings on this subject. From Leo XIII's *Arcanum divinae sapientiae* to the pastoral exhortation of John Paul II *Familiaris consortio*, this link is noted repeatedly.

2. When commenting on the inseparability by human choice of the unitive and procreative meanings of sexual intercourse, Frs. Benedict Ashley, O.P., and Kevin O'Rourke, O.P., conclude: "In our opinion, the insight into the way contraception contradicts the God-given meaning of sexuality, as revealed in scripture and tradition, expressed in *Humanae vitae*, and reaffirmed in the face of much criticism by John Paul II in collegial action with the 1980 synod and in *Familiaris consortio* (1981), is logically consistent and consistent also with the known data of human science and historical experience. The arguments brought against the teaching of the Church concerning the marital act have not demonstrated it to be fallacious nor provided an alternative consistent with the theological and scientific data." Benedict Ashley, O.P. and Kevin O'Rourke, O.P., *Healthcare Ethics*, Third Edition (St. Louis: Catholic Health Association, 1989), pp. 266–267.

3. The teaching of the Church on responsible parenthood is implicit in its insistence that procreation take place only in the context of marriage where the structures are in place to provide for the proper education and rearing of the child. Explicit mention of responsible parenthood is found throughout Magisterial teaching since the *Address to Italian Midwives* given by Pope Pius XII in 1951.

4. For a most telling critique of some contemporary fundamental option theories see: Germain Grisez, *The Way of the Lord Jesus, Vol. 1, Christian Moral Principles*, (Chicago: Franciscan Herald Press, 1983), chapter 16.

5. A different evaluation of this conflict is offered in Pope Paul's discussion of periodic continence. He writes: ". . . this discipline which is proper to the purity of married couples, far from harming conjugal love, rather confers on it a higher human value" (HV 21).

6. For a good discussion of the reinterpretation of the principle of double effect, and the birth of proportionalism see: Richard A. McCormick, *Ambiguity in Moral Choice*

(Milwaukee: Marquette University Press, 1973). In this monograph, McCormick discusses the writings of some of proportionalism's earliest proponents; most notably, Peter Knauer.

7. For a penetrating analysis of proportionalism see: Grisez, *The Way of the Lord Jesus, Vol. 1,* chapter 6.

8. Charles Curran, for example, argues that "non-contraceptive intercourse does not constitute a moral ideal or a human ideal. . ." and that to use contraception therefore does not require any moral justification. Charles E. Curran, *Transition and Tradition in Moral Theology,* (Notre Dame, Indiana: University of Notre Dame Press, 1979), p. 37.

9. Charles E. Curran, for example, has argued that the Church's teaching, especially on matters of human sexuality and medical ethics, is particularly reliant upon the version of natural law presented by the Roman lawyer Ulpian (c. 228); this view equates the natural law with the laws of nature. Charles E. Curran, *Ongoing Revision: Studies in Moral Theology,* (Notre Dame, Indiana: Fides Publishers), pp. 35–51.

10. *Ibid.,* p. 39.

11. The theological debate surrounding the issue has ranged from the accusation of biologism made by the dissenting theologians, to arguments among theologians who accept the Church's teaching as to the importance of man's biology. See: Janet E. Smith, *Humanae Vitae: A Generation Later,* (Washington, D.C.: Catholic University of America Press, 1991), appendix 4, for example, who has accused Grisez, *et al.* of attaching little to no importance to biological facts, while in fact Grisez *et al.* have continued to insist that they do see man's biology as important inasmuch as it discloses the meanings and purposes for which God has made the human person male and female. They maintain further that it is these meanings and purposes *known by man through use of his reason* that exclude the contraceptive choice, and not simply the biological finalities of the generative faculties. See: Germain Grisez, Joseph Boyle, Jr., John Finnis, and William E. May, *The Teaching of Humanae Vitae: A Defense* (San Francisco: Ignatius Press, 1988).

12. An illustration of this point is found in the condemnation of *coitus interruptus* as contraception.

13. Grisez, *et al., The Teaching of Human Vitae: A Defense.*

14. The object of the act is an integral part of the human act, and discloses a level of the agent's intention. That is, he intends that towards which the act itself is directed. This remains true irrespective of motive and circumstance.

15. Ashley and O'Rourke, *Healthcare Ethics,* p. 267.

16. John T. Noonan, Jr. *Contraception* (Cambridge, Massachusetts: Harvard University Press, 1986), p. 535.

17. Anthony Kosnik, *et al., New Directions in American Catholic Thought* (New York: Paulist Press, 1977). See also: Philip S. Keane, *Sexual Morality: A Catholic Perspective* (New York: Paulist Press, 1977).

18. Against those who would suggest that contraception does not involve grave matter and is thereby not the material for mortal sin, there is the testimony of *Humanae vitae.* The document presupposes that this violation of the law of God is gravely evil inasmuch as those who engage in it are instructed to have recourse to the Sacrament of Penance. As the Pope states: "And if sin should still keep its hold over them, let them not be discouraged, but rather have recourse with humble perseverance to the mercy of God, which is poured forth in the Sacrament of Penance" (HV 25). To suggest a pastoral approach that instructs contracepting couples to continue to receive the Eucharist without benefit of the Sacrament of Penance is to deny either the seriousness of the sin, or the importance true contrition and a firm purpose of amendment have to the integrity of the sacrament itself.

280

Chapter 20

THE IMPACT OF DISSENT ON CATHOLIC TEACHING AND CHRISTIAN LIFE

The Reverend Avery Dulles, S.T.D.

The theme of this afternoon's session, the 25th anniversary of *Humanae vitae,* has already been addressed by a moral theologian, Father Kevin McMahon. In my talk I shall not deal directly with questions of moral theology, a field in which I have no special competence. Speaking rather as an ecclesiologist, I shall reflect on how dissent from the encyclical has affected the life of the Church. Ideally this assessment should be made by someone skilled in sociology, a field in which I have no training. Perhaps Dr. Robert George, as a professor of politics, will be able to supplement my observations in this area.

When I heard in late July 1968 that the encyclical on birth control was about to be published I was greatly troubled. Personally I had nothing against a reaffirmation of the teaching of earlier popes on contraception. The doctrine of *Humanae vitae* was exactly what I had always believed as a Catholic and what I had been taught in my courses in ethics and moral theology. But I sensed that public opinion among Catholics had already swung so far in the direction of change that the pope's decision would be vehemently opposed. I was worried about the internal rifts that would arise in the Church.

My apprehensions were borne out by the events. Never, I suppose, has there been such vocal and organized dissent. Father Bernard Häring wrote at the time: "No papal teaching document has ever caused such an earthquake in the Church as the encyclical *Humanae vitae*."[1] About the same time a Protestant theologian, Robert McAfee Brown, wrote that the reaction of Catholics to the encyclical "shows conclusively that traditional views of papal authority simply cannot be taken seriously any more, and that Catholics feel no greater sense of being bound to unquestionable doctrine than do Protestants."[2]

In 1985 Andrew Greeley was still able to write: "The most obvious serious problem for American Catholicism in the years after the Vatican Council is the decline of support for certain components of its sexual ethic among large numbers of American Catholics."[3] With specific reference to *Humanae vitae* he adds, several pages later: "Certainly never in the history of American Catholicism, have so many Catholics in such apparent good faith decided that they can reject the official teaching of the church as to what is sexually sinful and what is not, and to do so while continuing the regular practice of Catholicism and even continuing the description of themselves as good, strong, solid Catholics."[4] According to public opinion polls only about 10% of American Catholics support the teaching of Paul VI on contraception. This figure has remained practically constant for nearly twenty years.

The dissent was occasioned by the convergence of many factors. The practice of birth control among Catholics, as among others, had been steadily increasing since the 1870s, and especially since the invention of the anovulant pill which was being marketed in the early 1960s. A number of distinguished moral theologians supported the pill as morally acceptable. All of this occurred in a period of rapid change, when many traditional Catholic positions were being revised. Vatican II was a part of this development. As interpreted in the American press, the Council was introducing a new spirit of modernization and democratization into the Catholic Church. The Church, it seemed, was acknowledging the responsibility of the human race to determine its own destiny and was liberating Catholics from a morality of external laws, including even laws imposed by God as a power above the world.

282

The heroes of the day were dissidents who dared to challenge the authorities and follow their own personal insights.

When Paul IV withdrew the question of birth control from the Council's agenda and referred it to the special commission on "Population, Family, and Birth" that had been set up by John XXIII, suspicions were aroused. But Pope Paul did attempt to make the commission genuinely representative by including in its membership not only bishops and theologians but also medical experts and married lay people. After several years of deliberation the commission, by a large majority, voted in favor of relaxing the traditional ban on contraception. Once the commission's reports had been leaked to the press in March 1967, theologians began to prepare the Catholic people for the expected change in official teaching.

A year later (on July 29, 1968) Paul VI, to the dismay of progressive Catholics, issued *Humanae vitae,* setting aside the majority report and decisively reaffirming the earlier teaching. But, for many Catholics, the decision came too late. During the five years since the papal commission had started its work, many Catholics had made up their minds to follow the less rigorous opinion, which was presented as solidly probable.

The encyclical put the bishops of the world in a difficult situation. Episcopal conferences, requested by the Holy See to write in support of the encyclical, gave varying interpretations. Several conferences assured Catholics that the practice of contraception, while always regrettable (and, as some said, "ontically" evil), was not always gravely sinful, and might not be sinful at all when warranted by serious reasons. Several conferences defended the legitimacy of conscientious dissent.

Many priests and theologians, going beyond the episcopal conferences, openly asserted that Paul VI was mistaken. As everyone here knows, a group of priest-theologians in this country organized a campaign of protest, calling press conferences to explain how wrong the pope had been. This group assured the faithful that to dissent from *Humanae vitae* was not only permissible but was the right course to adopt.

Although the theologians' advocacy of dissent presumably had some impact, I suspect that it was not the principal cause of the rejection of *Humanae vitae.* The theological dissent was itself a manifestation of the popular conviction that contraception was tolerable and sometimes necessary. Alarm over the growth of world population, the economics of supporting a large family, the perceived value of sexual intimacy for holding marriages intact, and the ready availability of cheap and efficient contraceptive devices all contributed to a mentality at odds with the encyclical.

However one interprets the causal relationships, the widespread disregard for official church teaching in this area is a serious matter in itself and one that has a ripple effect in many other areas of Catholic life. It threatens to frustrate many of the intentions of Vatican II. I shall briefly enumerate seven deleterious consequences.

1. The Church, according to Vatican II, is a sacrament of unity. The members are maintained in unity by common convictions, especially regarding faith and morality. When the emphatic and repeated teaching of the magisterium about key issues of sexual ethics falls on deaf ears and is widely rejected, the Church ceases to appear in the world as a sign of the unity God intends for the whole human family. Catholics no longer experience themselves, as much as they ought, as sharers in the same moral commitments. The more the hierarchy insists on adherence to *Humanae vitae,* the more alienated do the majority of the faithful feel. While they generally remain in the Church, they are marginalized.

2. Vatican II sought to give the laity an active role in the life of the Church and in the development of doctrine. It taught that the body of the faithful as a whole have a sense of the faith implanted in their hearts by the Holy Spirit, that the Spirit inclines them to accept authentic teaching, that they should be free to express their minds, and that they should place their experience at the service of the Church. The Council encouraged the hierarchy to consult the laity in deciding on doctrinal and practical questions.

Pope John Paul II, following up on the teaching of the Council, frequently mentions the participation of the laity in the prophetic office of the Church. In his apostolic exhortation on the Christian family he teaches that, thanks to the graces of the sacrament of matrimony, Christian spouses and parents have a special charism for authentic evangelical discernment regarding the proper ways of living out the relationships of family life.[5] The controversies about sexual ethics, however, impede the kind of consultation that should in principle occur. The lay members of the papal Commission on Population, Family and Birth appear to have supported the majority view against the position that the pope ultimately adopted. As long as the overwhelming majority of lay people are at odds with the hierarchy on the question of birth control, the process of consultation on marriage and family life will be gravely inhibited. The magisterium will find itself driven into an isolated clerical world.

3. Priests are placed in a difficult position as teachers, preachers and confessors. Even those priests who personally agree with the en-

cyclical are reluctant to insist on it because they do not wish to run the risk of antagonizing their hearers and turning them against the whole Catholic system. An individual priest who supports the encyclical finds himself outnumbered by colleagues who dispute his views. This is demoralizing for priests and confusing for the laity. Lay Catholics receive very little clear guidance of sexual matters from the clergy, who seem to be uncertain and indecisive, and usually end by telling the laity to "follow their own conscience." Regarding personal conscience as an acceptable alternative to church teaching, the faithful rarely mention contraception as a sin, even if and when they still go to confession.

4. The dissent about *Humanae vitae* has led to confusion about the authority of the magisterium. Those opposed to the encyclical tend to be critical of other church teachings, especially in the area of sexuality. The careful distinctions set forth in *Lumen gentium* no. 25 are obscured by tendentious interpretations. Although few Catholic theologians subscribe to Robert McAfee Brown's sweeping dismissal of papal teaching authority, opponents of the encyclical tend to minimize that authority. Some dispute the competence of the magisterium to speak on questions of natural law. Others deny the force of papal pronouncements that have not been reached through a collegial process. Still others regard all noninfallible teaching as legitimate matter for public dissent. At the opposite extreme, supporters of the encyclical sometimes treat the ordinary papal magisterium as though it were, at least in practice, infallible, even in matters on which revelation is silent.

The debate that occurred in 1989 and 1990 about the new profession of faith and the CDF Instruction on "The Ecclesial Vocation of the Theologian" is a case in point. The clauses referring to the obligation to assent to definitive nonrevealed doctrine and to authentic but nondefinitive doctrine were both interpreted as underhanded attempts to secure compliance with *Humanae vitae*. Possibly they were so intended. In the present polarized situation it is difficult to discuss any issues about the magisterium and dissent in a dispassionate and nonpartisan manner. Everyone is drawn into the battle for or against the encyclical.

5. The relations between bishops and theologians, which had been remarkably cordial during Vatican II, have become strained as a result of *Humanae vitae*. Bishops are tempted to regard theologians as sowers of dissent. Otherwise qualified theologians who dissent from *Humanae vitae* find themselves excluded from sensitive teaching positions and from appointments as consultors to episcopal committees. Scholars who continue to work cordially with the hierarchy are sometimes portrayed as sycophantic court theologians.

6. Another adverse effect of the dissent from *Humanae vitae* has to do with the appointment of bishops. Priests known to be opposed to the encyclical are, I am told, considered ineligible. Recommendations coming from the local church are in many cases rejected because of this or some similar issue. In nations where the pool of candidates is small, this restriction has been devastating. The debatable quality of some recent appointments has lowered the morale of Catholics in several countries. Rome is accused of spurning the doctrine of Vatican II on the relationship between the bishop and the local church, which he is obliged to serve and represent (LG 23; CD 11–21).

7. Finally, the development of episcopal conferences, which began so auspiciously at the close of Vatican II, has been stunted by the controversy about birth control. Paul VI had expected the conferences to give unequivocal support to his teaching, and was disappointed when a number of them, without overtly disagreeing, undermined the encyclical by their ambivalent responses. Partly for this reason the Holy See has tended to question the teaching authority of episcopal conferences and to insist on prior approval of conference statements.

In this connection it seems pertinent to mention national pastoral councils. The Dutch pastoral synod, which met in a mood of great enthusiasm from 1968 to 1970, diverged from *Humanae vitae* and several other official Catholic positions. As a result the Holy See discouraged the holding of national pastoral councils in other countries. The Detroit Call to Action Conference of 1976, which was held in lieu of a projected national pastoral council for the United States, repudiated the official teaching on contraception. When the bishops rejected this and other resolutions passed at Detroit, a "Call to Action" movement was launched to press for a comprehensive agenda of reform. This opposition movement still maintains its momentum.

Developments such as these show how difficult it is, in the prevailing climate of dissent, to realize the vision of a Church in which all the members actively participate in the formation of doctrine. Complaints are frequently heard to the effect that Rome is seeking to recentralize the Church, thus undoing the work of Vatican II. Dissent from *Humanae vitae* is not the sole source of difficulty, but in the United States and many other countries it is a major factor in preventing the decentralization, participation, and coresponsibility that were foreseen as resulting from the Council.

In a fuller treatment it would be possible to explore many other negative phenomena. We could investigate, for example, the degree to which dissent from *Humanae vitae* is linked with the decline of Mass attendance, with resignations from the active ministry, with the shortage of priestly vocations, and with the waning of financial contributions. Enough has been said, however, to make it clear that this dissent is a deep wound in the body of Christ. No one who loves and cares for the Church can be content to see the present state of affairs continue. But no quick and easy solution is at hand. I can at most suggest steps by which the evils might be alleviated.

1. The dissenters must recognize that public dissent by its very nature impairs the authority of the magisterium and weakens the Church as a community of faith and witness. Whatever may have been thought in 1968, when the encyclical was issued, it should by now be evident that protests in the public media will not compel the hierarchy to change its position. It is totally inappropriate for church doctrine to be determined by pressures of this kind. Demands for change usually provoke stronger assertions of the official teaching.

2. Those who are strongly convinced by the arguments for or against contraception should recognize the extreme difficulty of the question, and should therefore respect the intelligence and sincerity of those with whom they differ. If the moral judgment had been a simple matter, it would not have taken four years for the papal commission to reach its conclusion, nor would the vote have been divided. Nor would the pope have agonized so long in formulating his decision.

3. In making appointments to sensitive positions, such as seminary professorships, the hierarchy must take account of the candidates' general fidelity to Catholic doctrine. *Humanae vitae* should not be made the sole litmus test, but theologians who aggressively attack the encyclical would seem to disqualify themselves from receiving a canonical mission to teach with hierarchical approval. In sensitive areas such as catechesis and seminary training it is important that the official Catholic teaching be presented in a favorable light.

4. No amount of insistence by church authorities will bring about unanimity. Since *Humanae vitae* runs against the prevailing ethos of Western society, it is probably inevitable that large numbers of Catholics will be drawn into opposition. Possibly the Holy Spirit intends that the magisterium should learn some lesson from this massive disagreement. But even if the dissent comes from some other spirit, as in part it probably does, the parable of the wheat and the tares should be kept in mind. Overzealous efforts to uproot evil in the Church can be destructive of much good.

5. The issue of contraception should be addressed in the context of more general questions about family life and procreation. In our culture it is widely assumed that everyone has a right to sexual fulfillment in whatever manner, by whatever means, and with whatever partners one may choose, provided that the parties mutually consent. Premarital sex, adultery, and homosexual unions are becoming more

and more frequent. Children are increasingly regarded as an unwanted burden, almost an accident. In some traditionally Catholic countries the birth rate, constantly descending, has by now fallen below the replacement level. Sterilization and abortion are accepted methods of birth control.

Against this syndrome of permissiveness it may still be possible to raise an alarm that will be heard. Alliances can still be forged with people of good will, including non-Catholics and non-Christians, who wish to preserve and strengthen the traditional family. The issue of contraception is not totally separable from these larger questions because the deliberate exclusion of procreation from the sexual act has ramifications that go beyond the use of sex in marriage. Nevertheless, every opportunity should be used to promote common witness among all who oppose a merely hedonistic or recreational view of sex and who seek to discern the true meaning of sexuality in the framework of God's creative designs. Within the context of such an inquiry the teaching of Paul VI may appear less as a rigid clinging to the past than a prophetically inspired counter measure against the sexual revolution that was already in the making.

NOTES

1. Bernard Häring, "The Encyclical Crisis," *Commonweal* (8 September 1968): 588–94, at 588.

2. Robert McAfee Brown, "*Humanae Vitae:* An Ecumenical Boon?" *Commonweal* (8 September 1968): 595–97, at 595.

3. Andrew Greeley, *American Catholics since the Council: An Unauthorized Report* (Chicago: Thomas More, 1985), 81.

4. Ibid., 90.

5. John Paul II, *Familiaris consortio,* 5; in *Vatican Council II: More Postcondiliar Documents,* ed. Austin Flannery (Northport, N.Y.: Costello, 1982), 817–18.

Chapter 21

TEACHING EFFECTIVELY THE CHRISTIAN VISION OF RESPONSIBLE PARENTHOOD

Robert P. George, J.D., D. Phil.

You, our shepherds, who in union with each other and with our Holy Father speak to us with the sure voice of Jesus Christ, are in possession of a treasure more precious than the purest gold, namely, the authentic Catholic understanding and teaching regarding marriage, sex, and family life.

I would not be surprised, however, if sometimes this weighty treasure feels like it is attached to a chain you must wear around your necks. The moment you utter a word about, say, the value of chastity, the elite who guard the prevailing secularist orthodoxy, not to mention their fellow travelers within the Church, can be counted on to reproach you. If they are confident that no one they care about is listening to you anyway, they will merely dismiss your teaching as "unrealistic," and chide you for being "out of touch" with social reality. If, on the other hand, they have the slightest reason to fear that people might actually heed your words, they will accuse you of everything from encouraging child abuse, to spreading AIDS, to causing global warming. No one enjoys being dismissed as a fool, much less being vilified as an enemy of mankind; so I certainly sympathize with you, and thank God that I am not a bishop.

I hope that it is no way presumptous of me, though, to offer you a few words of encouragement. My message is simple: The Church is right; the cultural elite is wrong. Catholic teaching on sexual ethics and the sanctity of life is an intrinsic part of the saving Gospel of Jesus Christ. It is *good news,* and you should therefore preach it not only with confidence, but also with joy.

But, you may ask, how can we preach with joy a message which places upon people many heavy burdens? In a cultural climate in which, as Fr. Dulles points out, "it is widely assumed that everyone has a right to sexual fulfillment in whatever manner, by whatever means, and with whatever partners one may choose," how can we be joyful about telling people that they may not licitly do things that they wish to do and see no reason, apart from our teaching, not to do? And, after all, isn't it true that many of our most eminent theologians tell us that certain aspects of our teaching on sexual morality and the sanctity of life are doubtful and likely someday to change?

In response to the last question, let me simply report to you that the more I read and reflect on the efforts of dissenting theologians to cast doubt upon the validity of the Church's firm and constant teaching regarding masturbation, fornication, adultery, homosexual acts, contraception, *in vitro* fertilization, and abortion, the less impressed I am. In fact, I find that even the purely philosophical case for chastity and respect for human life, as these ideals have traditionally been understood, stands up remarkably well against their criticisms. Moreover, I am persuaded that certain of these teachings, including the teaching on contraception, can be affirmed with the most profound confidence because they are, in fact, proposed infallibly by the ordinary and universal magisterium.

Vatican II, in no uncertain terms, reaffirms the possibility of infallibility in the exercise of the ordinary and universal magisterium. In *Lumen gentium,* 25, the fathers state that the bishops may proclaim infallibly the teaching of Christ on a matter of faith or morals

> even when they are dispersed throughout the world, provided that they remain in communion with each other and with the successor of Peter and that in authoritatively teaching on a

matter of faith or morals they agree in one judgment as that to be held definitively.

All responsible Catholics, regardless of their views on particular morally controversial matters, affirm this teaching. However, few seem to have reflected on the question of whether the firm and constant teaching of the ordinary and universal magisterium on chastity and respect for human life fulfills the conditions for infallibility set forth in *Lumen gentium*. However, in a brilliant article that I warmly commend to all of you, the late John C. Ford, S.J. and Germain Grisez cogently argue that these conditions have in fact been fulfilled in the case of the Church's teaching on contraception and, by implication, I think, her teachings on abortion, masturbation, fornication, adultery, and homosexual acts.[1] I certainly do not doubt the intelligence or sincerity of those Catholic moralists who in the face of such scholarship continue to defend contraception or any of these other acts and argue that the Church's teaching is wrong and can and should be changed. It is just that I find their arguments less and less compelling as the debate proceeds.[2]

Let me return, though, to the alleged burdensomeness of the Church's teaching on these matters.

It is sometimes said that the Church's moral teachings are a parade of negatives: no, don't do this; no, you mustn't do that; no, you can't do the other thing; no! no! no! And it is true that loyal and well-intentioned people have sometimes presented the Church's teachings in such negative terms. The reality, however, is that a profoundly positive truth is at the core of these teachings: Human life is intrinsically and immeasurably *good*.

The truth about the goodness of life bears virtually unlimited repetition: You just can't remind people of it often enough. Because human life, though it is a condition of the realization and enjoyment of every other human good, is no mere means, but is, rather, good-in-itself, it is worth transmitting, nurturing, preserving, protecting, and in all things treating with the greatest respect. In important ways, it is because of the unique and intrinsic value of each human life that the institutions of marriage and family have a singular role and a profound goodness, though their value (we must never forget) is also intrinsic and is not reducible to the status of mere means to other ends (even the ends of transmitting, nurturing, and protecting life). Because the intrinsic good of marital union has an intelligibility that partly depends on and is partly specified by its unique role and value in transmitting life to new human persons, and in nurturing and educating such persons, human sexuality has a correspondingly profound dignity and moral significance.

People who recognize the truth that human life is intrinsically good—and this must include every truly faithful Christian and Jew—can never accept the notion of "morally indifferent sex" that is widely propagated in our culture and promoted by apologists for sexual permissiveness.[3] Faithful persons will believe that sex can be reasonable and unreasonable, right and wrong—anything but "morally indifferent." They will understand that people can have sex for *reasons,* and not merely for the sake of satisfying desires. The reasons spouses should engage in chaste acts of sexual intercourse are provided by the intelligible human goods of transmitting life to new persons and expressing, in a profound and unique way, their marital commitment.[4] By the same token, they will understand that even spouses can sometimes have reasons not to have sex, and that sometimes (as in all cases of possible nonmarital intercourse, as well as sometimes in cases of possible marital intercourse) these reasons will be conclusive.

Above all, people who fully grasp the great goodness of human life will recognize the importance of always choosing compatibly with a will that is oriented positively toward that good. They will perceive the unreasonableness, the immorality, of choosing to destroy a human life that has already begun, or even to impede the coming to be of a new human life. Even where there are good reasons (as sometimes there are) for spouses to avoid the possible bad side effects of a new person's coming to be, they will never treat the good of a new person's coming to be as if it were not an intrinsic-good-to-be-respected (though they have reasons to refrain from acting for that good here and now), but rather an evil-to-be-avoided. They will see the point of abstaining from intercourse rather than adopting by choice a proposal to prevent a possible person's coming to be.[5]

People who appreciate the true value of human life, or any other intrinsic good, will recognize that, in choosing, one integrates the objects of one's choice, the goods or evils one intends, into one's will, effecting a sort of synthesis between oneself and what one sets oneself to do. Because human choices *last* in the personality of the choosing subject (establishing, reinforcing, or, as the case may be, reversing a good or bad moral character) the moral quality of our choices—whatever their intended or unintended consequences—bears upon a crucial interest of the choosing person, namely the worth of his own character. Because the possession of a morally good character is itself intrinsically valuable, and no mere means to other ends, people have reason to care about their own moral integrity; and this is why sexual immorality, apart from its manifest bad consequences in terms of venereal diseases, broken marriages and unhappy families, the feminization of poverty, and the like, is always harmful: It is, in short, morally self-destructive of those who engage in it.

One needn't be a Catholic or even a Christian (or a believer at all) to grasp, in some way, the intrinsic value of human life and, thus, the moral significance of human sexual choices. In the light of Catholic faith, however, one perceives a fuller significance to choosing in this and other domains of morally significant action. Our good choices, whether or not they are effective in bringing about the states of affairs in the world we seek, and, indeed, even if they are nothing more than choices not to do evil, *last even into eternity*. They are contributions to the building up of the Heavenly Kingdom, where, as *Gaudium et spes* teaches, we will find them again, "burnished and freed from stain." Thus, even choices made for the sake of moral good which to the purely secular mind seem pointless (e.g., an abandoned spouse's fidelity to a spouse who, having divorced him or her, remarries) have profound value. Christ himself gives them to the Father as nothing less than a costly contribution of the good of, say, marital fidelity to the Kingdom.

People who understand the great positive truths that undergird the negative norms of Catholic moral teaching are, in general, unlikely to find these norms too burdensome. The positive truths provide the point, the reason for, the negative norms. That is why it is important to teach these norms in the context of a clear affirmation of the principle that human life, and, relatedly, marriage and family life, are great goods. And it is important to stress that, whatever the sacrifices involved, uprightness in sexual matters contributes profoundly to the integrity of marriages and to the good character of every upright person.

In the context of the anti-life ethos which Pope Paul VI all-too-accurately foresaw, it is particularly important that people be made to understand the connection between the negative norms and the great positive truths regarding the value of human life and the corresponding dignity of marriage and family life. In a cultural milieu in which people are constantly confronted with temptations to unchastity, many people will indeed find it difficult to live up to the Church's teaching. Nothing will help them better to resist these temptations than to communicate to them a sound understanding of the reasons for the teaching. And this means that post-conciliar moral teaching must truly overcome the legalism of a pre-conciliar moral theology (a legalism with which the thought of dissenting Catholic moralists remains imbued).

God does not impose upon us norms governing sexuality as a challenge or test of our obedience and worthiness of heaven. Nor is hell a punishment for failing the test. True, immoral sexual choices, like other grave immoralities, self-determine people in ways that are incompatible with a sharing in divine life; but if, by unrepented immoral choices, one permanently refuses God's gracious offer of eternal life, *one consigns oneself to hell.* For his part, God does everything short of obliterating our free wills in order to prevent our self-destruction. It is by God's choice and action, not ours, that sin and death are conquered; and it is through his grace that we have the possibility of repentance, reformation, and forgiveness and the hope of life with him in heaven.

The critical point against all forms of legalism is that moral norms are not arbitrary impositions of the divine will, much less ecclesiastical whim. As Grisez has pointed out,

> [G]iven that [God] has made us what we are, he has no choice about the content of morality. God is free and all-powerful, but even he cannot make ... what is humanly destructive to be humanly fulfilling. Therefore God commands us to act only in morally good ways, not because he wants to impose anything, but because, loving us, he wants us to do what is for our own good.[6]

Moral norms are not pointless impositions. They are, rather, the intelligible requirements of respect for the true human goods that give us reasons for action and restraint. Specifically with regard to sexuality, God's law reflects and supports the reasons we all have (rooted, ultimately, in the great and intrinsic goodness of human life and, relatedly, of marriage and family life) to be chaste. The fundamental reason we should all be chaste—indeed, the reason God commands us to be chaste—is that chastity is good for us; and unchastity, like every other form of immorality, is bad for us. Chastity, however difficult to practice, enriches and ennobles our lives; unchastity eats away at our integrity, corrupts and debases us.

Chastity, like other virtues, requires us to resist wayward desires. Thus, it will indeed seem burdensome to those who have no appreciation of its point, that is to say, of the true human goods it preserves and protects. In the cultural climate that Fr. Dulles described, it really is unlikely that very many people who understand the Church's teaching in a legalistic way will accept and abide by it. It is therefore important that the Catholic faithful be taught to appreciate the true point and the true value of chastity. They must come to a fuller appreciation of the goods of life and marriage and family life that give them reasons to be chaste.

294

The way to lessen the burden on the faithful is most decidedly not to "hush up" the Church's authentic teaching, even for the sake of "leaving people in good faith." Only someone who was still caught in the grip of legalism would urge that strategy. Once one recognizes the inherently self-destructive nature of unchastity and other vices, one will see that Catholic moral teaching, including the Church's teaching on sex, really is a treasure to be shared fully with the faithful. As Fr. Dulles says, what people need is "the clear guidance of the Church," and, as he also suggests, too often they are not getting it.

We should not, however, leave unremarked the good things that are happening and signs of good things to come. First of all, the clear leadership of Pope John Paul II, and, particularly, his influential "personalist" approach to sexual ethics, is helping Catholics to overcome legalism and contributing greatly to the firming of the Church's mind on contraception and other disputed teachings. Secondly, as the result of efforts often led by courageous lay people, the availability of effective noncontraceptive natural family planning techniques is becoming more widely known and, when presented in the light of a nonlegalistic account of the Church's teachings, is accepted by Catholic married couples. Thirdly, and relatedly, among the new generation of priests now emerging from our seminaries are many young men whose willingness to question the secular orthodoxy about the meaning and significance of sex opens them to appreciate, and thus empowers them to communicate, the Church's teachings on chastity. It is well known, though remarkably underreported, that in several large seminaries where *Humanae vitae* is taught wisely and well the overwhelming majority of students agree with the Church's teaching.

If you are to share fully with the faithful and all men and women of goodwill the treasure of authentic Catholic teaching on marriage, sex, and the family you would do well to encourage these positive developments. I would suggest, for example, that you help to publicize and disseminate the Pope's writings on marriage, sex, and family life. I would urge you to promote sound NFP programs in your dioceses and make them a regular part of marriage preparation. I would encourage you to be joyful and, indeed, fearless, in communicating and defending the Church's teaching, thus setting an example that the younger (and, since nothing is impossible with God, even some of the older) priests in your dioceses will want to emulate.

Finally, if I may be so bold, I would exhort you not to be so fearful of disunity that you fail to be a "sign of contradiction" in the cultural climate that obtains today. The Church's teaching is true and good; and the only sort of unity worth having is unity around principles of truth and goodness. If we are willing to stand for truth and goodness—

even at the cost of being countercultural—surely Our Lord will not deny us the unity that he promises and we so urgently desire.

NOTES

1. "Contraception and the Infallibility of the Ordinary Magisterium," *Theological Studies,* 39 (1978), 258–312; reprinted in *The Teaching of Humanae Vitae: A Defense* (San Francisco: Ignatius Press, 1988), pp. 117–219.

2. In all candor, I must confess that I do not share Fr. Dulles's perception of "the extreme difficulty" of the question of contraception. (I do think, however, that the question whether the anovulent pill was a contraceptive method of birth regulation and thus fell under the traditional moral prohibition was, in the early 1960s, a perfectly legitimate one.) On any premises that a Catholic ought to be willing to accept, contraception cannot be morally right. One cannot choose to contracept without forming a contralife will. A more difficult question, I think, is whether married couples may legitimately practice natural family planning. This question turns on whether NFP can be practiced *without* a contraceptive intent. I agree with Pope Paul VI that it can be so practiced, though, to be sure, sometimes people do use NFP as a form of contraception. For a careful and comprehensive treatment of all of these points see Germain Grisez, Joseph Boyle, John Finnis, and William E. May, " 'Every Marital Act Ought to be Open to New Life': Toward A Clearer Understanding," *The Thomist,* 52 (1988), 365–426; reprinted in *The Teaching of Humanae Vitae: A Defense, supra,* note 1, pp. 33–116.

3. For a defense of the idea of "morally indifferent sex, " see Richard Posner, *Sex and Reason* (Cambridge, MA: Harvard University Press, 1992). I offer a response to Posner in Robert P. George, "Can Sex Be Reasonable?," *Columbia Law Review,* 93, (1993), forthcoming.

4. Because marital union is itself intrinsically good, spouses have a reason to have sex even when, through no choice of theirs, conception is temporarily or even permanently impossible. Indeed, where spouses have reason to avoid the bad side effects of bringing a new person into being, it may be perfectly reasonable for them to restrict their intercourse to infertile periods.

5. The morally crucial difference between contraception and noncontraceptive natural family planning is that in contraception someone always adopts by choice a proposal to prevent a new person's coming to be; in natural family planning no one need adopt such a proposal (though it is possible for people to practice NFP as a method of contraception and, thus, immorally). For a careful explanation of these points, see Grisez, Boyle, Finnis, and May, "Every Marital Act," *supra,* note 2.

6. Germain Grisez, "Legalism, Moral Truth, and Pastoral Practice," *Anthropotes,* 6 (1990), 111–121, 114.